The Big Book of ALL HIT
for Acoustic Guitar

Wise Publications
London/New York/Paris/Sydney/Copenhagen/Madrid/Tokyo

Exclusive Distributors:
Music Sales Limited
8/9 Frith Street,
London W1D 3JB, England.
Music Sales Pty Limited
120 Rothschild Avenue,
Rosebery, NSW 2018,
Australia.

Order No. AM969529
ISBN 0-7119-8761-0
This book © Copyright 1998, 2001 by Wise Publications
(Previously published as three separate volumes: Rock for Acoustic Guitar,
Love Songs for Acoustic Guitar & 90's Hits for Acoustic Guitar.)

Edited by Arthur Dick
New music arrangements by Eric Roche
New music engravings by Paul Ewers Music Design
Cover design by Chloë Alexander
Printed in Great Britain

Your Guarantee of Quality
As publishers, we strive to produce every book to the highest
commercial standards.
This book has been carefully designed to minimise awkward
page turns and to make playing from it a real pleasure.
Particular care has been given to specifying acid-free, neutral-
sized paper made from pulps which have not been elemental
chlorine bleached. This pulp is from farmed sustainable forests
and was produced with special regard for the environment.
Throughout, the printing and binding have been planned to
ensure a sturdy, attractive publication which should give years
of enjoyment.
If your copy fails to meet our high standards, please inform us
and we will gladly replace it.

Music Sales' complete catalogue describes thousands of titles
and is available in full colour sections by subject, direct from
Music Sales Limited. Please state your areas of interest and
send a cheque/postal order for £1.50 for postage to:
Music Sales Limited, Newmarket Road, Bury St. Edmunds,
Suffolk IP33 3YB.

www.musicsales.com

Part 1
ROCK CLASSICS

GUITAR TABLATURE EXPLAINED

Guitar music can be notated three different ways: on a musical stave, in tablature, and in rhythm slashes

RHYTHM SLASHES are written above the stave. Strum chords in the rhythm indicated. Round noteheads indicate single notes.

THE MUSICAL STAVE shows pitches and rhythms and is divided by lines into bars. Pitches are named after the first seven letters of the alphabet.

TABLATURE graphically represents the guitar fingerboard. Each horizontal line represents a string, and each number represents a fret.

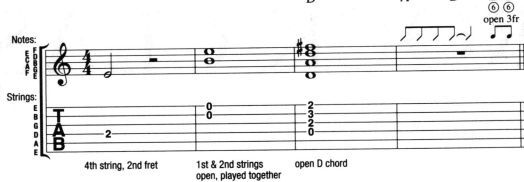

4th string, 2nd fret   1st & 2nd strings open, played together   open D chord

Definitions for special guitar notation

SEMI-TONE BEND: Strike the note and bend up a semi-tone (1/2 step).

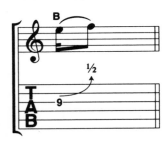

WHOLE-TONE BEND: Strike the note and bend up a whole-tone (whole step).

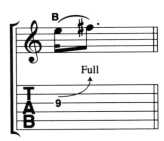

GRACE NOTE BEND: Strike the note and bend as indicated. Play the first note as quickly as possible.

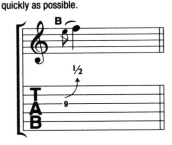

QUARTER-TONE BEND: Strike the note and bend up a 1/4 step.

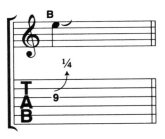

BEND & RELEASE: Strike the note and bend up as indicated, then release back to the original note.

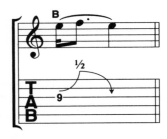

COMPOUND BEND & RELEASE: Strike the note and bend up and down in the rhythm indicated.

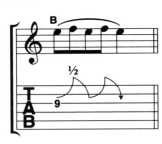

PRE-BEND: Bend the note as indicated, then strike it.

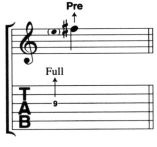

PRE-BEND & RELEASE: Bend the note as indicated. Strike it and release the note back to the original pitch.

UNISON BEND: Strike the two notes simultaneously and bend the lower note up to the pitch of the higher.

BEND & RESTRIKE: Strike the note and bend as indicated then restrike the string where the symbol occurs.

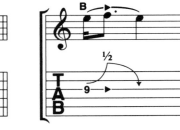

BEND, HOLD AND RELEASE: Same as bend and release but hold the bend for the duration of the tie.

BEND AND TAP: Bend the note as indicated and tap the higher fret while still holding the bend.

VIBRATO: The string is vibrated by rapidly bending and releasing the note with the fretting hand.

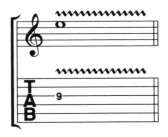

HAMMER-ON: Strike the first (lower) note with one finger, then sound the higher note (on the same string) with another finger by fretting it without picking.

PULL-OFF: Place both fingers on the notes to be sounded, Strike the first note and without picking, pull the finger off to sound the second (lower) note.

LEGATO SLIDE (GLISS): Strike the first note and then slide the same fret-hand finger up or down to the second note. The second note is not struck.

NOTE: The speed of any bend is indicated by the music notation and tempo.

SHIFT SLIDE (GLISS & RESTRIKE): Same as legato slide, except the second note is struck.

TRILL: Very rapidly alternate between the notes indicated by continuously hammering on and pulling off.

TAPPING: Hammer ("tap") the fret indicated with the pick-hand index or middle finger and pull off to the note fretted by the fret hand.

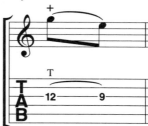

PICK SCRAPE: The edge of the pick is rubbed down (or up) the string, producing a scratchy sound.

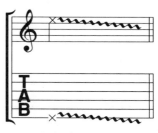

MUFFLED STRINGS: A percussive sound is produced by laying the fret hand across the string(s) without depressing, and striking them with the pick hand.

NATURAL HARMONIC: Strike the note while the fret-hand lightly touches the string directly over the fret indicated.

Harm.

PINCH HARMONIC: The note is fretted normally and a harmonic is produced by adding the edge of the thumb or the tip of the index finger of the pick hand to the normal pick attack.

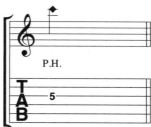

P.H.

HARP HARMONIC: The note is fretted normally and a harmonic is produced by gently resting the pick hand's index finger directly above the indicated fret (in parentheses) while the pick hand's thumb or pick assists by plucking the appropriate string.

H.H.

PALM MUTING: The note is partially muted by the pick hand lightly touching the string(s) just before the bridge.

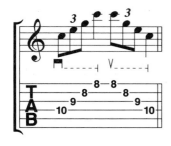

P.M.

RAKE: Drag the pick across the strings indicated with a single motion.

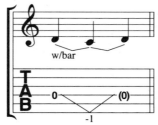

rake

TREMOLO PICKING: The note is picked as rapidly and continuously as possible.

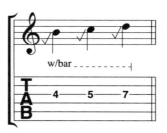

ARPEGGIATE: Play the notes of the chord indicated by quickly rolling them from bottom to top.

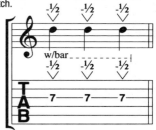

SWEEP PICKING: Rhythmic downstroke and/or upstroke motion across the strings.

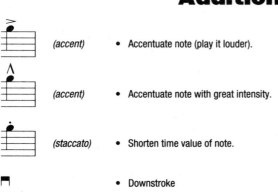

VIBRATO DIVE BAR AND RETURN: The pitch of the note or chord is dropped a specific number of steps (in rhythm) then returned to the original pitch.

w/bar

VIBRATO BAR SCOOP: Depress the bar just before striking the note, then quickly release the bar.

w/bar

VIBRATO BAR DIP: Strike the note and then immediately drop a specific number of steps, then release back to the original pitch.

w/bar

Additional musical definitions

	(accent)	• Accentuate note (play it louder).
	(accent)	• Accentuate note with great intensity.
	(staccato)	• Shorten time value of note.
		• Downstroke
V		• Upstroke

D.%. al Coda

• Go back to the sign (%), then play until the bar marked *To Coda* ⊕ then skip to the section marked ⊕ *Coda*.

D.C. al Fine

• Go back to the beginning of the song and play until the bar marked *Fine* (end).

tacet

• Instrument is silent (drops out).

• Repeat bars between signs.

1. **2.**

• When a repeated section has different endings, play the first ending only the first time and the second ending only the second time.

NOTE: Tablature numbers in parentheses mean:
1. The note is sustained, but a new articulation (such as hammer on or slide) begins.
2. A note may be fretted but not necessarily played.

A DESIGN FOR LIFE

Music by James Dean Bradfield & Sean Moore
Lyrics by Nicky Wire

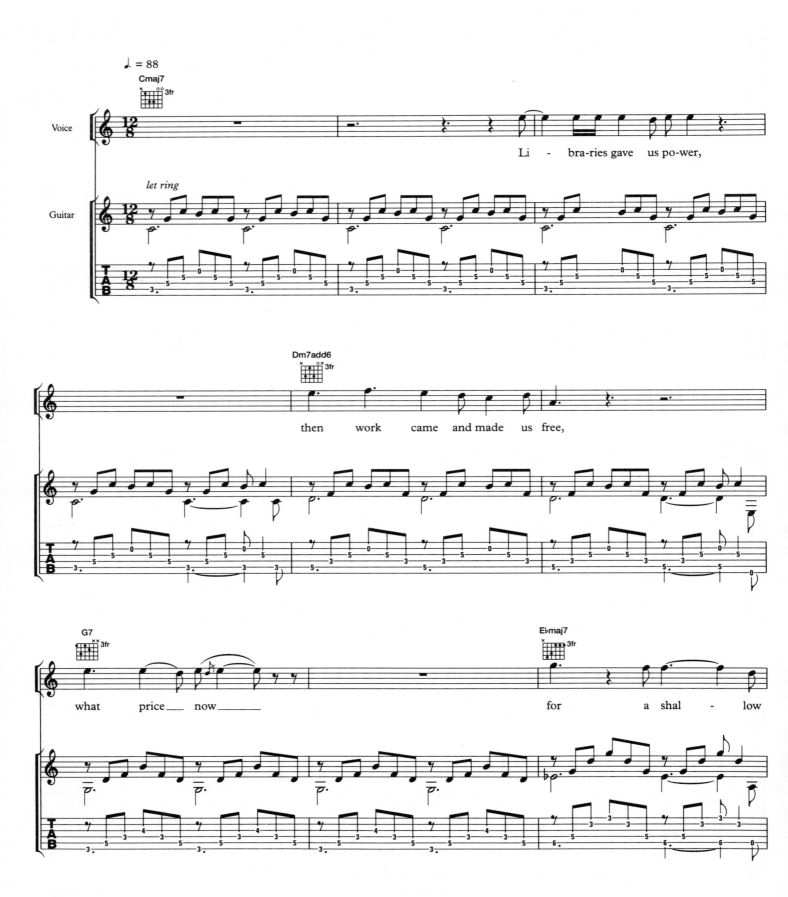

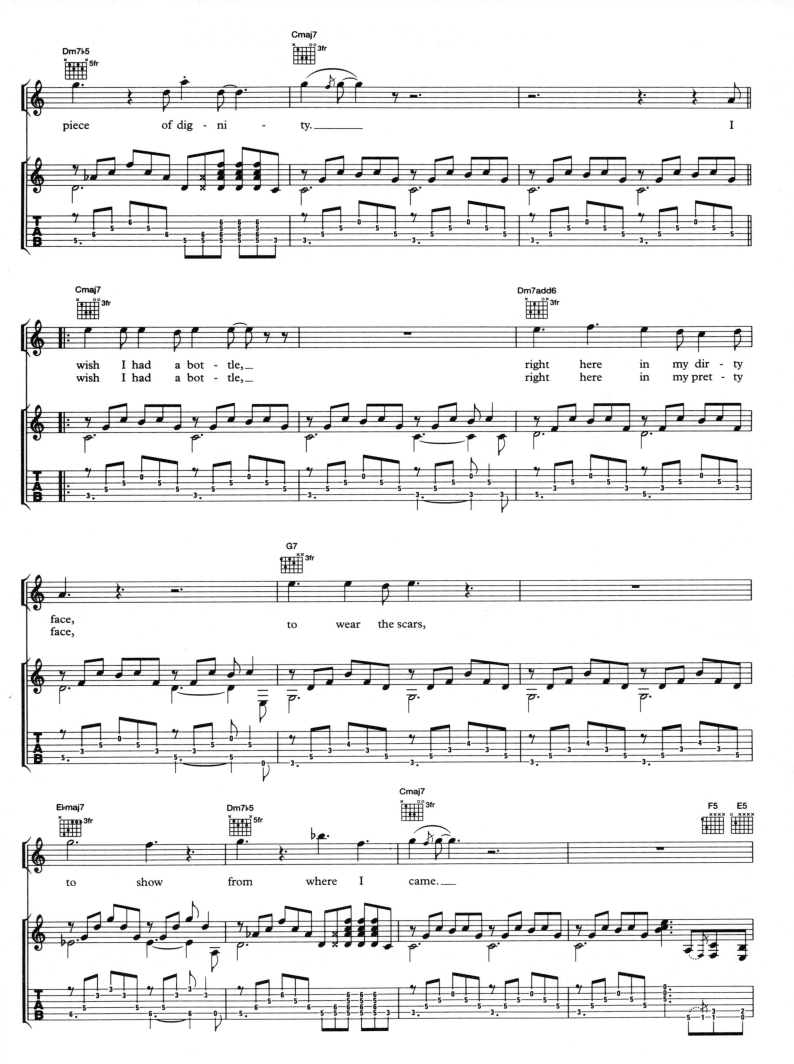

A DAY IN THE LIFE

Words & Music by John Lennon & Paul McCartney

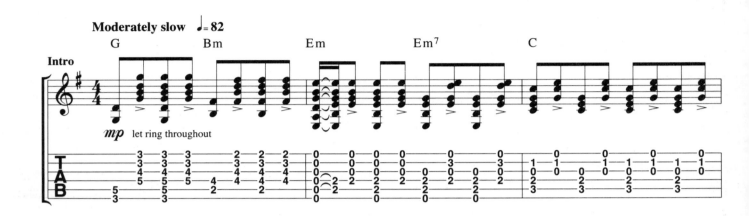

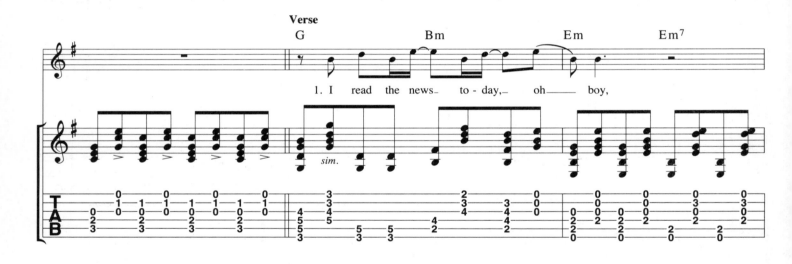

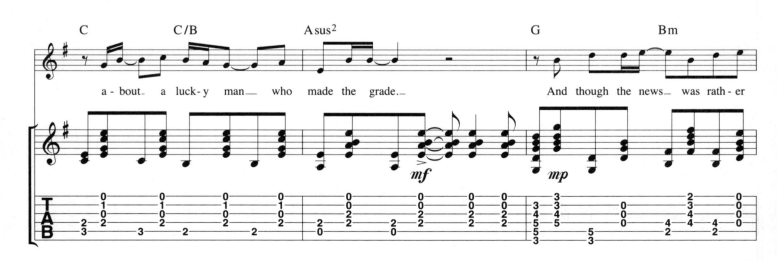

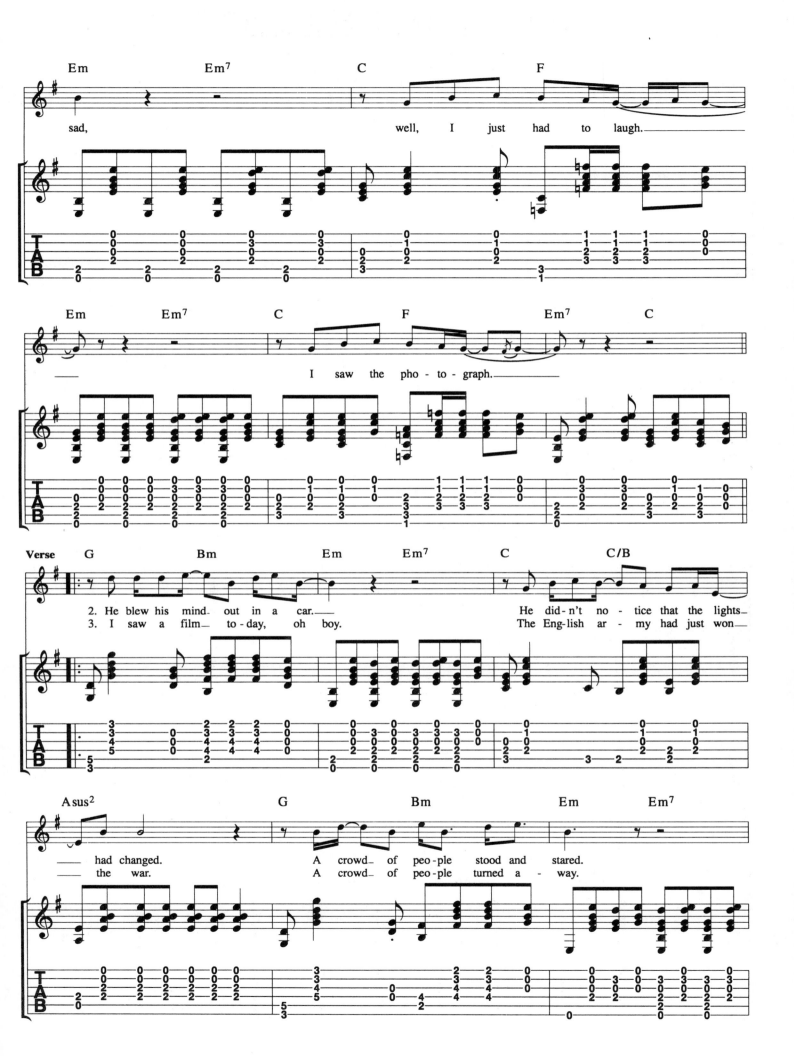

They'd seen his face be-fore.— No-bo-dy was real-ly sure if he was from the House of Lords.—
But I just had to look,—

hav-ing read the book.— I'd love to

Orchestral Interlude
Double-time ♩=164
Gtr. tacet N.C.(B)

turn_____ you_____ on._____

Spoken: Four, five, six, sev-en. *etc.*

E

Woke up, fell out of bed, dragged a comb a-cross my head.__ Found my way down-stairs and drank__ a cup, and look-ing up__ I no-ticed I was late. Found my coat and grabbed my hat,__ made the

CHARMLESS MAN

Words & Music by Damon Albarn, Alex James, Graham Coxon & Dave Rowntree

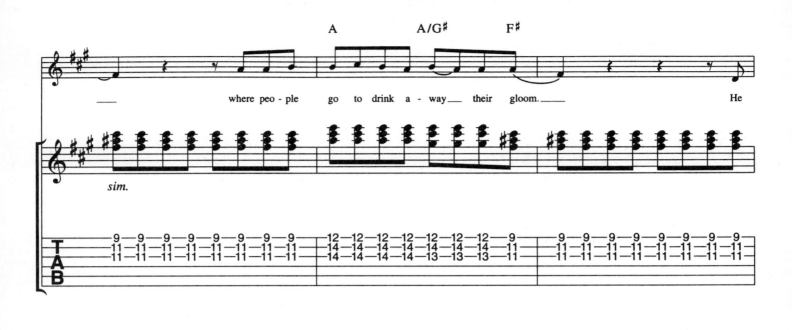

where peo - ple go to drink a - way___ their gloom.___ He

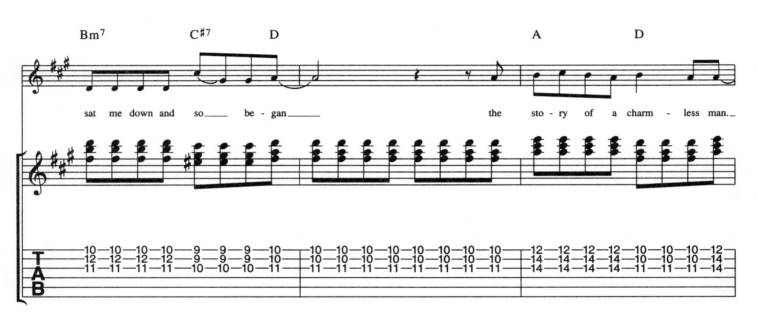

sat me down and so___ be - gan___ the sto - ry of a charm - less man.___

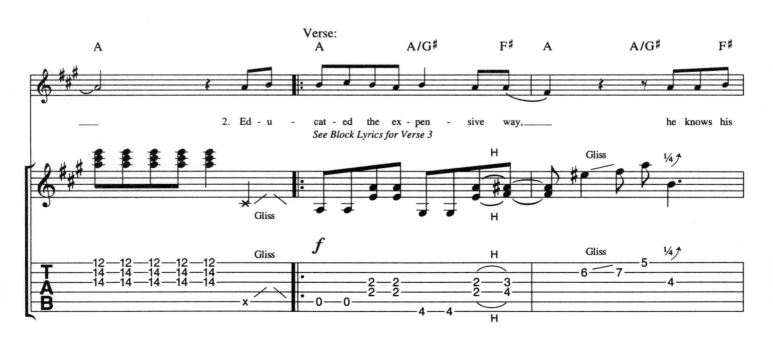

Verse:

2. Ed - u - cat - ed the ex - pen - sive way,___ he knows his

See Block Lyrics for Verse 3

Cla - ret from his Beau - jol - ais._____ I think he'd like to have been Ron - nie Kray,_____

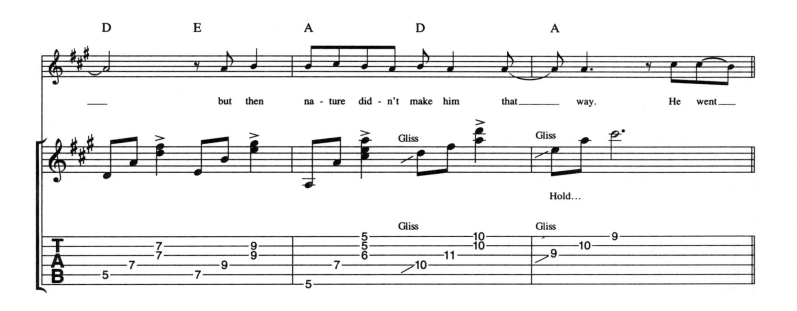

_____ but then na - ture did - n't make him that_____ way. He went_____

Hold...

Chorus:

na na na na na na na,_____ na na na na na na na na.

See Block Lyrics for Chorus 2:

Bend Hold...

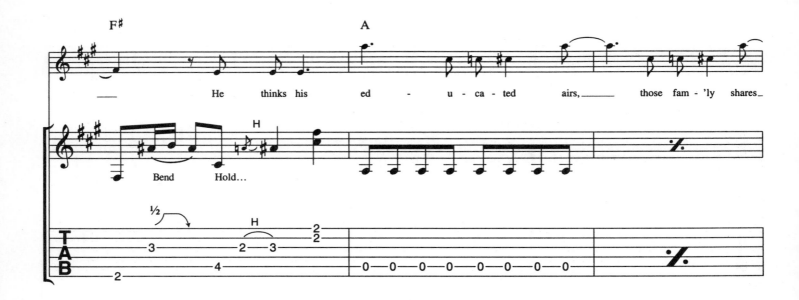

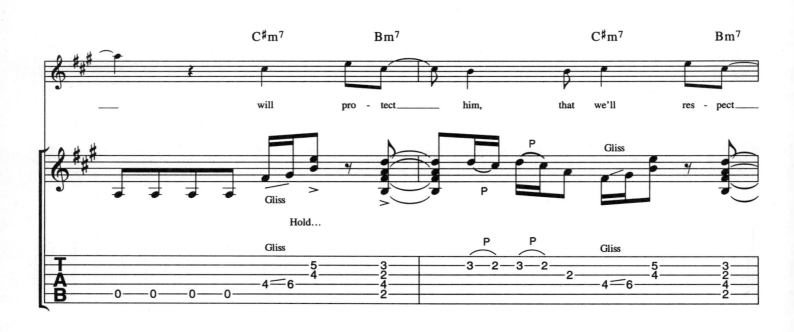

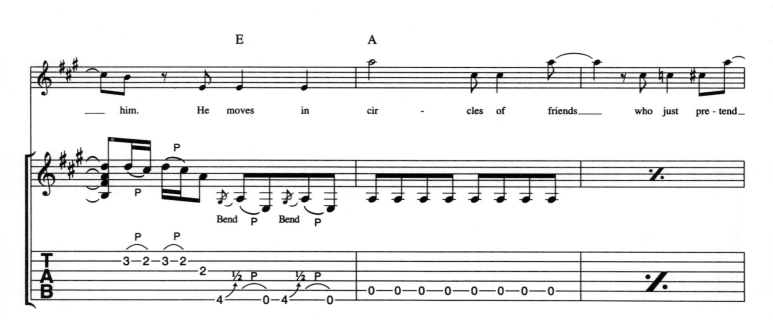

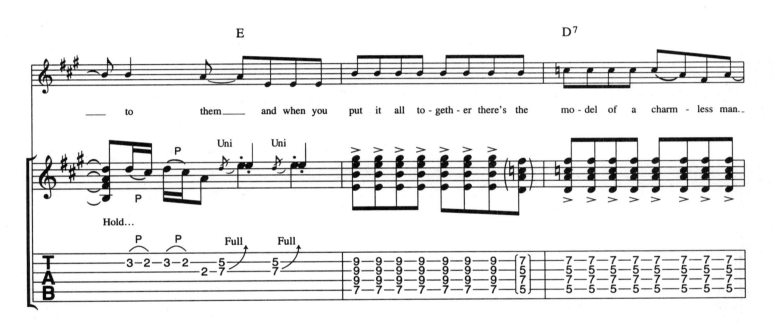

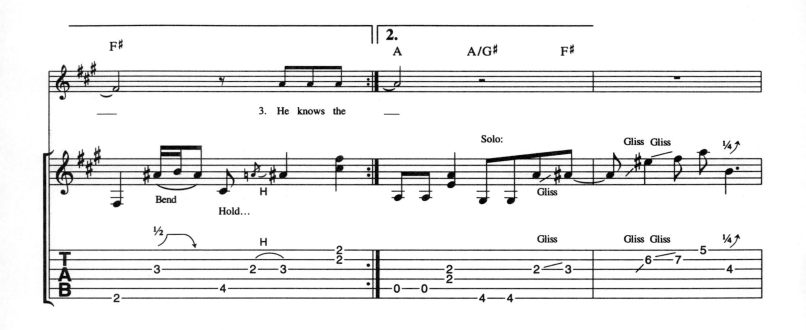

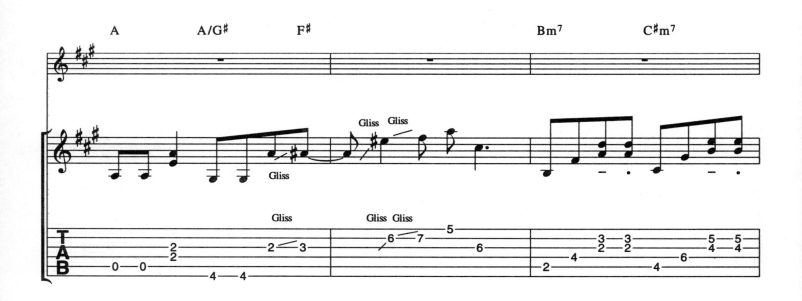

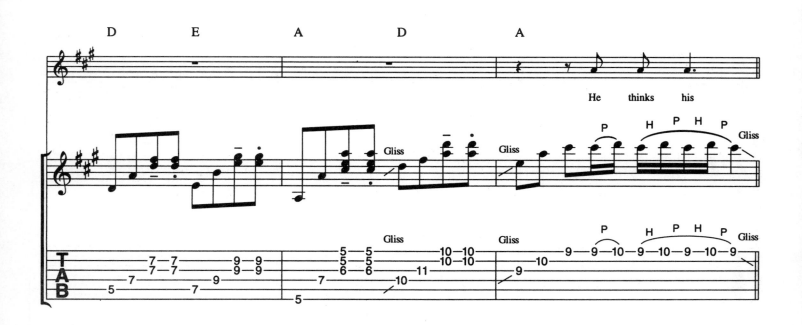

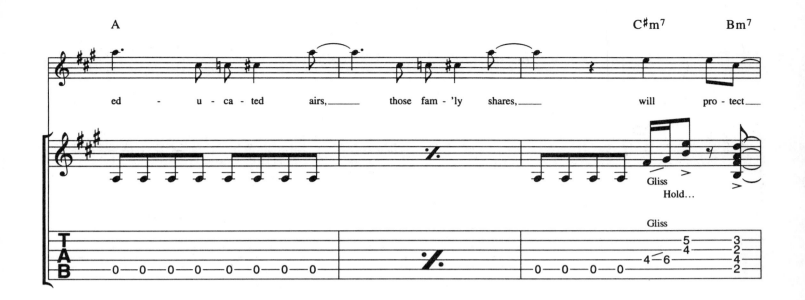

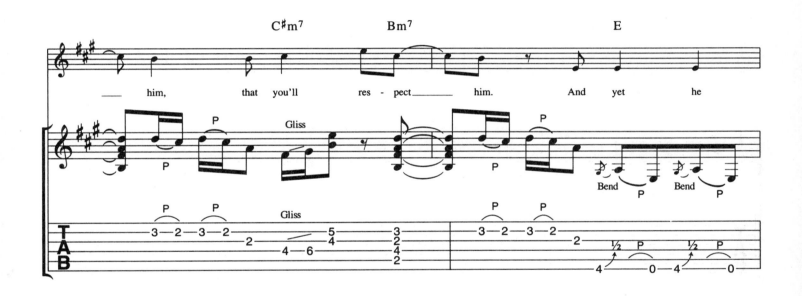

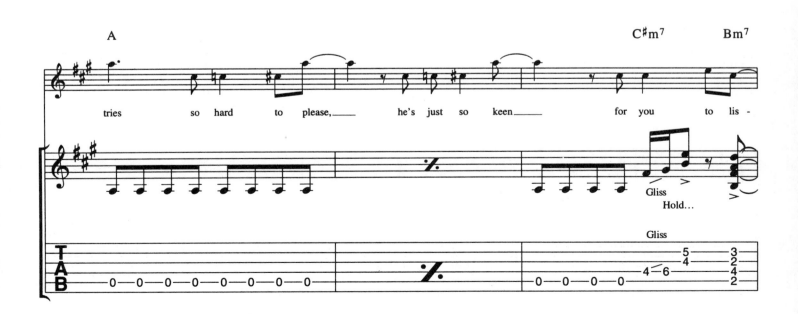

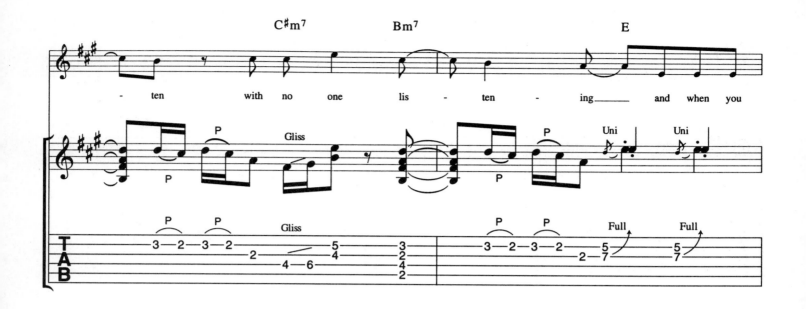

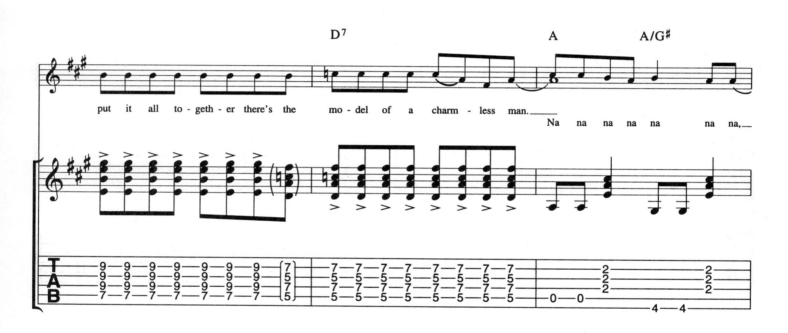

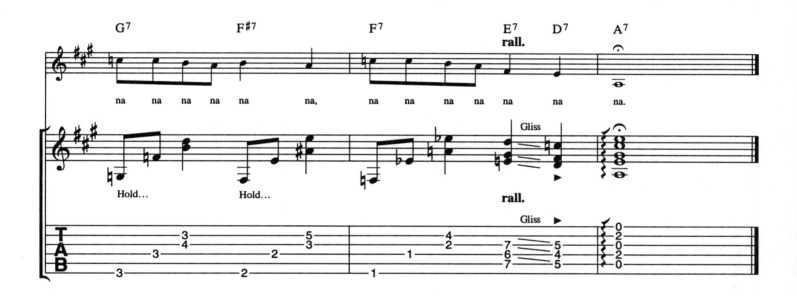

Verse 3:
He knows the swingers and their cavalry
Says he can get in anywhere for free
I began to go a little cross-eyed
And from this charmless man I just had to hide.

Chorus 2:
He went na na na na na na na
Na na na na na na na na na
He talks at speed, he gets nose bleeds
He doesn't see his days
Are tumbling down upon him
And yet he tries so hard to please
He's just so keen for you to listen
But no one is listening
And when you put it all together
There's the model of a charmless man.

DISCO 2000

Music by Pulp
Lyrics by Jarvis Cocker

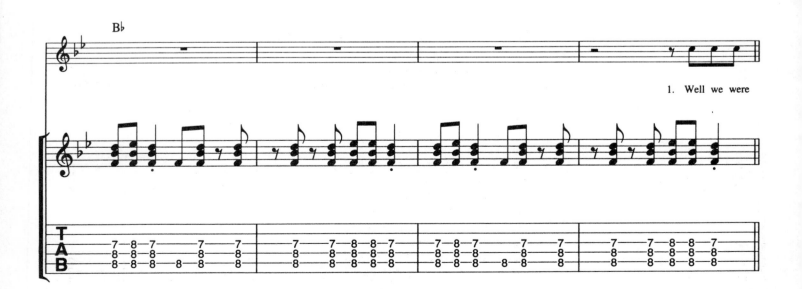

1. Well we were

Verse:

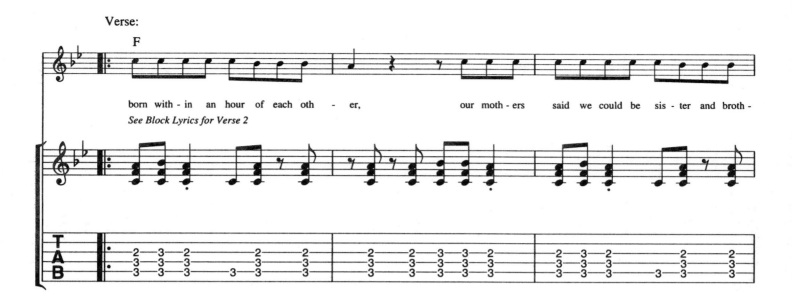

born with-in an hour of each oth - er, our moth-ers said we could be sis-ter and broth-
See Block Lyrics for Verse 2

- er, your name is De-bo-rah, De-bo-rah,_____ it nev-er

suit-ed ya. And they said that when we grew up____
on 𝄋 Do it!

we'd get mar - ried and nev - er split up,_____ oh,____ we nev - er

Oh, yeah,

did it, al - though I of - ten thought of it.____ Oh,

oh, yeah.

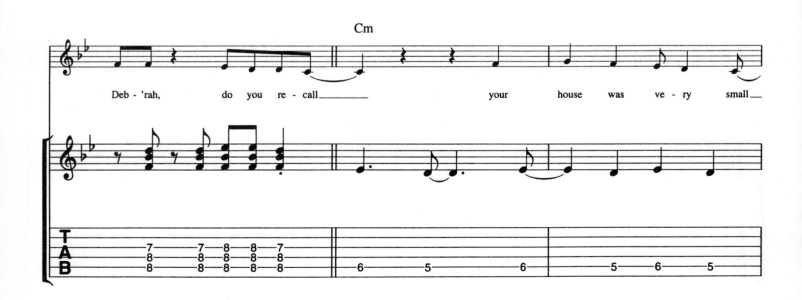

Deb - 'rah, do you re - call_____ your house was ve - ry small___

with wood-chip on the wall_____ when I_____ came round_ to call_

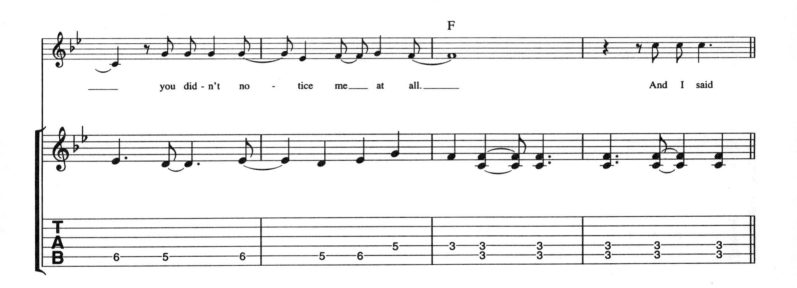

F

_____ you did-n't no - tice me___ at all._____ And I said

Chorus:

B♭   Dm

Let's all meet up_____ in the year_____ two thou - sand, won't it be strange___ when we're___

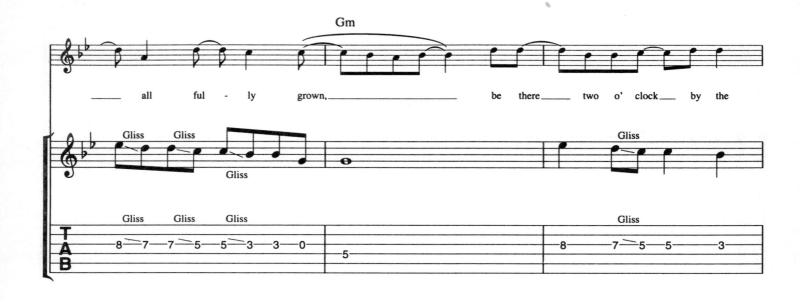

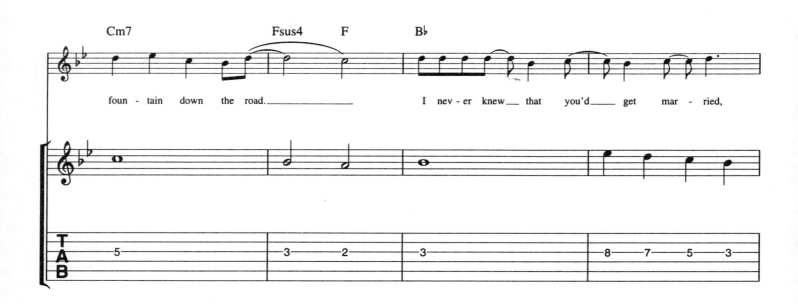

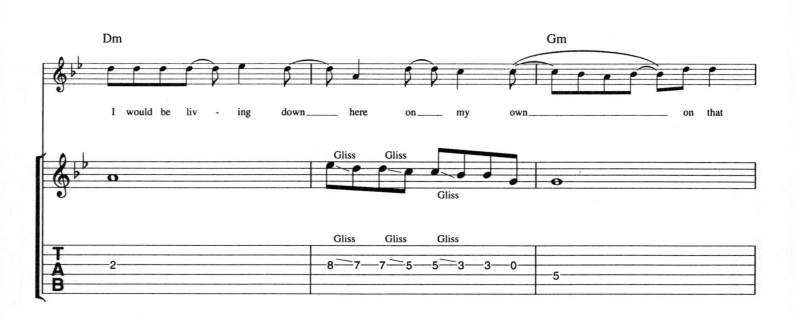

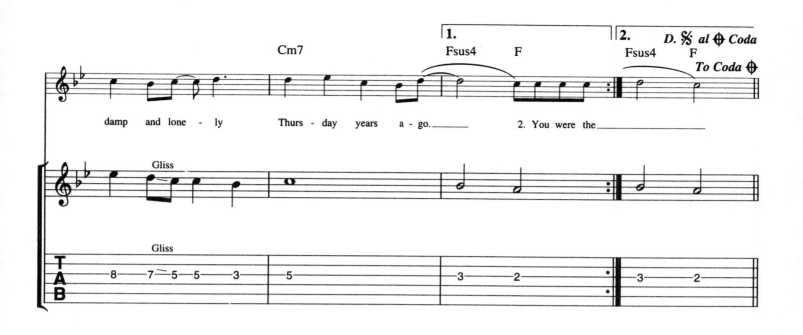

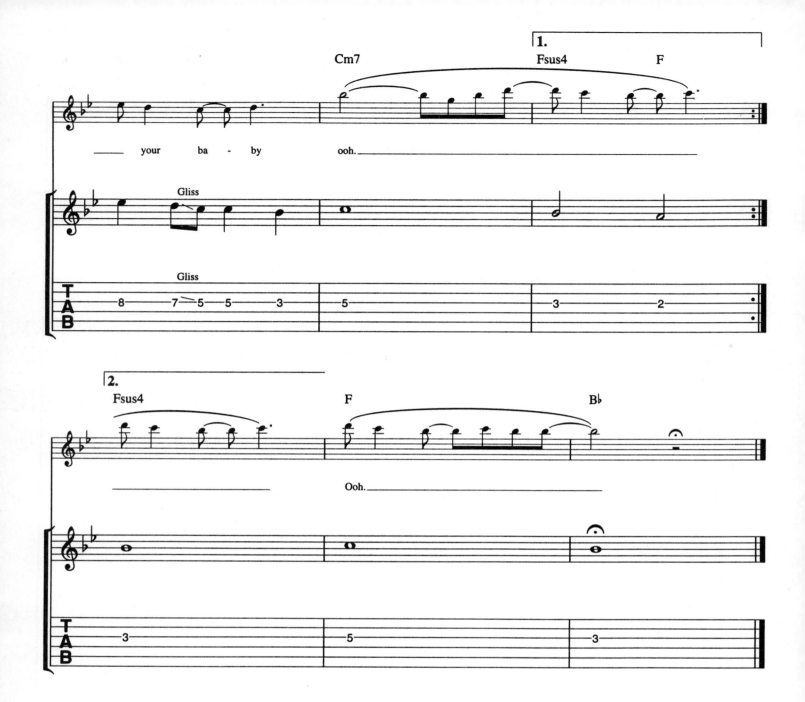

Verse 2:
You were the first girl at school to get breasts
Martyn said that yours were the best
The boys all loved you but I was a mess
I had to watch them try and get you undressed
We were friends, that was as far as it went
I used to walk you home sometimes but it meant
Oh, it meant nothing to you
'Cause you were so popular.

GET UP, STAND UP

Words & Music by Bob Marley & Peter Tosh

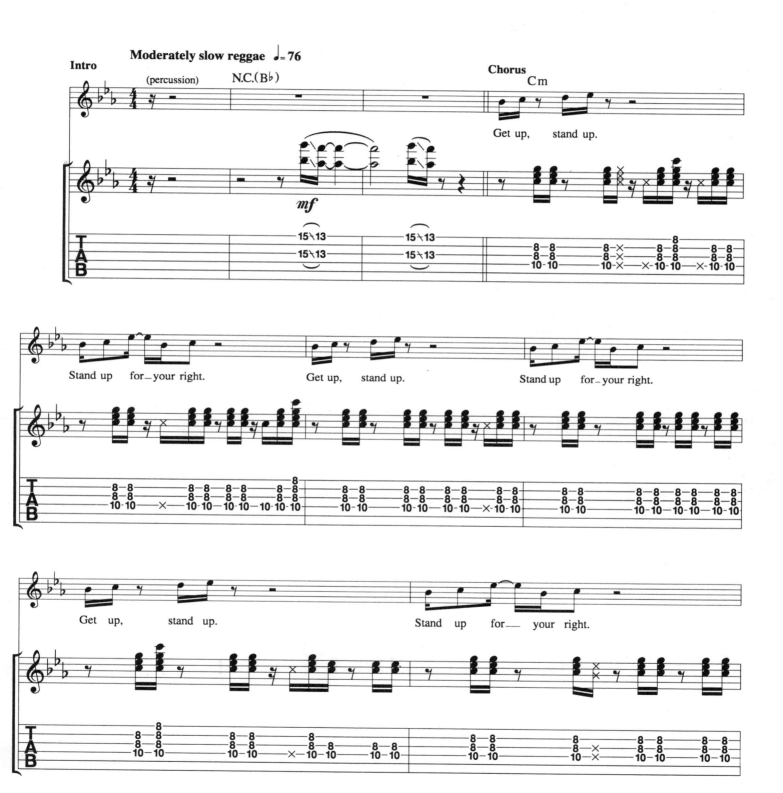

HAND IN MY POCKET

Words & Music by Alanis Morissette & Glenn Ballard

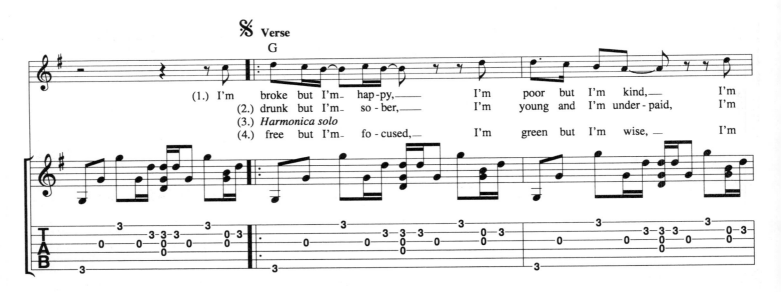

(1.) I'm broke but I'm hap-py, _____ I'm poor but I'm kind, _____ I'm
(2.) drunk but I'm so-ber, _____ I'm young and I'm under-paid, _____ I'm
(3.) *Harmonica solo*
(4.) free but I'm fo-cused, _____ I'm green but I'm wise, _____ I'm

short but I'm_ health - y, yeah. _____ I'm_ high but I'm ground - ed, I'm
tired but I'm_ work - ing, yeah. _____ I care but I'm rest - less, I'm
hard but I'm_ friend - ly ba - by. I'm_ sad but I'm laugh - ing, I'm

JAILHOUSE ROCK

Words & Music by Jerry Leiber & Mike Stoller

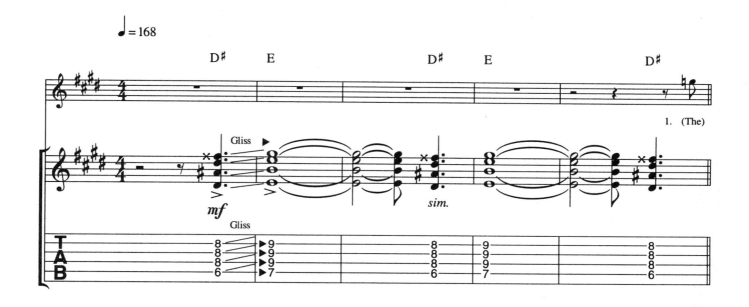

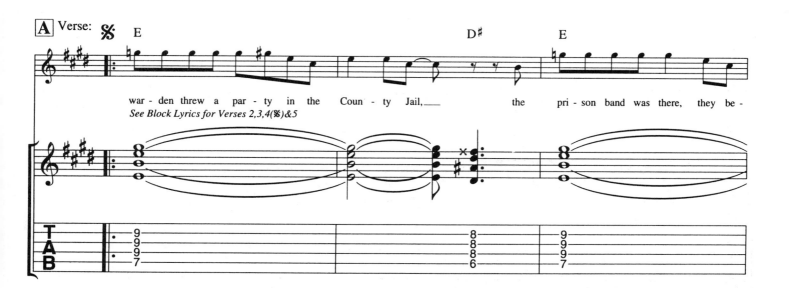

war - den threw a par - ty in the Coun - ty Jail, ___ the pri - son band was there, they be -

See Block Lyrics for Verses 2,3,4(%)&5

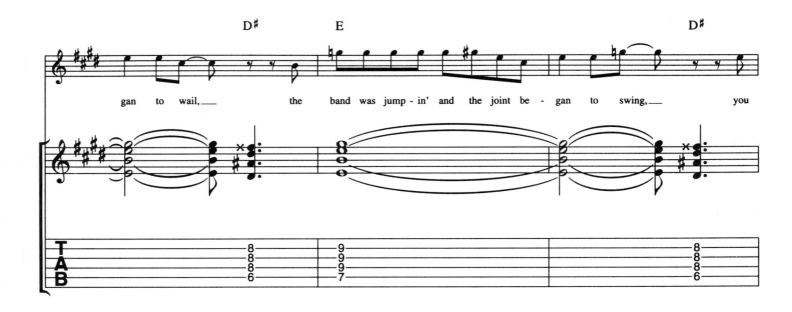

gan to wail,___ the band was jump-in' and the joint be - gan to swing,___ you

B Chorus:

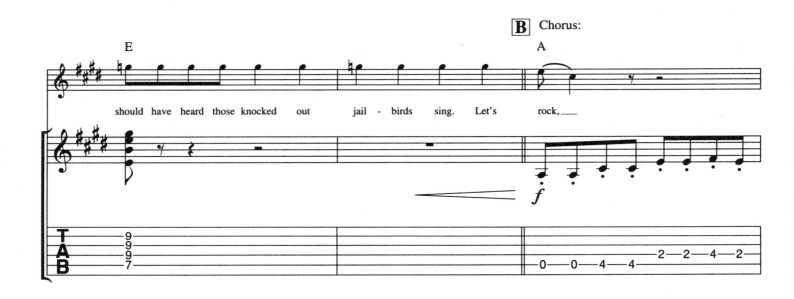

should have heard those knocked out jail - birds sing. Let's rock,___

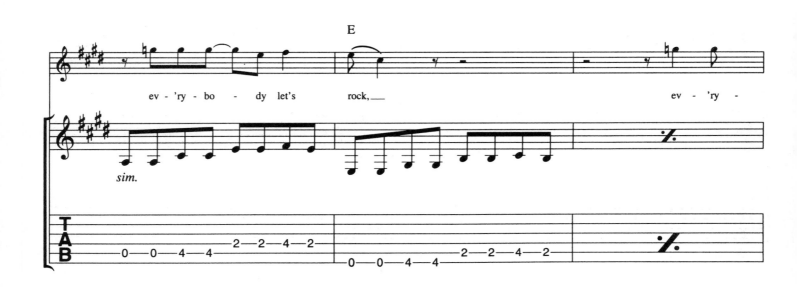

ev - 'ry-bo - dy let's rock,___ ev - 'ry -

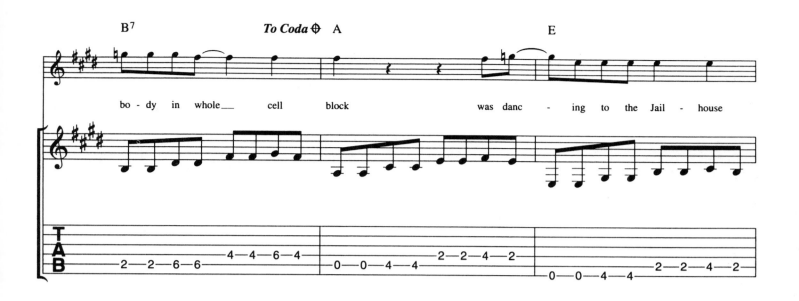

bo - dy in whole___ cell block   was danc   - ing to the Jail - house

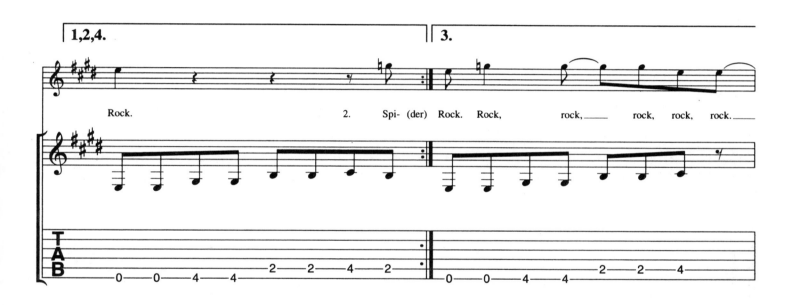

Rock.   2. Spi- (der) Rock. Rock,   rock,___   rock, rock, rock.___

C Guitar solo:

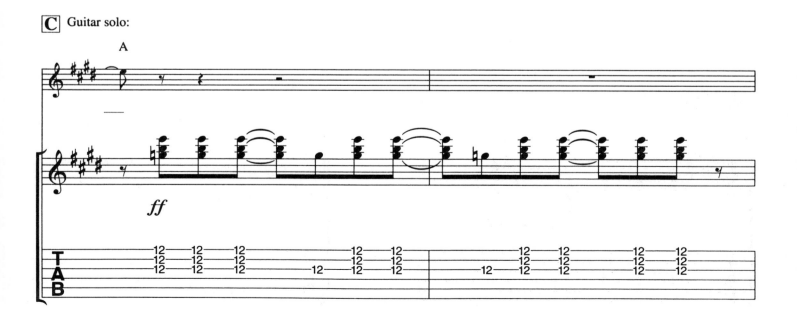

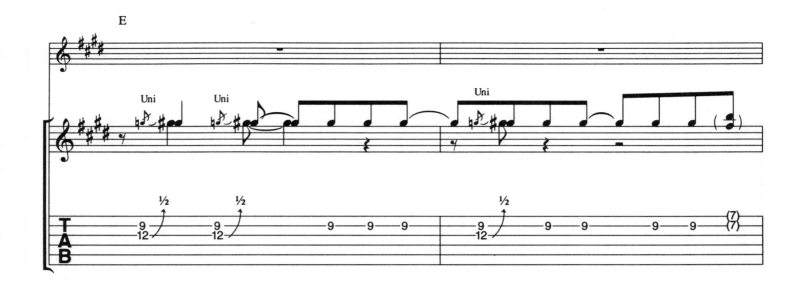

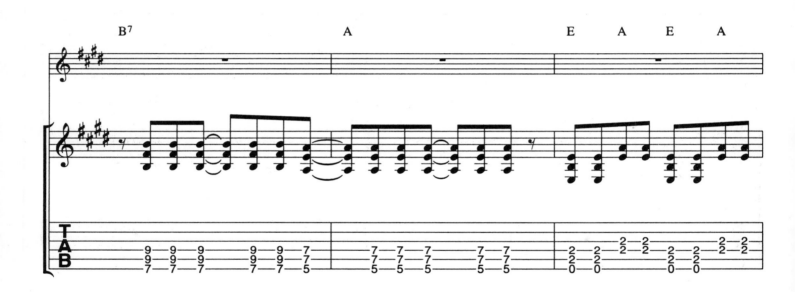

D.%. al ⊕ Coda
with repeat

⊕ *Coda*

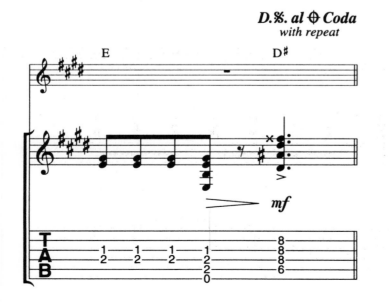

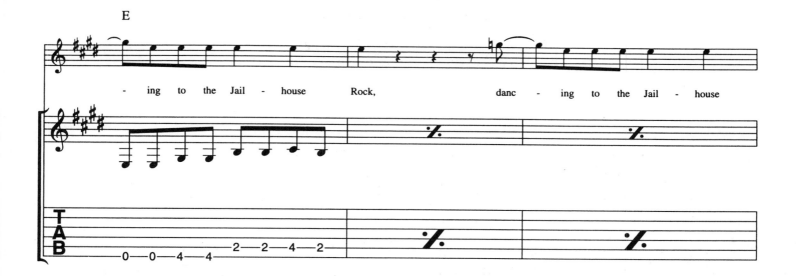

Verse 2:
Spider Murphy played his tenor saxophone
Little Joe was blowin' on the slide trombone
The drummer boy from Illinois went crash, boom, bang
The whole rhythm section was a purple gang.

Let's rock *etc...*

Verse 4(𝄋):
The sad sack was sittin' on a block of stone
Way over in the corner weepin' all alone
The warden said, "Hey buddy, don't you be no square"
If you can't find a partner, use a wooden chair."

Let's rock *etc...*

Verse 3:
Number Forty Seven said to Number Three
That "You're the cutest jailbird I ever did see
I sure would be delighted with your company
Come on and do the Jailhouse Rock with me."

Let's rock *etc...*

Verse 5:
Shifty Henry said to Bugs, "For Heaven's sake
No one's lookin' out, now's our chance to make a break"
Bugsy turned to Shifty and he said, "Nix, nix
I wanna stick around a while and get my kicks."

Let's rock *etc...*

IRONIC

Music by Alanis Morissette & Glenn Ballard
Lyrics by Alanis Morissette

*Symbols in parentheses represent chord names with respect to capoed guitar.
Symbols above reflect actual sounding chords.

Verse 2:

Mister Play It Safe was afraid to fly
He packed his suitcase and kissed his kids goodbye
He waited his whole damn life to take that flight
And as the plane crashed down he thought, "Well isn't this nice?"

It's like rain...*etc.*

LINGER

Music by Dolores O'Riordan & Noel Hogan
Words by Dolores O'Riordan

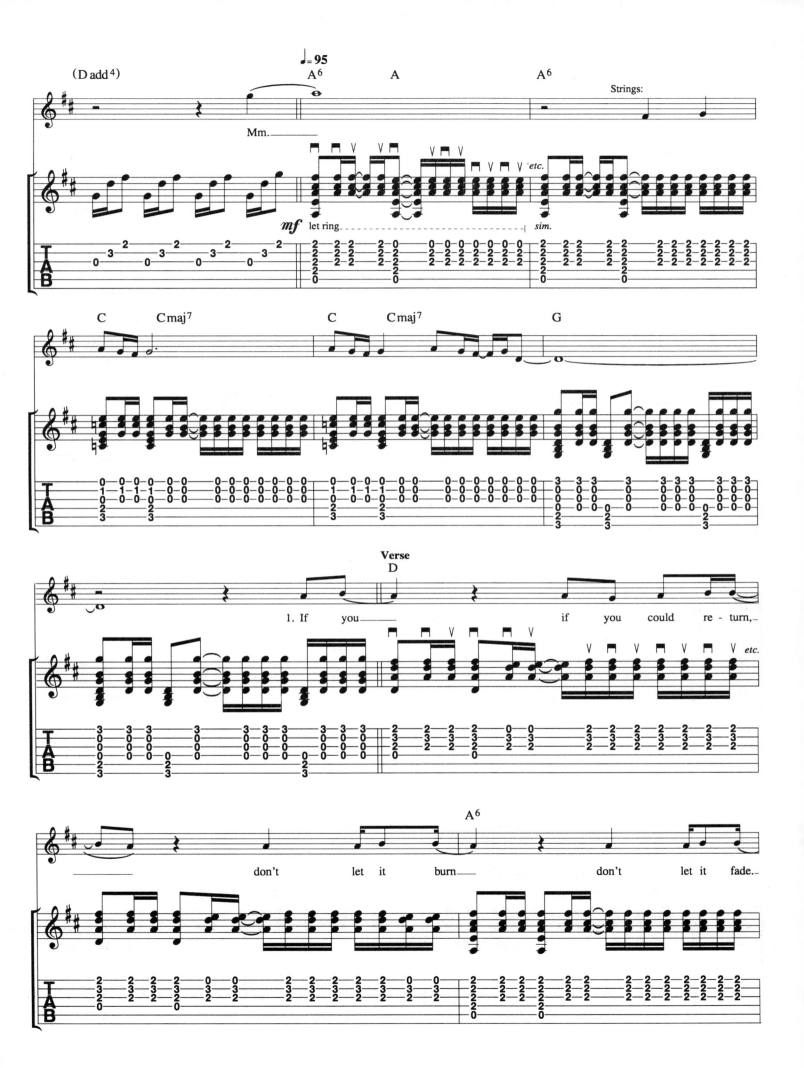

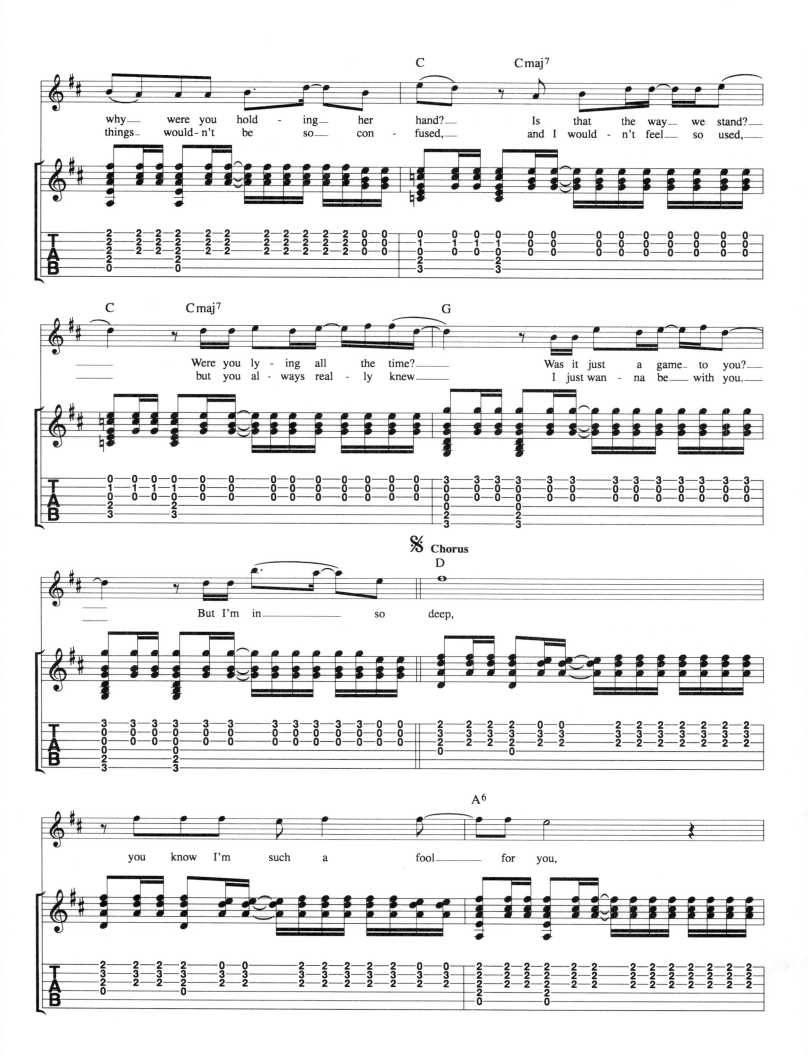

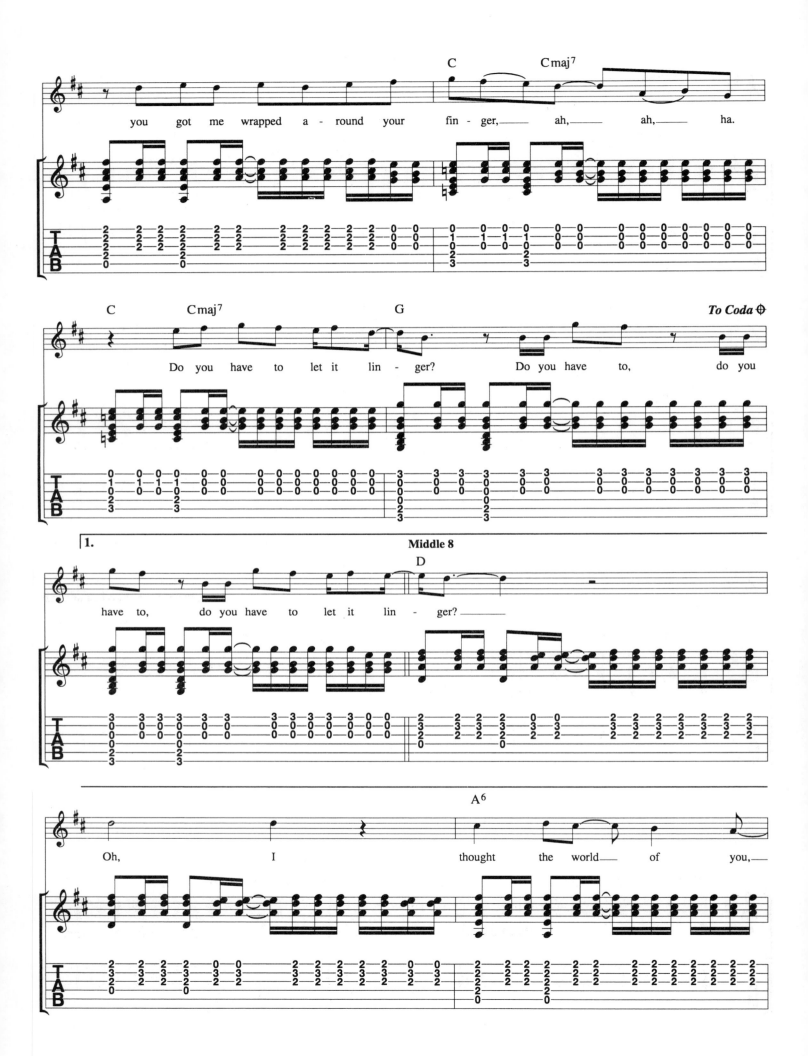

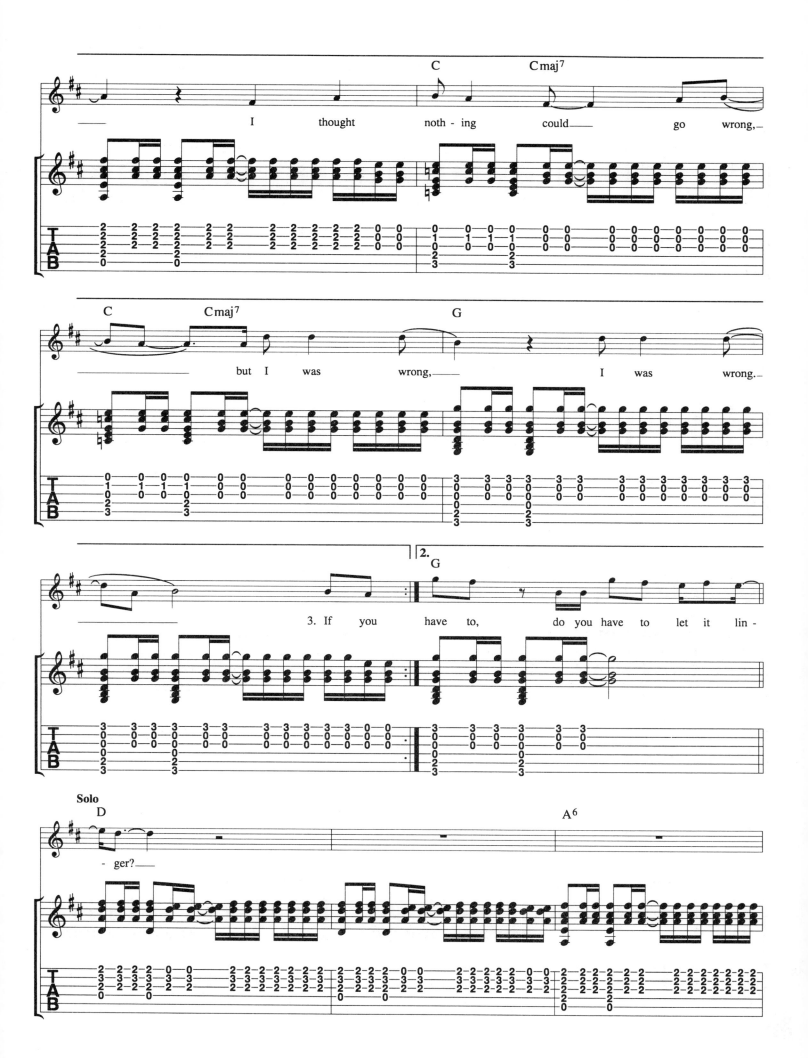

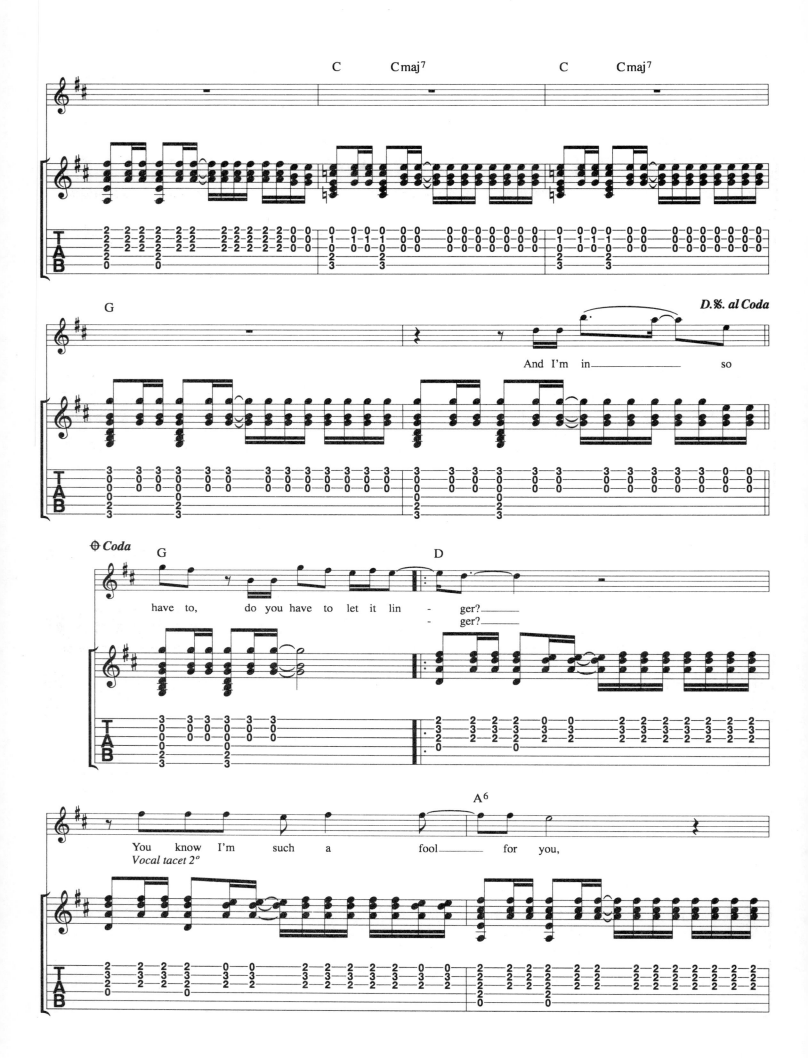

LAYLA
(Acoustic Version)

Words & Music by Eric Clapton & Jim Gordon

2nd and 3rd Verses

2. Tried to give you con-sol-a-tion, __ your old man had let you down. __

3. Make the best of the sit-u-a-tion, __ before I fin-ally go in-sane. __

Like __ a __ fool, I fall in love __ with you.

Please __ don't say we'll nev-er find __ a way.

beg-gin' darl-in', please. _ Lay-la, _____ darl-in' won't you ease my wor-ried mind. __

MESSAGE IN A BOTTLE

Words & Music by Sting

F#madd9   C#madd9   Aadd9   Badd9   F#madd9

_ oh. __   More   lone - li - ness __   than

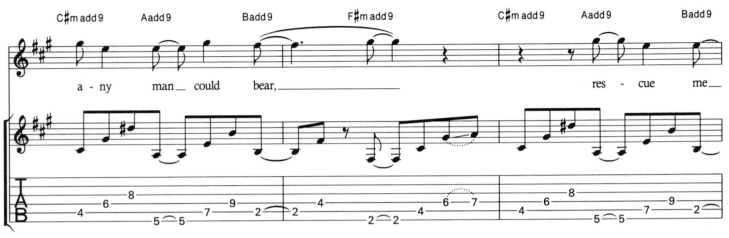

C#madd9   Aadd9   Badd9   F#madd9   C#madd9   Aadd9   Badd9

a - ny   man __   could   bear, _____   res - cue   me

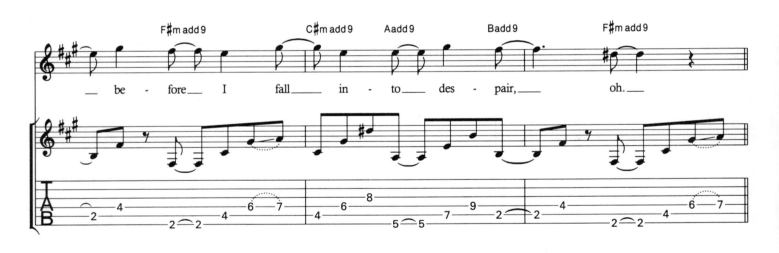

F#madd9   C#madd9   Aadd9   Badd9   F#madd9

_ be - fore __   I   fall __   in - to __   des - pair, __   oh. __

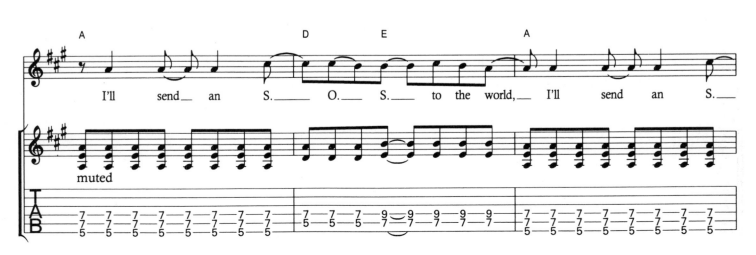

A   D   E   A

I'll   send __   an   S. __   O. __   S.   to the world, __   I'll   send   an   S. __

muted

68

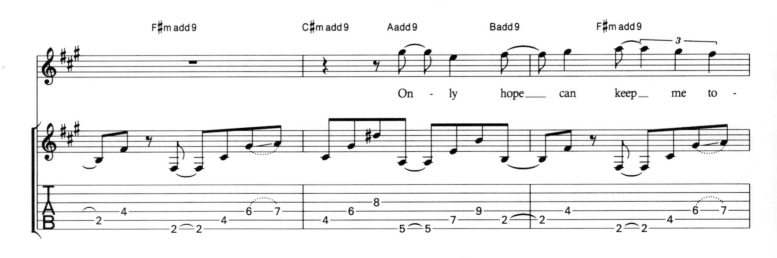

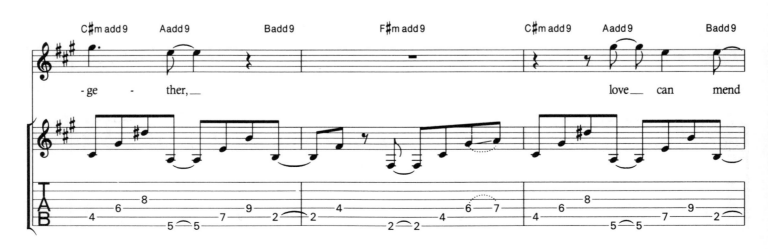

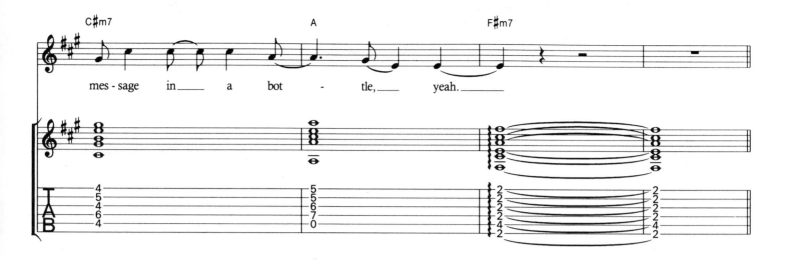

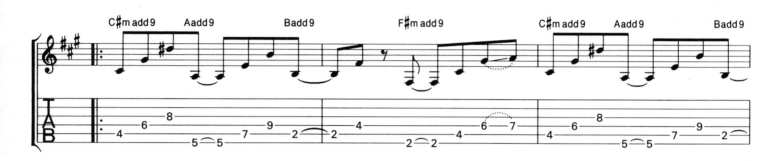

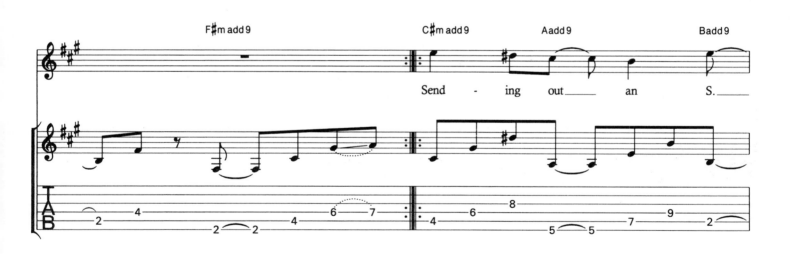

MR TAMBOURINE MAN

Words & Music by Bob Dylan

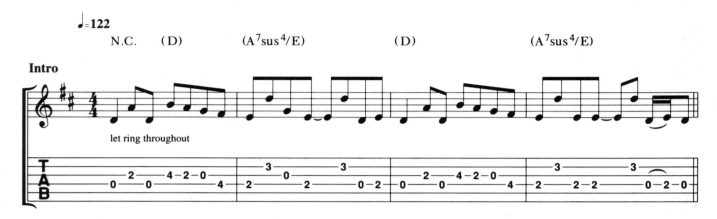

79

ONLY WOMEN BLEED

Words & Music by Alice Cooper & Dick Wagner

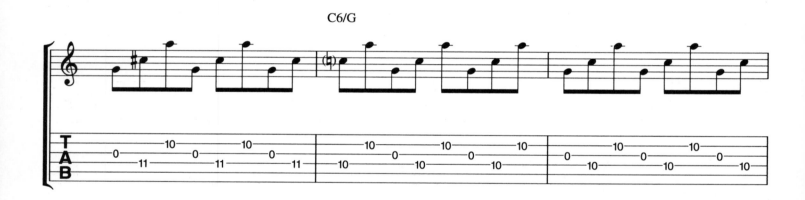

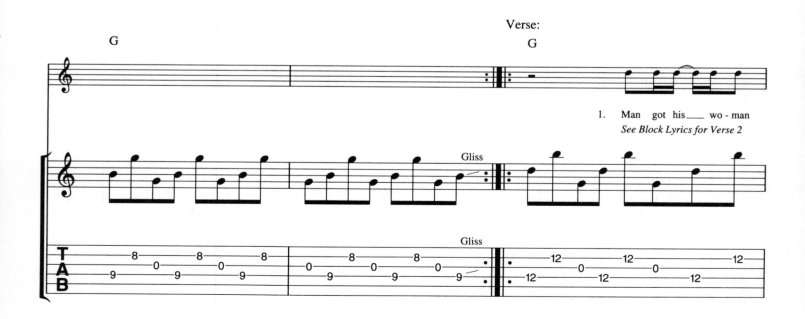

1. Man got his___ wo - man
See Block Lyrics for Verse 2

to take his seed,_____

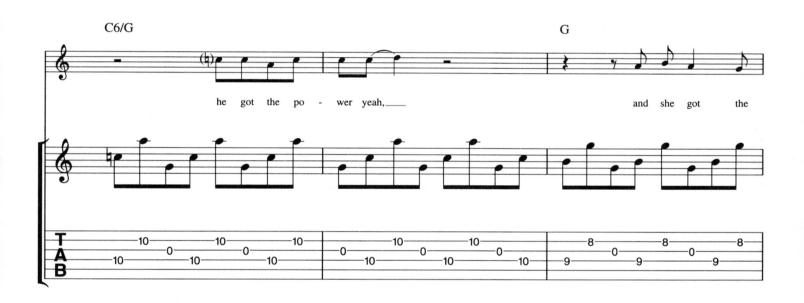

he got the po - wer yeah,_____

and she got the

need.

She spends her life_____ through

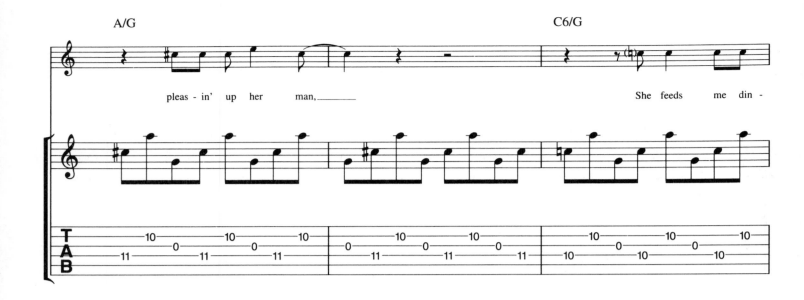

pleas - in' up her man,_____ She feeds me din -

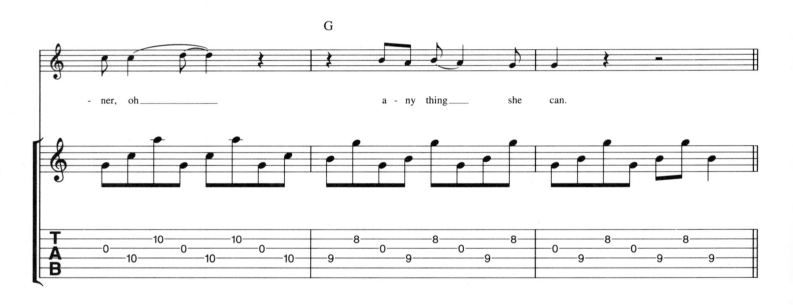

- ner, oh_____ a - ny thing___ she can.

Bridge:

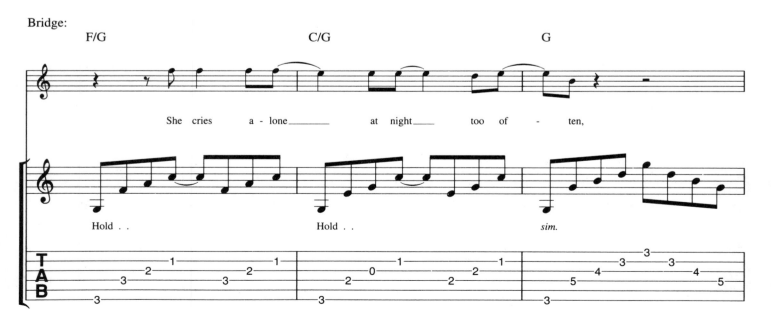

She cries a - lone_____ at night___ too of - ten,

Hold . .   Hold . .   *sim.*

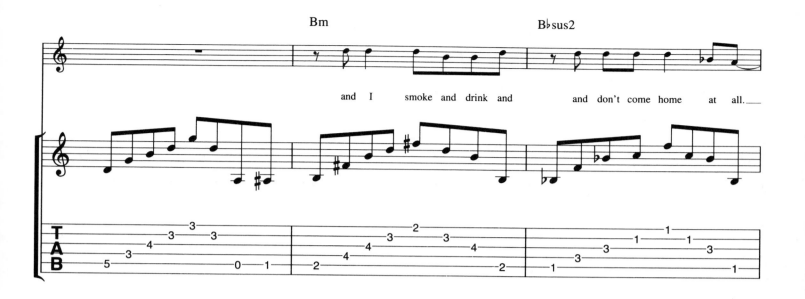

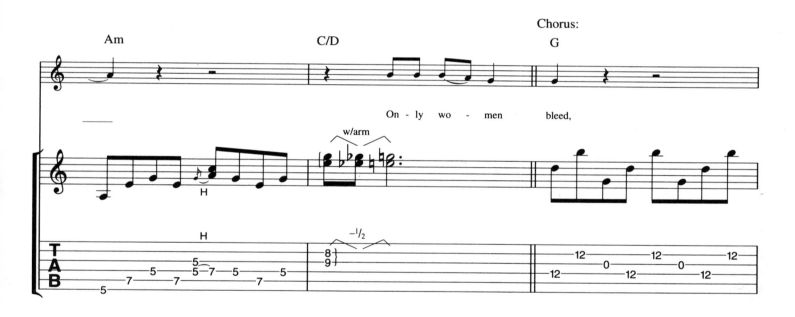

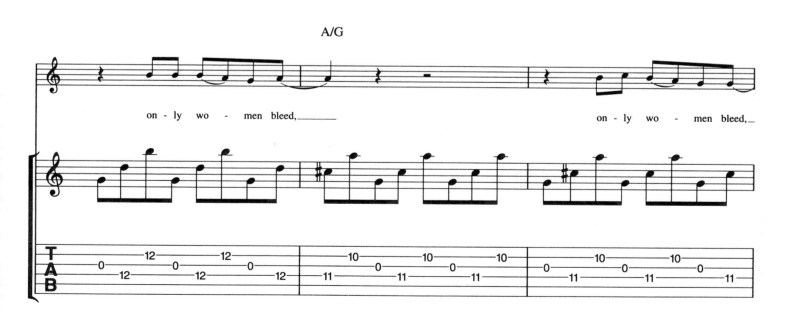

only wo - men bleed._____

Black eyes_____ all of the time,_____ don't spend a dime,_____

(Vocal tacet 1x)

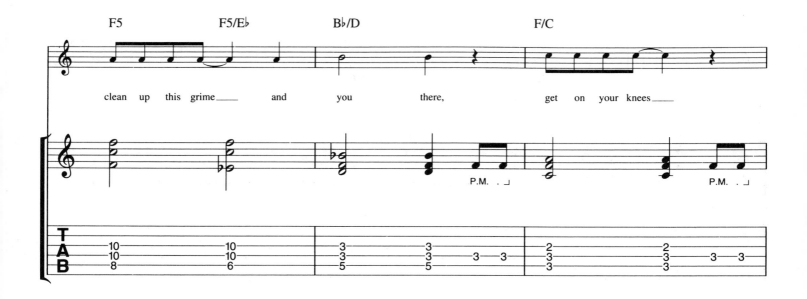

clean up this grime___ and you there, get on your knees___

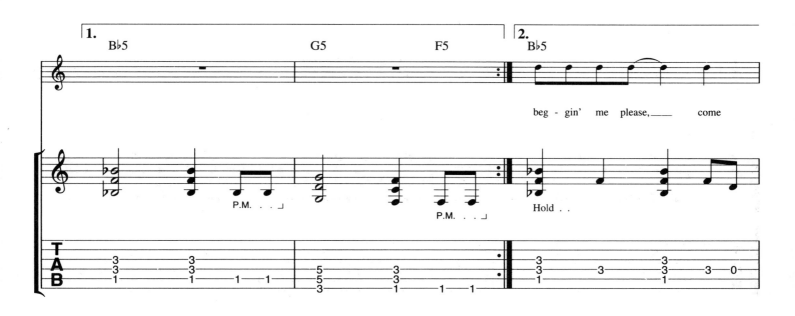

1. beg - gin' me please,___ come

2.

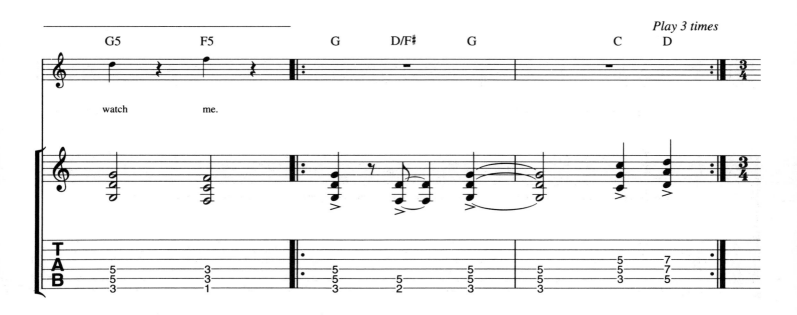

watch me.

Play 3 times

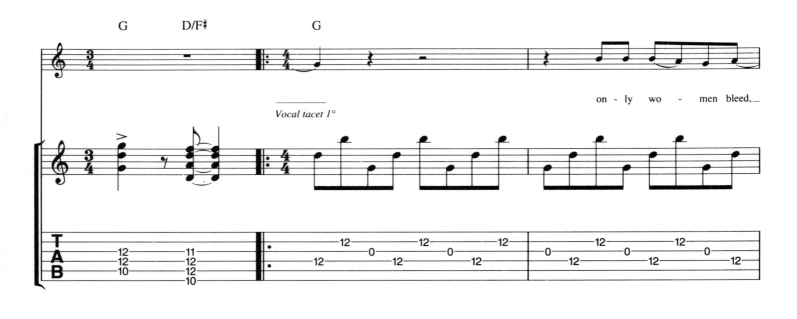

on - ly wo - men bleed,

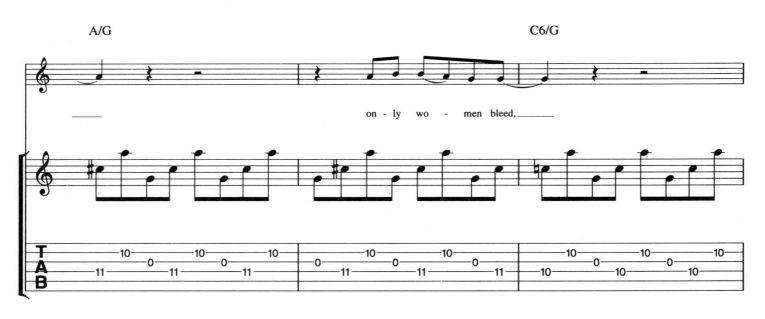

on - ly wo - men bleed,_____

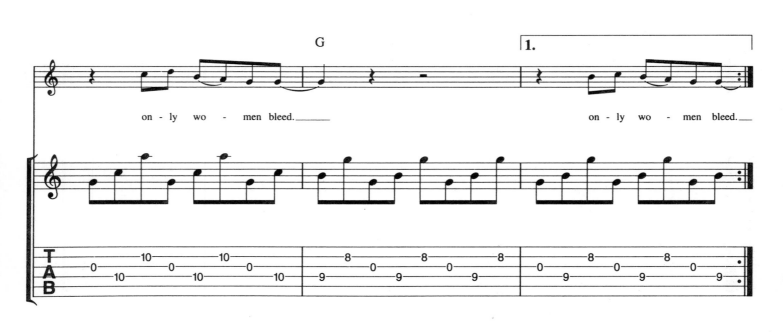

on - ly wo - men bleed._____

on - ly wo - men bleed.

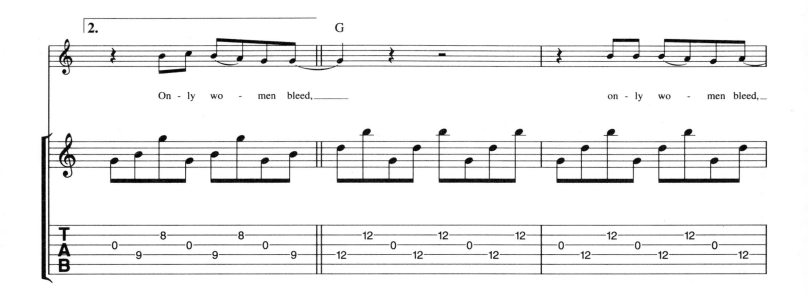

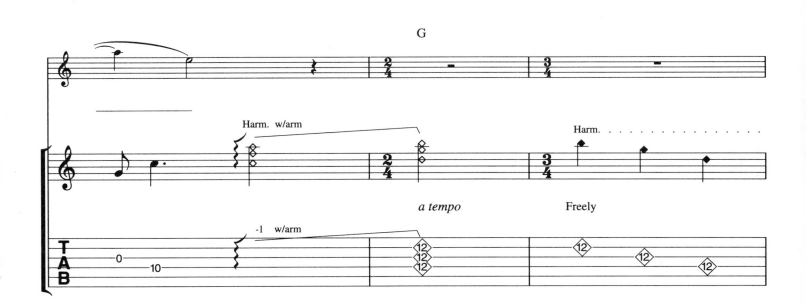

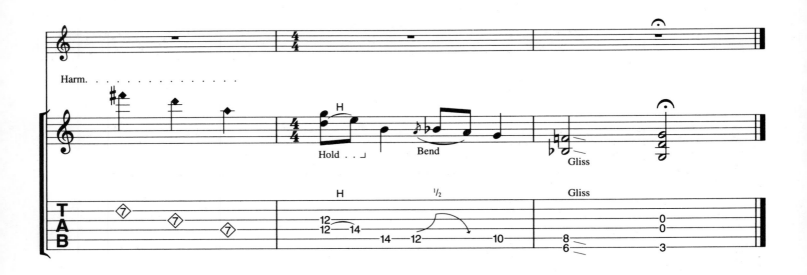

Verse 2:

        Now man makes your hair grey
        I'm a last mistake
        And all she's really lookin' for
        Is just an even break.

        I lied right at her
        You know she hates that game
        I slap her once in a while
        She lives in love and pain.

RIKKI DON'T LOSE THAT NUMBER

Words & Music by Walter Becker & Donald Fagen

1. We hear you're leav-ing, that's O. K.

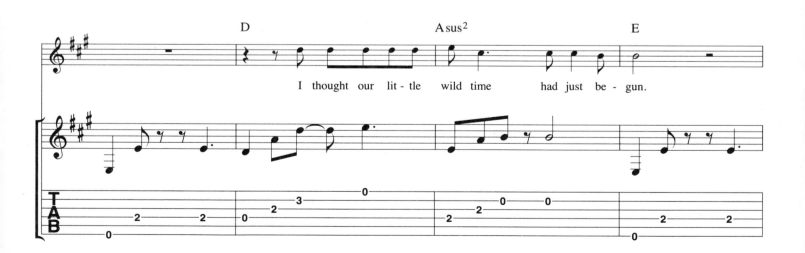

I thought our lit-tle wild time had just be-gun.

93

SUNDAY BLOODY SUNDAY

Words & Music by U2

Bm   D   G⁶

Bo - dies strewn a - cross the dead - end street.
there's ma - ny lost but tell me who has won?

Bm   D   G⁶

But I won't heed the bat - tle call,
The trench - es dug with in our hearts,

Bm   D   G⁶

it puts my back up, puts my back up a - gainst the wall.
and moth - er's chil - dren, broth - ers sis - ters torn a - part.

Chorus

Bm   D   G⁶   Bm   D

Sun - day, blood - y Sun - day.   Sun - day, blood - y Sun-

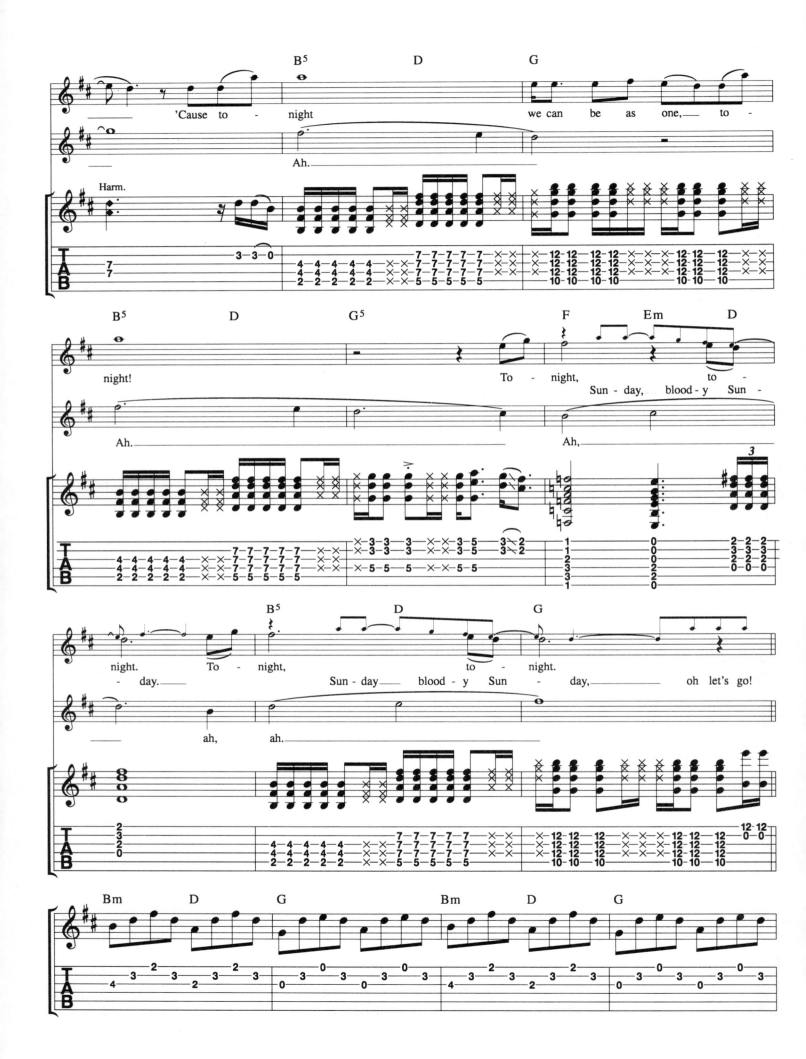

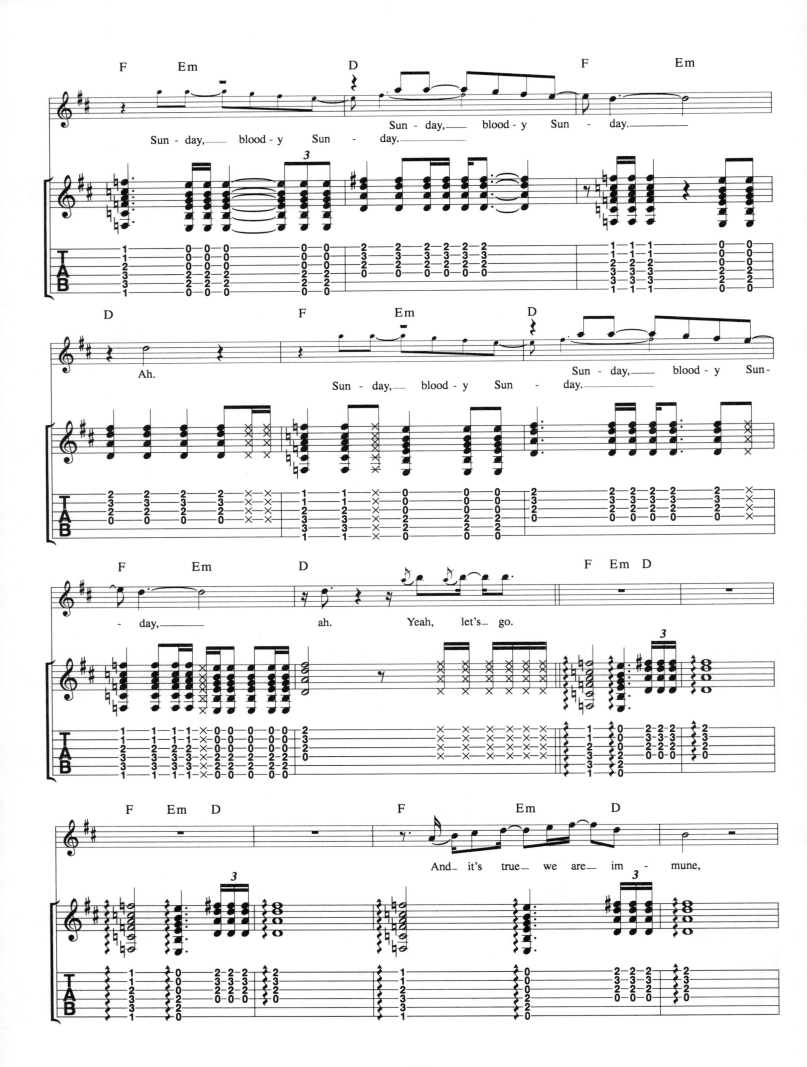

THAT'S ENTERTAINMENT

Words & Music by Paul Weller

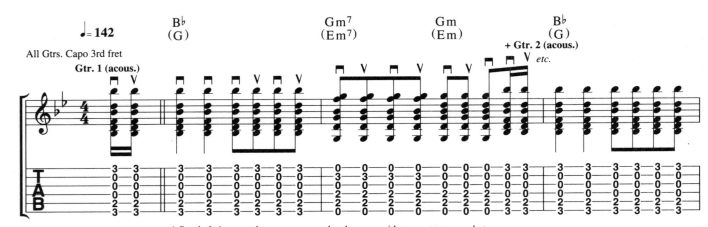

* Symbols in parentheses represent chord names with respect to capoed gtrs.

Tab 0 = 3rd fret. Symbols above reflect actual sounding chords.

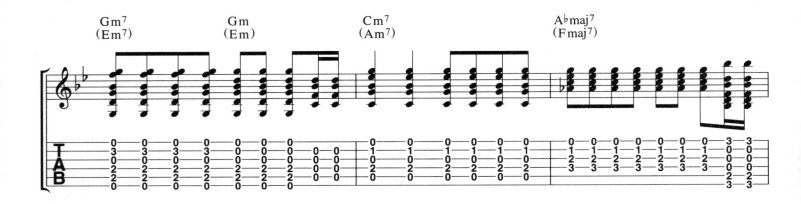

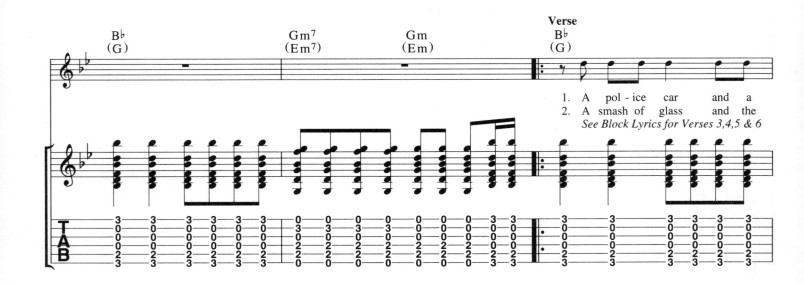

1. A pol - ice car and a
2. A smash of glass and the

See Block Lyrics for Verses 3,4,5 & 6

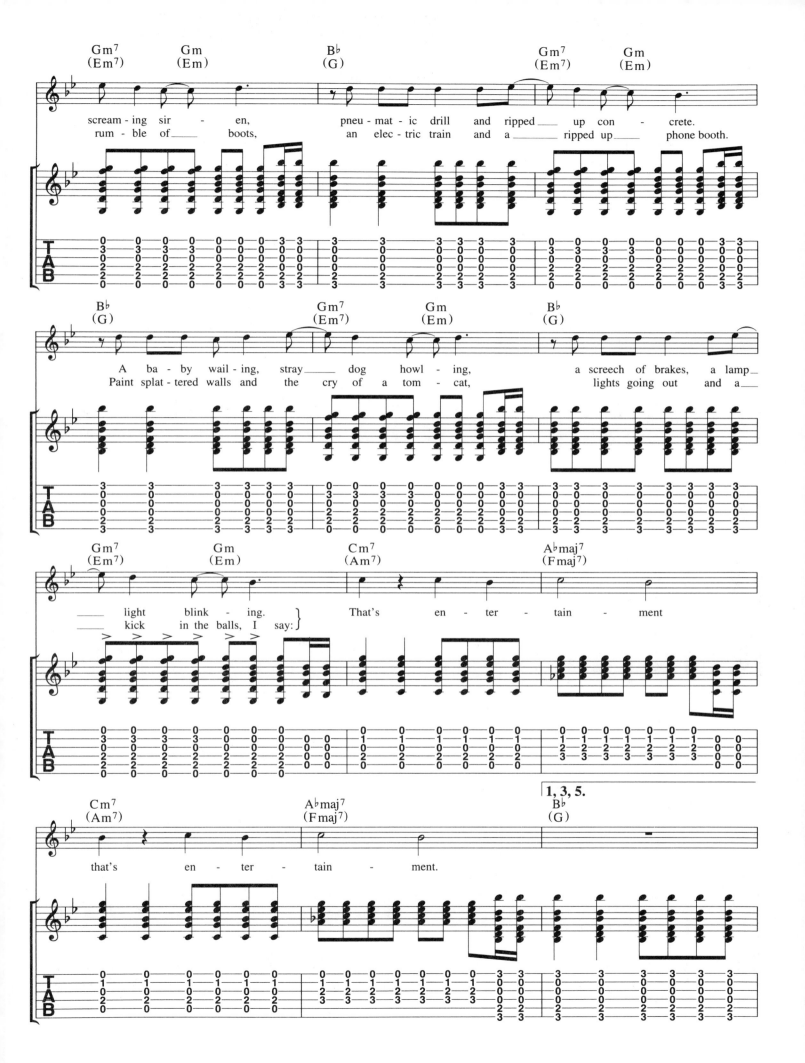

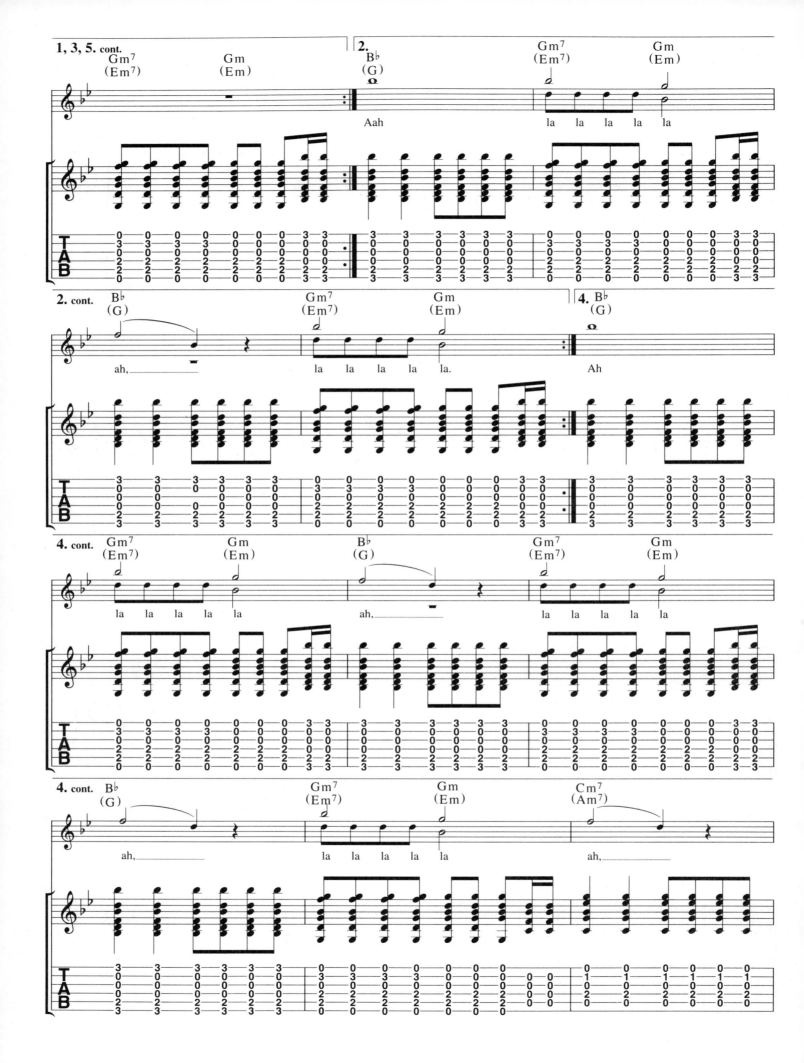

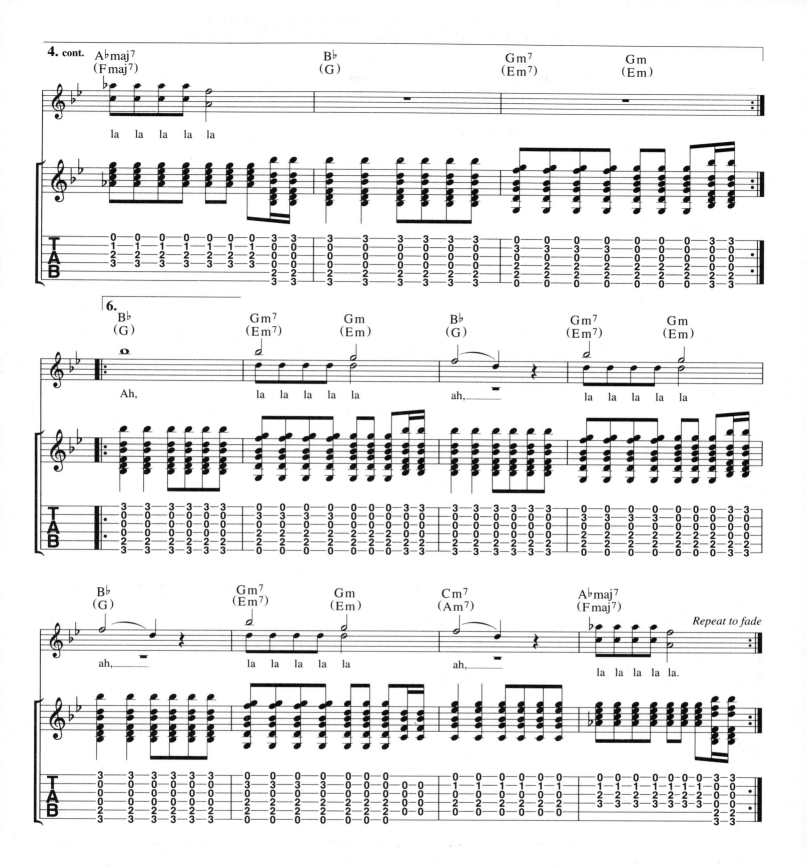

Verse 3: Days of speed and slow time Mondays
Pissing down with rain on a boring Wednesday
Watching the news and not eating your tea
A freezing cold flat and damp on the walls, I say:

Verse 4: Waking up at 6 a.m. on a cool warm morning
Opening the windows and breathing in petrol
An amateur band rehearsing in a nearby yard
Watching the telly and thinking about your holidays.

Verse 5: Waking up from bad dreams and smoking cigarettes
Cuddling a warm girl and smelling stale perfume
A hot summer's day and sticky black tarmac
Feeding ducks in the park and wishing you were far away.

Verse 6: Two lovers kissing amongst the scream of midnight
Two lovers missing the tranquility of solitude
Getting a cab and travelling on buses
Reading the grafitti about slashed seat affairs.

THE CHANGINGMAN

Words & Music by Paul Weller & Brendan Lynch

THE UNIVERSAL

Words & Music by Damon Albarn, Graham Coxon, Alex James & Dave Rowntree

yes, the fu-ture's been sold. Ev-'ry night___ we're___ gone, and to

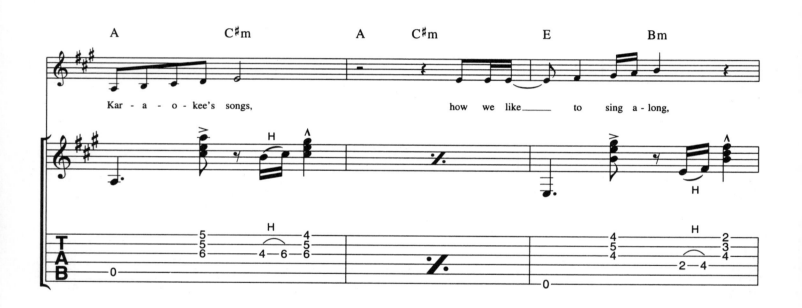

Kar - a - o - kee's songs, how we like___ to sing a - long,

Chorus:

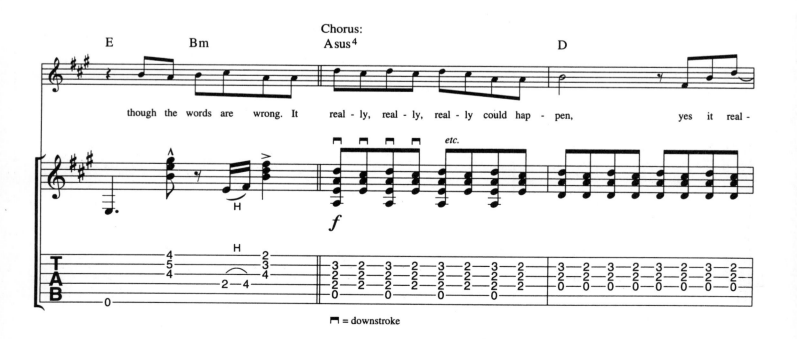

though the words are wrong. It real - ly, real - ly, real - ly could hap - pen, yes it real -

⊓ = downstroke

Verse 2:
No one here is alone
Satellites in every home
Yes, the Universal's here
Here for everyone.

Every paper that you read
Says tomorrow's your lucky day
Well, here's your lucky day.

WATERFALL

Words & Music by Ian Brown & John Squire

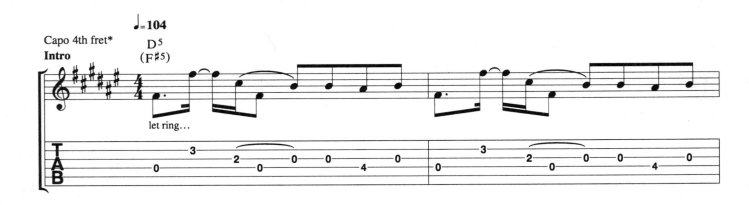

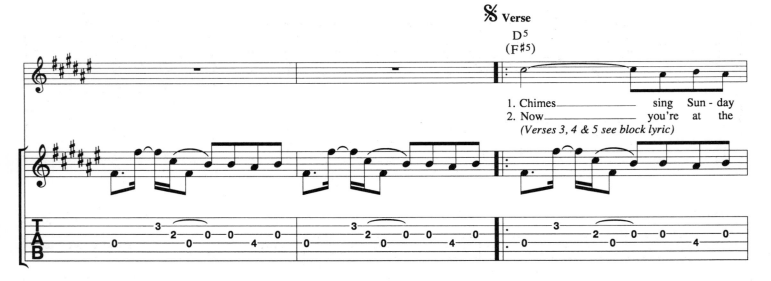

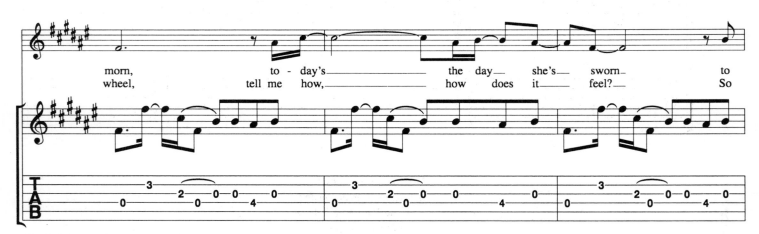

*Symbols in parentheses represent chord names with respect to capoed guitars (Tab 0 = 4th fret)
 Symbols above represent actual sounding chords

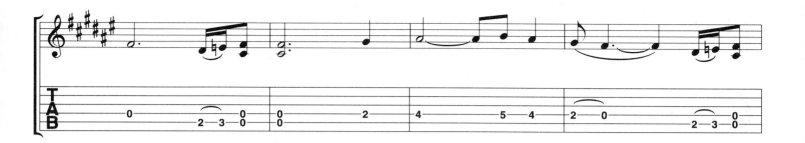

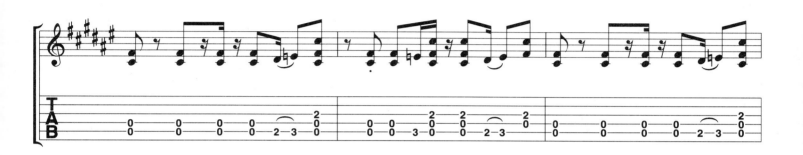

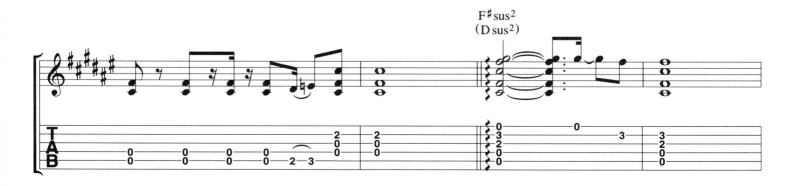

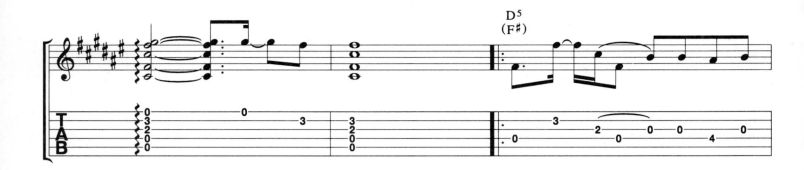

Repeat to fade

Verse 3:
As the miles they disappear
See land begin to clear
Free from the filth and the scum
This American satellite's won.

Verse 4:
See the steeple pine
The hills as old as time
Soon to be put to the test
To be whipped by the winds of the west.

Verse 5:
Stands on shifting sands
The scales held in her hands
The wind it just whips her and wails
And fills up her brigantine sails.

WIDE OPEN SPACE

Words & Music by Paul Draper

PRÉSENTATION DE LA TABLATURE DE GUITARE

Il existe trois façons différentes de noter la musique pour guitare : à l'aide d'une portée musicale, de tablatures ou de barres rythmiques

Les BARRES RYTHMIQUES sont indiquées au-dessus de la portée. Jouez les accords dans le rythme indiqué. Les notes rondes indiquent des notes réciles.

La PORTÉE MUSICALE indique les notes et rythmes et est divisée en mesures. Cette division est représentée par des lignes. Les notes sont : do, ré, mi, fa, sol, la, si.

La PORTÉE EN TABLATURE est une représentation graphique des touches de guitare. Chaque ligne horizontale correspond à une corde et chaque chiffre correspond à une case.

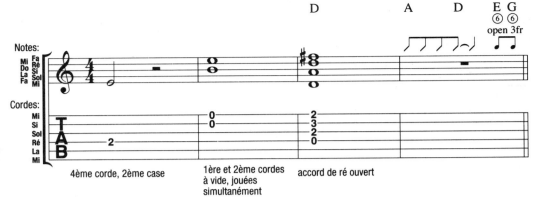

4ème corde, 2ème case

1ère et 2ème cordes à vide, jouées simultanément

accord de ré ouvert

Notation Spéciale De Guitare : Définitions

TIRÉ DEMI-TON : Jouez la note et tirez la corde afin d'élever la note d'un demi-ton (étape à moitié).

TIRÉ PLEIN : Jouez la note et tirez la corde afin d'élever la note d'un ton entier (étape entière).

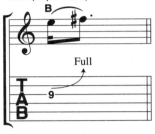

TIRÉ D'AGRÉMENT : Jouez la note et tirez la corde comme indiqué. Jouez la première note aussi vite que possible.

TIRÉ QUART DE TON : Jouez la note et tirez la corde afin d'élever la note d'un quart de ton.

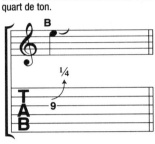

TIRÉ ET LÂCHÉ : Jouez la note et tirez la corde comme indiqué, puis relâchez, afin d'obtenir de nouveau la note de départ.

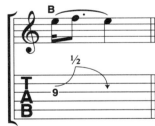

TIRÉ ET REJOUÉ : Jouez la note et tirez la corde comme indiqué puis rejouez la corde où le symbole apparaît.

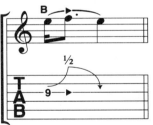

PRÉ-TIRÉ : Tirez la corde comme indiqué puis jouez cette note.

PRÉ-TIRÉ ET LÂCHÉ : Tirez la corde comme indiqué. Jouez la note puis relâchez la corde afin d'obtenir le ton de départ.

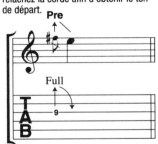

HAMMER-ON: Jouez la première note (plus basse) avec un doigt puis jouez la note plus haute sur la même corde avec un autre doigt, sur le manche mais sans vous servir du médiator.

PULL-OFF: Positionnez deux doigts sur les notes à jouer. Jouez la première note et sans vous servir du médiator, dégagez un doigt pour obtenir la deuxième note, plus basse.

GLISSANDO : Jouez la première note puis faites glisser le doigt le long du manche pour obtenir la seconde note qui, elle, n'est pas jouée.

GLISSANDO ET REJOUÉ : Identique au glissando à ceci près que la seconde note est jouée.

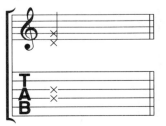

HARMONIQUES NATURELLES : Jouez la note tandis qu'un doigt effleure la corde sur le manche correspondant à la case indiquée.

PICK SCRAPE (SCRATCH) : On fait glisser le médiator le long de la corde, ce qui produit un son éraillé.

ÉTOUFFÉ DE LA PAUME : La note est partiellement étouffée par la main (celle qui se sert du médiator). Elle effleure la (les) corde(s) juste au-dessus du chevalet.

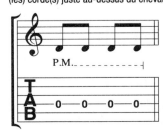

CORDES ÉTOUFFÉES : Un effet de percussion produit en posant à plat la main sur le manche sans relâcher, puis en jouant les cordes avec le médiator.

NOTE: La vitesse des tirés est indiquée par la notation musicale et le tempo.

ERLÄUTERUNG ZUR TABULATURSCHREIBWEISE

Es gibt drei Möglichkeiten, Gitarrenmusik zu notieren: im klassichen Notensystem, in Tabulaturform oder als rhythmische Akzente

RHYTHMISCHE AKZENTE werden über dem Notensystem notiert. Geschlagene Akkorde werden rhythmisch dargestellt. Ausgeschriebene Noten stellen Einzeltöne dar.

Im **NOTENSYSTEM** werden Tonhöhe und rhythmischer Verlauf festgelegt; es ist durch Taktstriche in Takte unterteilt. Die Töne werden nach den ersten acht Buchstaben des Alphabets benannt.
Beachte: "B" in der anglo-amerkanischen Schreibweise entspricht dem deutschen "H"!

DIE TABULATUR ist die optische Darstellung des Gitarrengriffbrettes. Jeder horizontalen Linie ist eine bestimmte Saite zugeordnet, jede Zahl bezeichnet einen Bund.

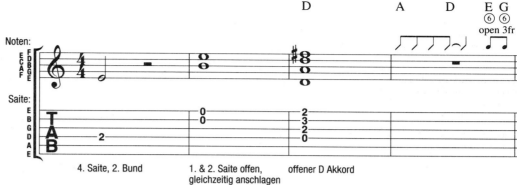

4. Saite, 2. Bund | 1. & 2. Saite offen, gleichzeitig anschlagen | offener D Akkord

Erklärungen zur speziellen Gitarennotation

HALBTON-ZIEHER: Spiele die Note und ziehe dann um einen Halbton höher (Halbtonschritt).

GANZTON-ZIEHER: Spiele die Note und ziehe dann einen Ganzton höher (Ganztonschritt).

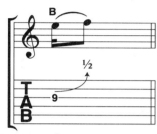

ZIEHER MIT VORSCHLAG: Spiele die Note und ziehe wie notiert. Spiele die erste Note so schnell wie möglich.

VIERTELTON-ZIEHER: Spiele die Note und ziehe dann einen Viertelton höher (Vierteltonschritt).

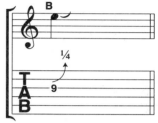

ZIEHEN UND ZURÜCKGLEITEN: Spiele die Note und ziehe wie notiert; lasse den Finger dann in die Ausgangsposition zurückgleiten. Dabei wird nur die erste Note angeschlagen.

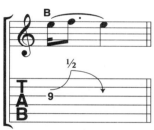

ZIEHEN UND NOCHMALIGES ANSCHLAGEN: Spiele die Note und ziehe wie notiert, schlage die Saite neu an, wenn das Symbol "▶" erscheint und lasse den Finger dann zurückgleiten.

ZIEHER VOR DEM ANSCHLAGEN: Ziehe zuerst die Note wie notiert; schlage die Note dann an.

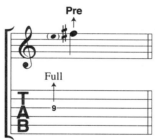

ZIEHER VOR DEM ANSCHLAGEN MIT ZURÜCKGLEITEN: Ziehe die Note wie notiert; schlage die Note dann an und lasse den Finger auf die Ausgangslage zurückgleiten.

AUFSCHLAGTECHNIK: Schlage die erste (tiefere) Note an; die höhere Note (auf der selben Saite) erklingt durch kräftiges Aufschlagen mit einem anderen Finger der Griffhand.

ABZIEHTECHNIK: Setze beide Finger auf die zu spielenden Noten und schlage die erste Note an. Ziehe dann (ohne nochmals anzuschlagen) den oberen Finger der Griffhand seitlich - abwärts ab, um die zweite (tiefere) Note zum klingen zu bringen.

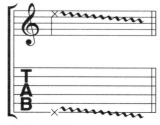

GLISSANDOTECHNIK: Schlage die erste Note an und rutsche dann mit dem selben Finger der Griffhand aufwärts oder abwärts zur zweiten Note. Die zweite Note wird nicht angeschlagen.

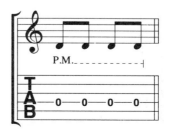

GLISSANDOTECHNIK MIT NACHFOLGENDEM ANSCHLAG: Gleiche Technik wie das gebundene Glissando, jedoch wird die zweite Note angeschlagen.

NATÜRLICHES FLAGEOLETT: Berühre die Saite über dem angegebenen Bund leicht mit einem Finger der Griffhand. Schlage die Saite an und lasse sie frei schwingen.

PICK SCRAPE: Fahre mit dem Plektrum nach unten über die Saiten - klappt am besten bei umsponnenen Saiten.

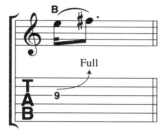

DÄMPFEN MIT DER SCHLAGHAND: Lege die Schlaghand oberhalb der Brücke leicht auf die Saite(n).

DÄMPFEN MIT DER GRIFFHAND: Du erreichst einen percussiven Sound, indem du die Griffhand leicht über die Saiten legst (ohne diese herunterzudrücken) und dann mit der Schlaghand anschlägst.

AMMERKUNG: Das Tempo der Zieher und Glissandos ist abhängig von der rhythmischen Notation und dem Grundtempo.

SPIEGAZIONI DI TABLATURA PER CHITARRA

La musica per chitarra può essere annotata in tre diversi modi: sul pentagramma, in tablatura e in taglio ritmico

IL TAGLIO RITMICO è scritto sopra il pentagramma. Percuotere le corde al ritmo indicato Le teste arrotondate delle note indicano note singole.

IL PENTAGRAMMA MUSICALE mostra toni e ritmo ed è divisa da linee in settori. I toni sono indicati con le prime sette lettere dell'alfabeto.

LA TABLATURA rappresenta graficamente la tastiera della chitarra. Ogni linea orizzontale rappresenta una corda, ed ogni corda rappresenta un tasto.

4° corda, 2° tasto   1° e 2° corda aperte, suonate insieme   accordo D aperto

Definizioni Per Annotazioni Speciali Per Chitarra

SEMI-TONO CURVATO: percuotere la nota e curvare di un semitono (1/2 passo).

TONO CURVATO: Percuotere la nota e curvare di un tono (passo intero).

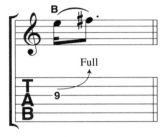

NOTA BREVE, CURVATA: percuotere la nota e curvare come indicato. Suonare la prima nota il più velocemente possibile.

QUARTO DI TONO, CURVATO: Percuotere la nota e curvare di un quarto di passo.

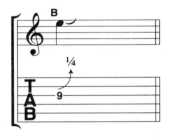

CURVA E LASCIA: Percuotere la nota e curvare come indicato, quindi rilasciare indietro alla nota originale.

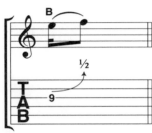

CURVA E RIPERCUOTI: Percuotere la nota e curvare come indicato poi ripercuotere la corda nel punto del simbolo.

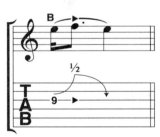

PRE-CURVA: Curvare la nota come indicato e quindi percuoterla.

PRE-CURVA E RILASCIO: Curvare la nota come indicato. Colpire e rilasciare la nota indietro alla tonalità indicata.

MARTELLO-COLPISCI: Colpire la prima nota (in basso) con un dito; quindi suona la nota più alta (sulla stessa corda) con un altro dito, toccandola senza pizzicare.

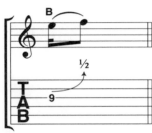

TOGLIERE: Posizionare entrambe le dita sulla nota da suonare. Colpire la prima nota e, senza pizzicare, togliere le dita per suonare la seconda nota (più in basso).

LEGATO SCIVOLATO (GLISSATO): Colpire la prima nota e quindi far scivolare lo stesso dito della mano della tastiera su o giù alla seconda nota. La seconda nota non viene colpita.

CAMBIO SCIVOLATO (GLISSARE E RICOLPIRE): Uguale al legato - scivolato eccetto che viene colpita la seconda nota.

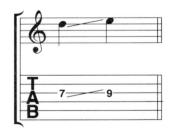

ARMONICA NATURALE: Colpire la nota mentre la mano della tastiera tocca leggermente la corda direttamente sopra il tasto indicato.

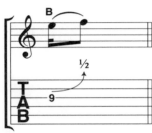

PIZZICA E GRAFFIA: Il limite del pizzicato è tirato su (o giù) lungo la corda, producendo un suono graffiante.

SORDINA CON IL PALMO: La nota è parzialmente attenuata dalla mano del pizzicato toccando la corda (le corde) appena prima del ponte.

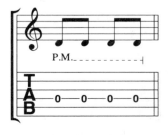

CORDE SMORZATE: Un suono di percussione viene prodotto appoggiando la mano della tastiera attraverso la corda (le corde) senza premere, e colpendole con la mano del pizzicato.

NOTA: La velocità di ogni curvatura è indicata dalle annotazioni musicali e dal tempo.

Part 2
LOVE SONGS

GUITAR TABLATURE EXPLAINED

Guitar music can be notated three different ways: on a musical stave, in tablature, and in rhythm slashes

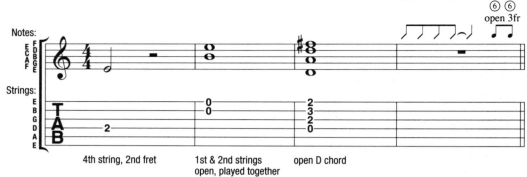

RHYTHM SLASHES are written above the stave. Strum chords in the rhythm indicated. Round noteheads indicate single notes.

THE MUSICAL STAVE shows pitches and rhythms and is divided by lines into bars. Pitches are named after the first seven letters of the alphabet.

TABLATURE graphically represents the guitar fingerboard. Each horizontal line represents a string, and each number represents a fret.

4th string, 2nd fret   1st & 2nd strings open, played together   open D chord

Definitions for special guitar notation

SEMI-TONE BEND: Strike the note and bend up a semi-tone (1/2 step).

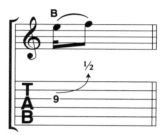

WHOLE-TONE BEND: Strike the note and bend up a whole-tone (whole step).

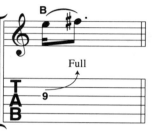

GRACE NOTE BEND: Strike the note and bend as indicated. Play the first note as quickly as possible.

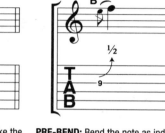

QUARTER-TONE BEND: Strike the note and bend up a 1/4 step.

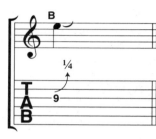

BEND & RELEASE: Strike the note and bend up as indicated, then release back to the original note.

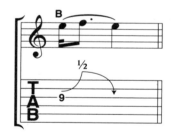

COMPOUND BEND & RELEASE: Strike the note and bend up and down in the rhythm indicated.

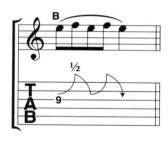

PRE-BEND: Bend the note as indicated, then strike it.

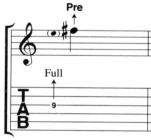

PRE-BEND & RELEASE: Bend the note as indicated. Strike it and release the note back to the original pitch.

UNISON BEND: Strike the two notes simultaneously and bend the lower note up to the pitch of the higher.

BEND & RESTRIKE: Strike the note and bend as indicated then restrike the string where the symbol occurs.

BEND, HOLD AND RELEASE: Same as bend and release but hold the bend for the duration of the tie.

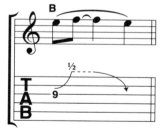

BEND AND TAP: Bend the note as indicated and tap the higher fret while still holding the bend.

VIBRATO: The string is vibrated by rapidly bending and releasing the note with the fretting hand.

HAMMER-ON: Strike the first (lower) note with one finger, then sound the higher note (on the same string) with another finger by fretting it without picking.

PULL-OFF: Place both fingers on the notes to be sounded, Strike the first note and without picking, pull the finger off to sound the second (lower) note.

LEGATO SLIDE (GLISS): Strike the first note and then slide the same fret-hand finger up or down to the second note. The second note is not struck.

NOTE: The speed of any bend is indicated by the music notation and tempo.

SHIFT SLIDE (GLISS & RESTRIKE): Same as legato slide, except the second note is struck.

TRILL: Very rapidly alternate between the notes indicated by continuously hammering on and pulling off.

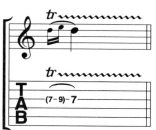

TAPPING: Hammer ("tap") the fret indicated with the pick-hand index or middle finger and pull off to the note fretted by the fret hand.

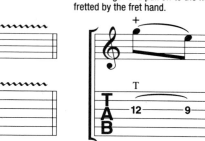

PICK SCRAPE: The edge of the pick is rubbed down (or up) the string, producing a scratchy sound.

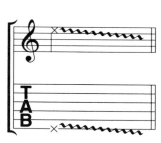

MUFFLED STRINGS: A percussive sound is produced by laying the fret hand across the string(s) without depressing, and striking them with the pick hand.

NATURAL HARMONIC: Strike the note while the fret-hand lightly touches the string directly over the fret indicated.

Harm.
12

PINCH HARMONIC: The note is fretted normally and a harmonic is produced by adding the edge of the thumb or the tip of the index finger of the pick hand to the normal pick attack.

P.H.
5

HARP HARMONIC: The note is fretted normally and a harmonic is produced by gently resting the pick hand's index finger directly above the indicated fret (in parentheses) while the pick hand's thumb or pick assists by plucking the appropriate string.

H.H.
7 (19)

PALM MUTING: The note is partially muted by the pick hand lightly touching the string(s) just before the bridge.

P.M.
0 0 0 0

RAKE: Drag the pick across the strings indicated with a single motion.

rake
5

TREMOLO PICKING: The note is picked as rapidly and continuously as possible.

5   7

ARPEGGIATE: Play the notes of the chord indicated by quickly rolling them from bottom to top.

5
5
5

SWEEP PICKING: Rhythmic downstroke and/or upstroke motion across the strings.

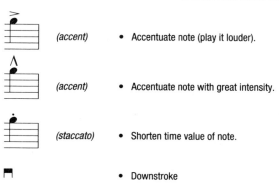

VIBRATO DIVE BAR AND RETURN: The pitch of the note or chord is dropped a specific number of steps (in rhythm) then returned to the original pitch.

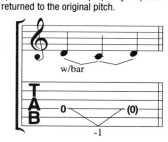

w/bar
0   (0)
-1

VIBRATO BAR SCOOP: Depress the bar just before striking the note, then quickly release the bar.

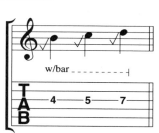

w/bar
4   5   7

VIBRATO BAR DIP: Strike the note and then immediately drop a specific number of steps, then release back to the original pitch.

-½   -½   -½
w/bar
-½   -½   -½
7   7   7

Additional musical definitions

> (accent)	• Accentuate note (play it louder).	
∧ (accent)	• Accentuate note with great intensity.	
• (staccato)	• Shorten time value of note.	
⊓	• Downstroke	
V	• Upstroke	

D.%. al Coda

D.C. al Fine

tacet

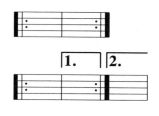

1.   2.

• Go back to the sign (%), then play until the bar marked *To Coda* ⊕ then skip to the section marked ⊕ *Coda*.

• Go back to the beginning of the song and play until the bar marked *Fine* (end).

• Instrument is silent (drops out).

• Repeat bars between signs.

• When a repeated section has different endings, play the first ending only the first time and the second ending only the second time.

NOTE: Tablature numbers in parentheses mean: 1. The note is sustained, but a new articulation (such as hammer on or slide) begins.
2. A note may be fretted but not necessarily played.

ALL I REALLY WANT TO DO

Words & Music by Bob Dylan

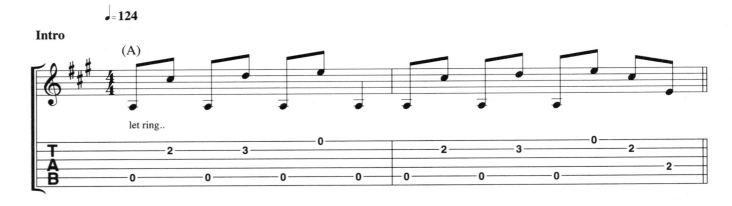

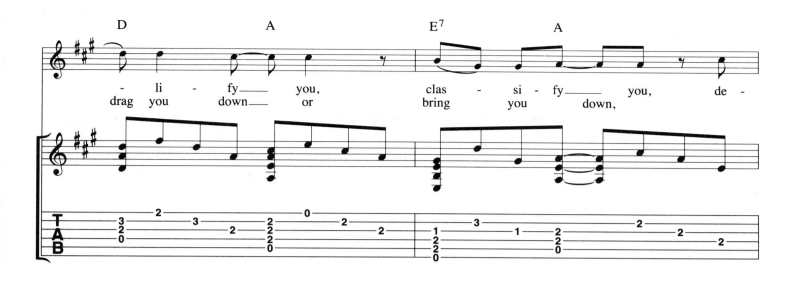

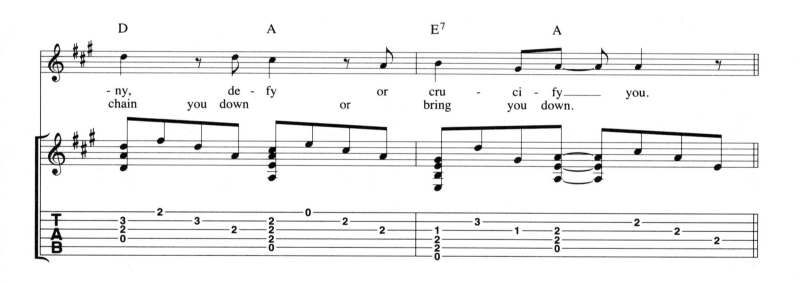

7

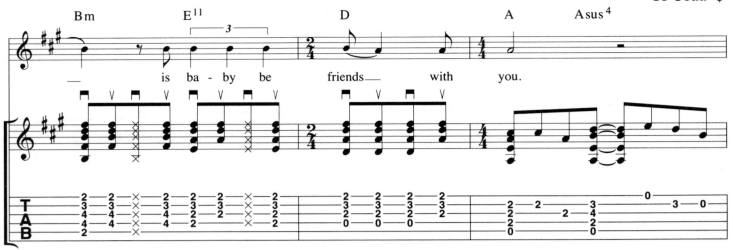

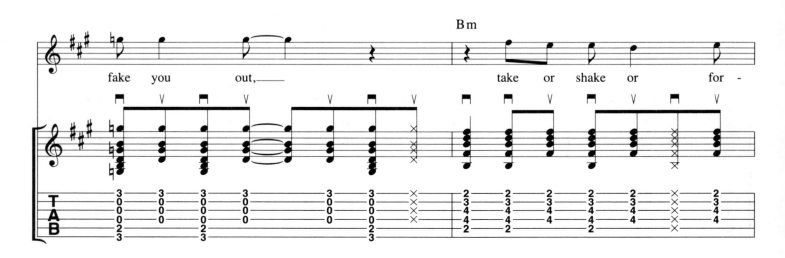

8

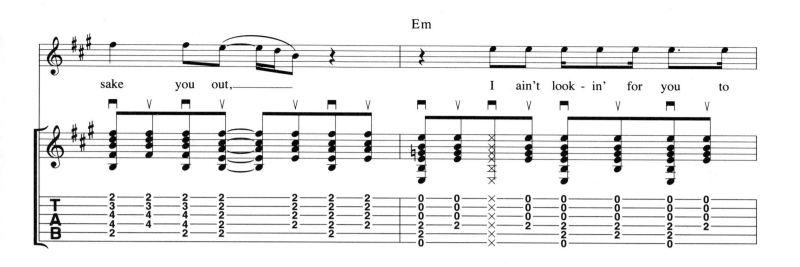

Em

sake you out,_____ I ain't look-in' for you to

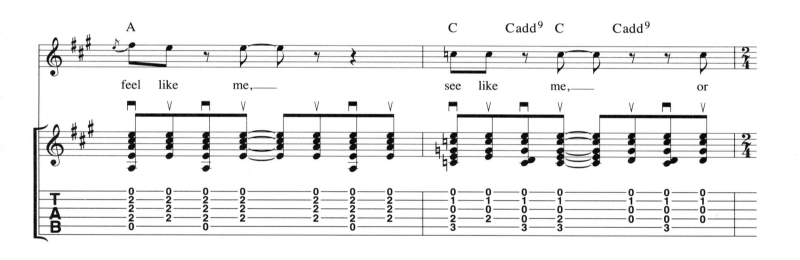

A   C   Cadd⁹ C   Cadd⁹

feel like me,_____ see like me,_____ or

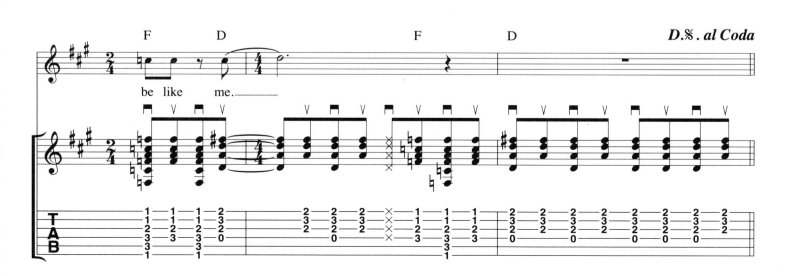

F   D   F   D   D.𝄋. al Coda

be like me._____

9

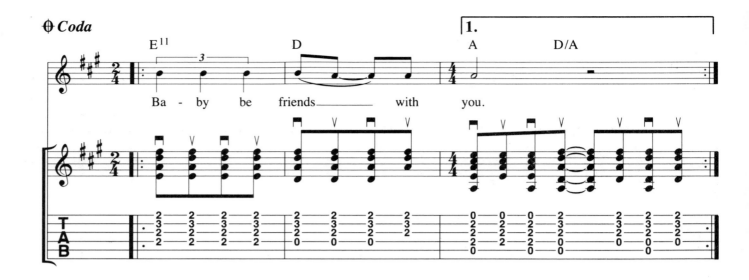

Ba - by be friends_____ with you.

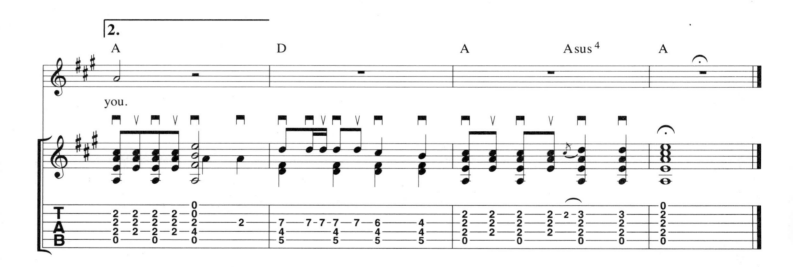

you.

Verse 3 (%):
I don't want to meet your kin
Make you spin, or do you in
Or select you, or dissect you
Or inspect you, or reject you.

ALWORDS

ALWAYS

Words & Music by Jon Bon Jovi

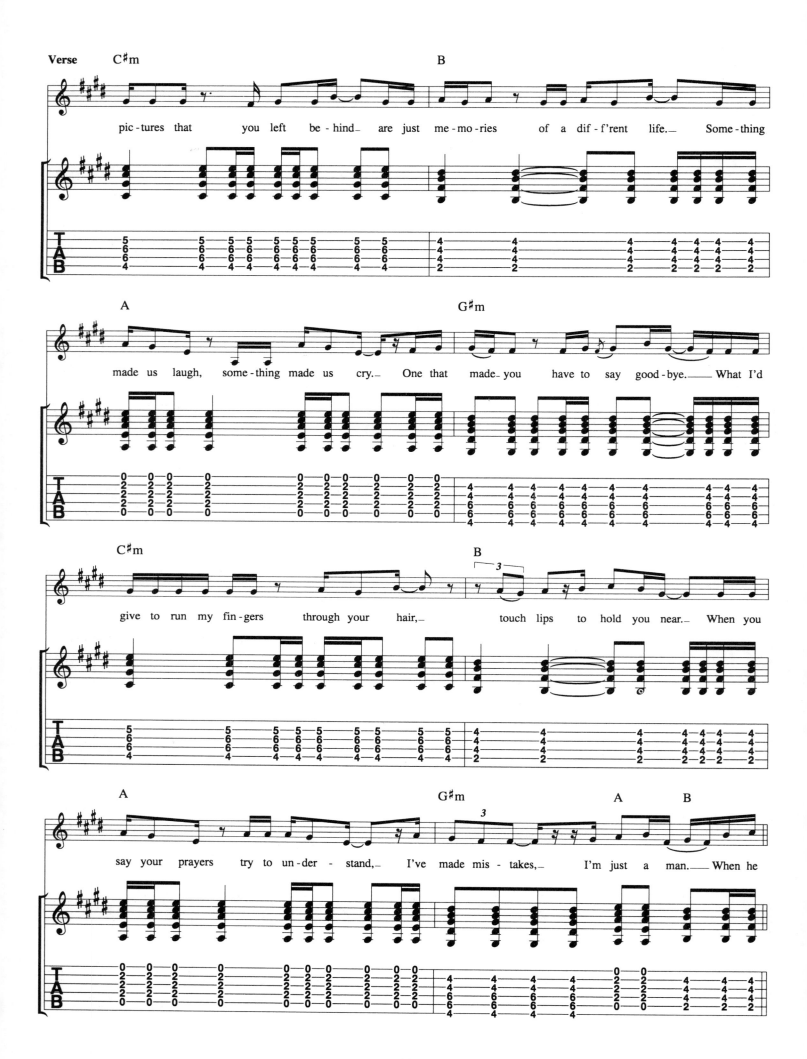

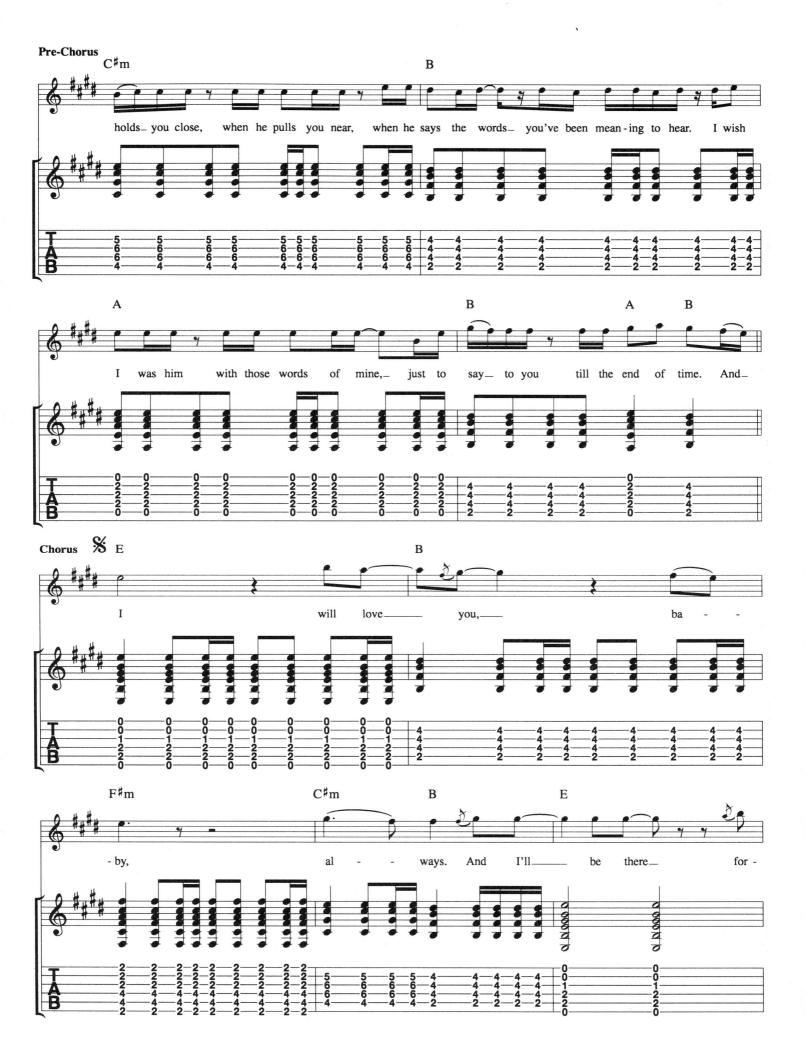

17

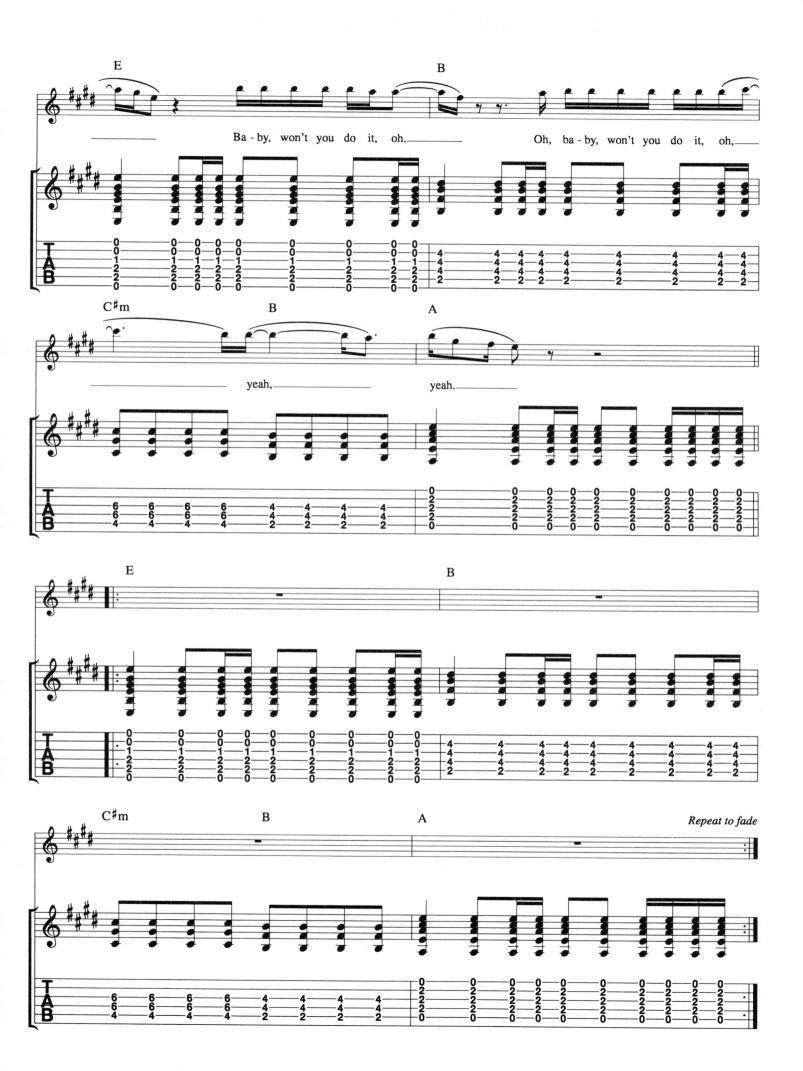

FRIDAY I'M IN LOVE

Words by Robert Smith

Music by Robert Smith, Simon Gallup, Porl Thompson, Boris Williams & Perry Bamonte

Capo on 1st fret: original key E♭

end Rhythm figure 1

21

to Coda ⊕

___ too late. ___ But Fri - day ne - ver hes - i - tate. ___

let ring ----------------------- | *let ring* ----------------- *let ring* -----------------------

with Rhythm figure 1

3. I don't care ___ if Mon - day's black, ___ Tues - day, Wednes - day, heart _

___ at - tack. ___ Thurs - day ne - ver look - ing back, ___ it's Fri -

with Rhythm figures 1 and 2

day I'm in love. _____

guitar 2

guitar 3

Rhythm figure 3

24

25

Tues - day's grey and Wednes - day too. ___ Thurs - day I don't care _

___ a-bout ___ you, ___ it's Fri - day I'm in love. _____

6. Mon - day you can fall _____ a -part, _____ Tues - day, Wednes -day, break _

___ my heart. ___ Thurs - day does - n't ev - en start, ___ it's Fri -

with Rhythm figures 1 (twice) and 1a
add Rhythm figure 3 on repeat

vocal ad lib

day I'm in love. _____

guitar 1

guitar 2

guitar 3

29

GOD ONLY KNOWS

Words & Music by Brian Wilson & Tony Asher

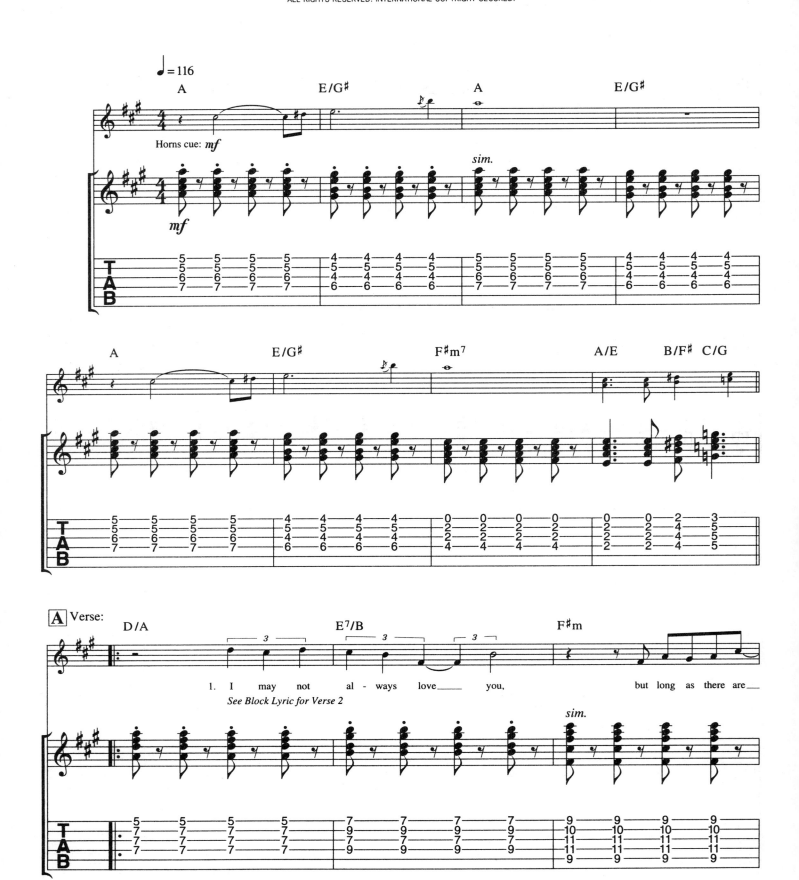

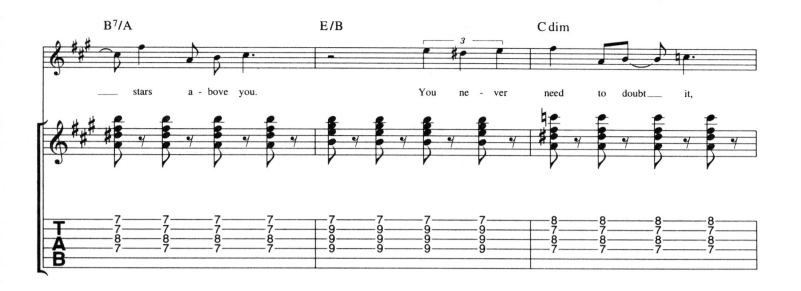

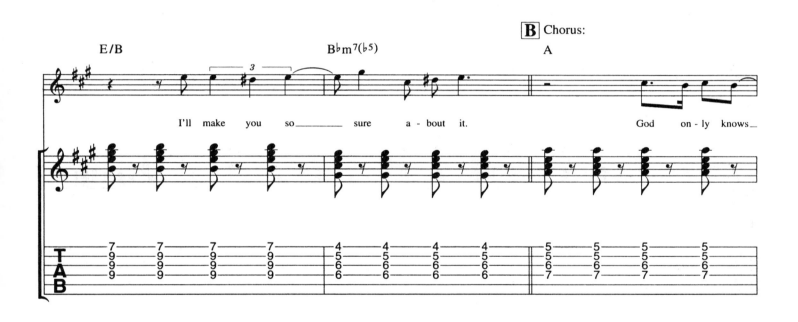

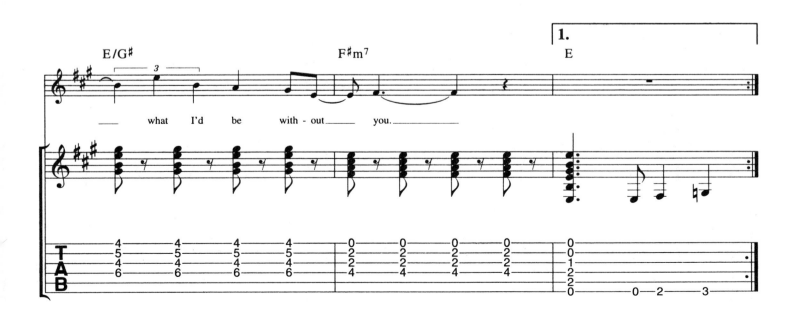

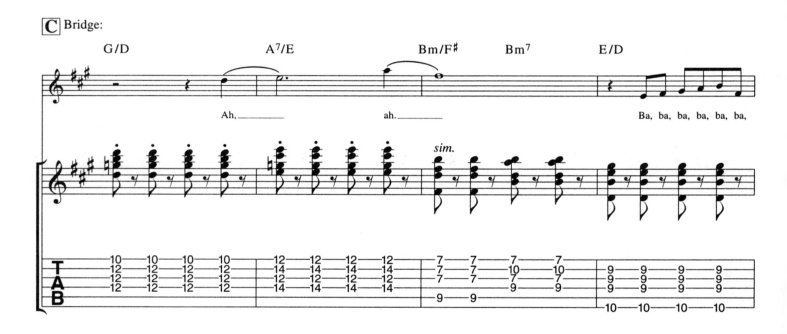

D Chorus:

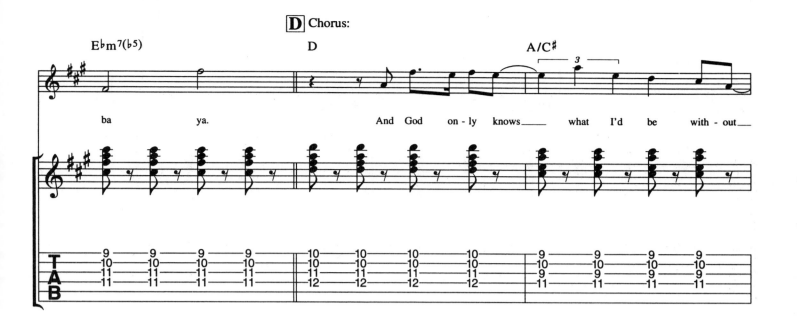

ba   ya.   And God on-ly knows___ what I'd be with-out___

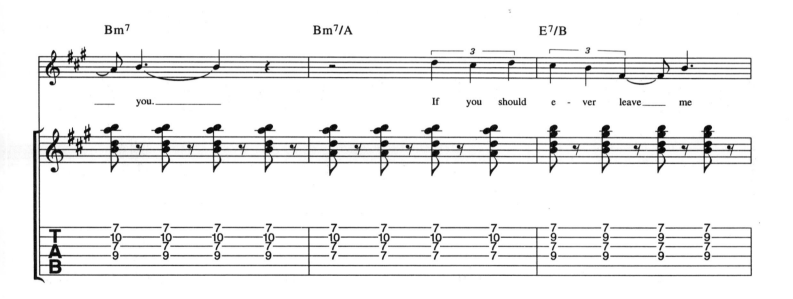

___ you.___   If you should e-ver leave___ me

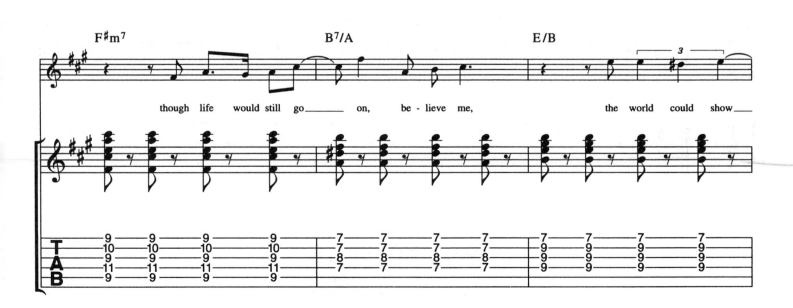

though life would still go___ on, be-lieve me,   the world could show___

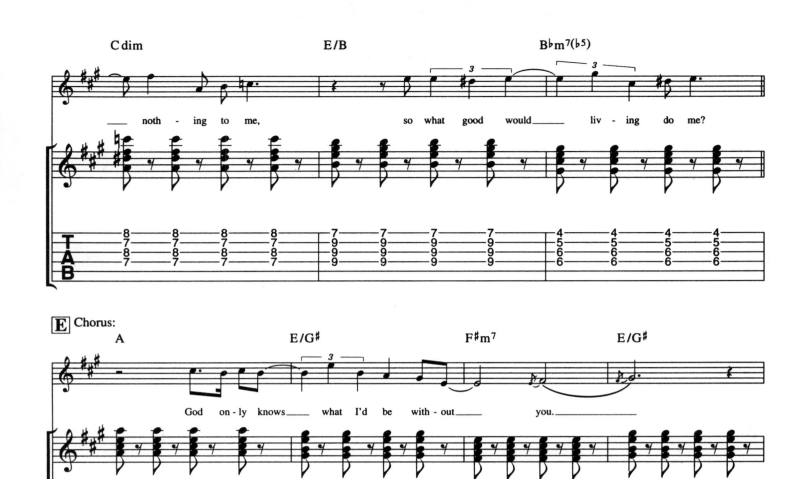

nothing to me, so what good would living do me?

E Chorus:

God only knows what I'd be without you.

And God only knows what I'd be without you.

Repeat to fade

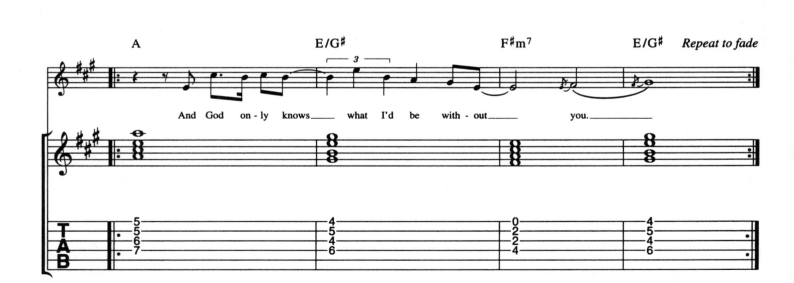

Verse 2:
If you should ever leave me
Well, life would still go on, believe me
The world could show nothing to me
So what good would living do me?

LADY FRIEND

Words & Music by David Crosby

35

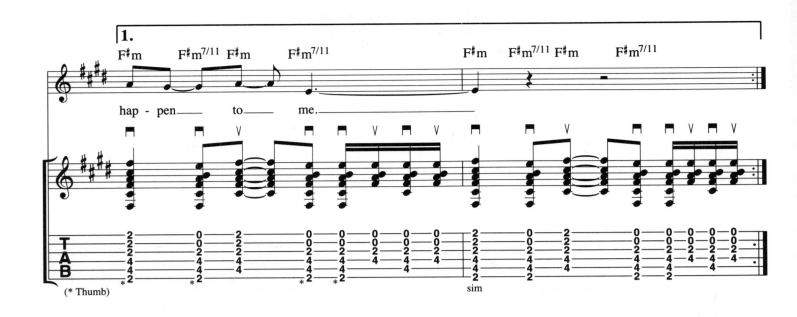

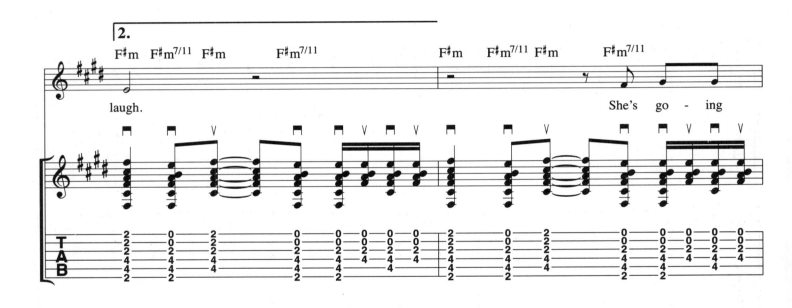

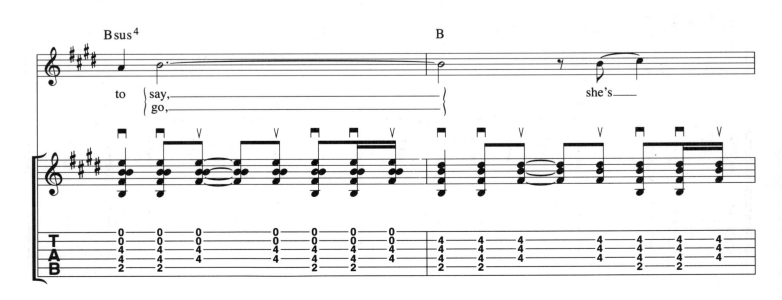

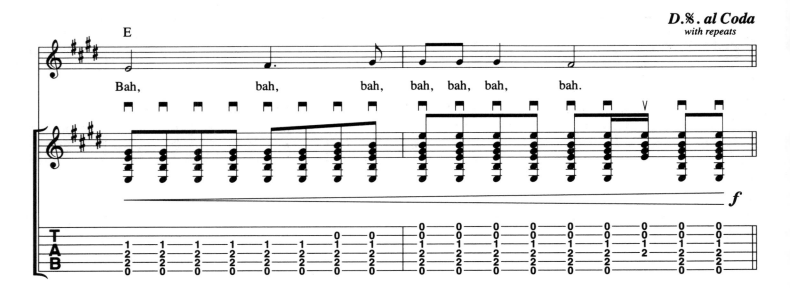

Bah,   bah,   bah, bah, bah, bah,   bah.

⊕ *Coda*

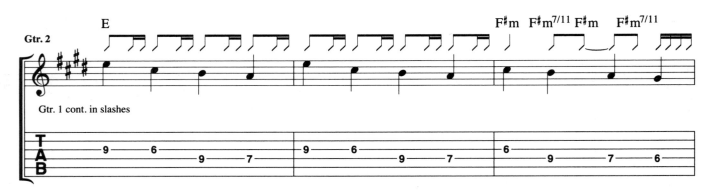

Gtr. 2

Gtr. 1 cont. in slashes

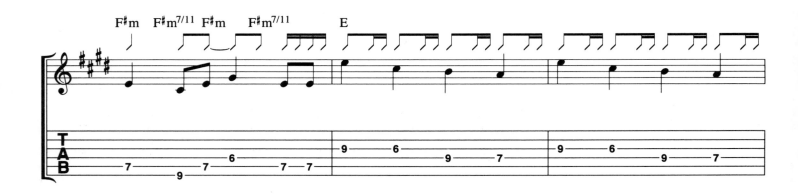

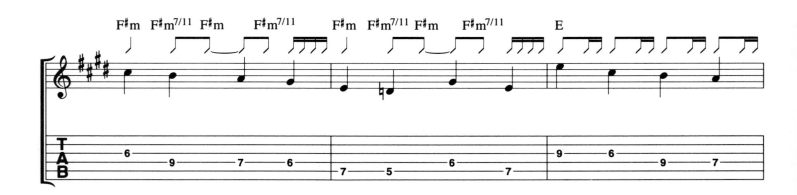

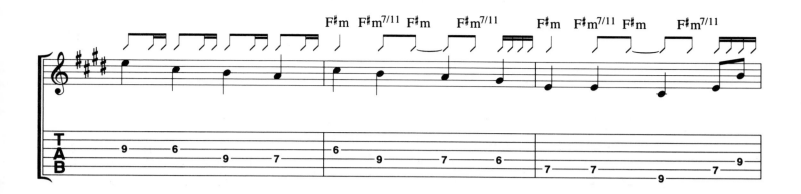

Verse 2:

Here it comes
It looks just like the last wave I drowned in
Here it comes
And I'm so far from shore.

Verse 3 (𝄋):

Here it comes again
The night is going too far
Here it comes
She's going to say "Goodbye".

LET IT GROW

Words & Music by Eric Clapton

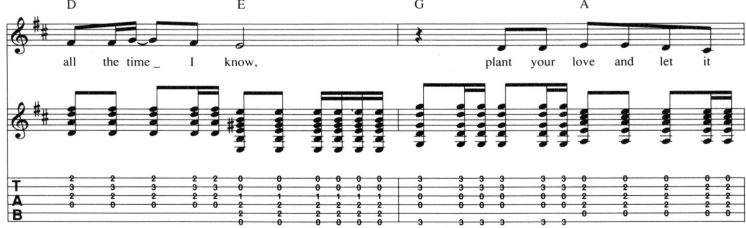

E   B   A

grow.   let it blos- som, let _ it flow.

to Coda ⊕

B

In the sun, _ the rain, _ the snow,   love is love - ly, ___

E   B

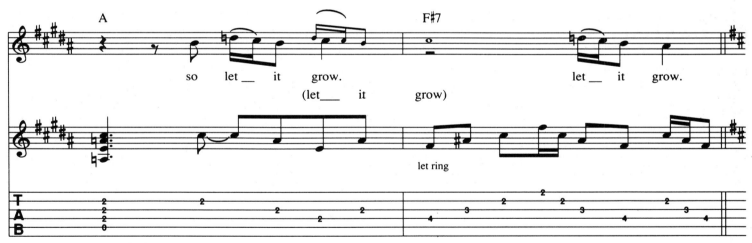

A   F#7

so let _ it grow.   let _ it grow.

(let___ it grow)

let ring

Instrumental
Electric Guitar

B

G   D/F#   Em   Bm   A   (Dobro pick up)

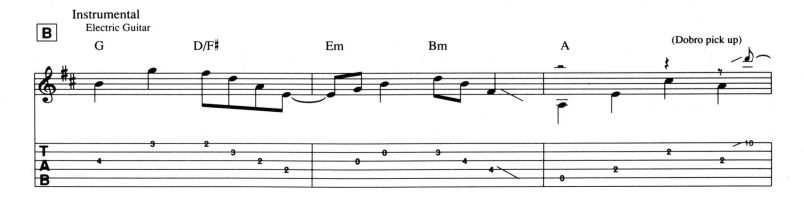

LINGER

Music by Dolores O'Riordan & Noel Hogan
Words by Dolores O'Riordan

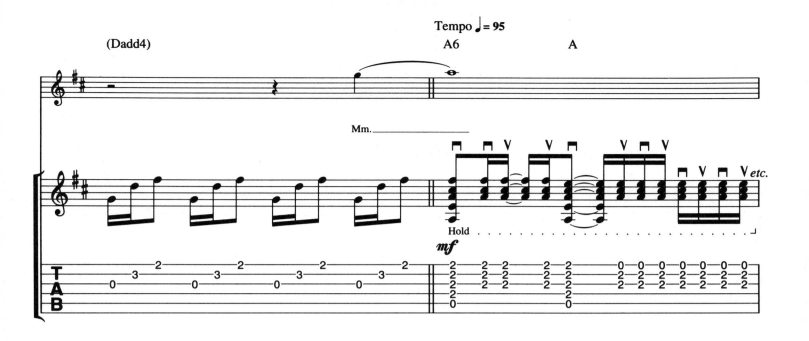

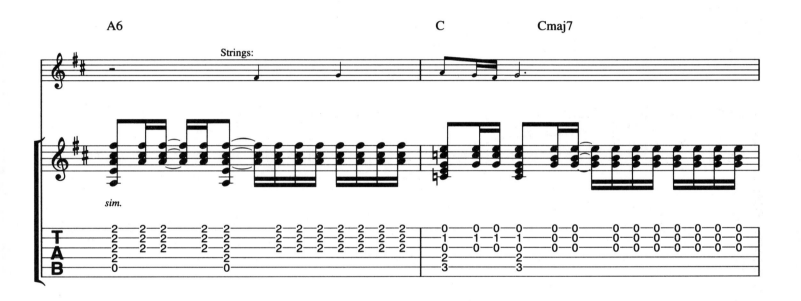

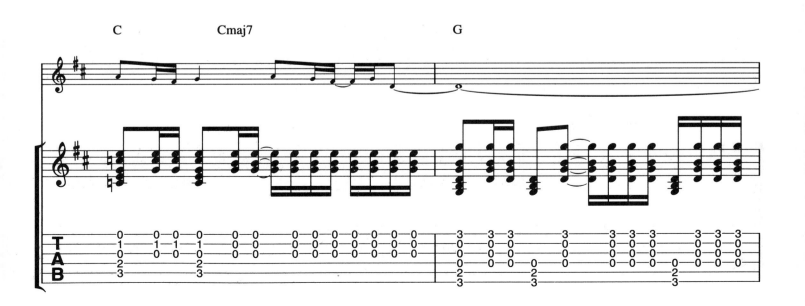

Verse

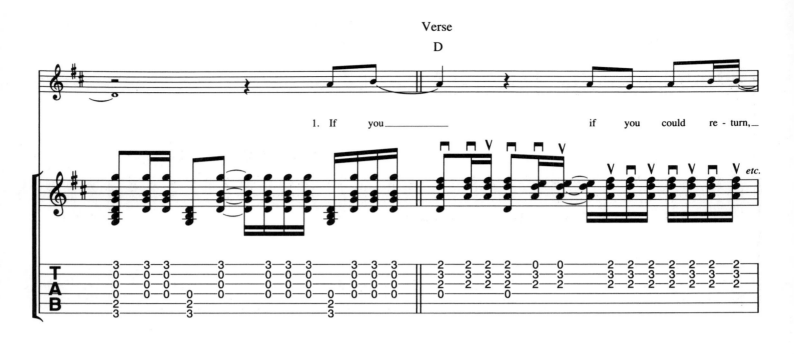

1. If you_____ if you could re - turn,

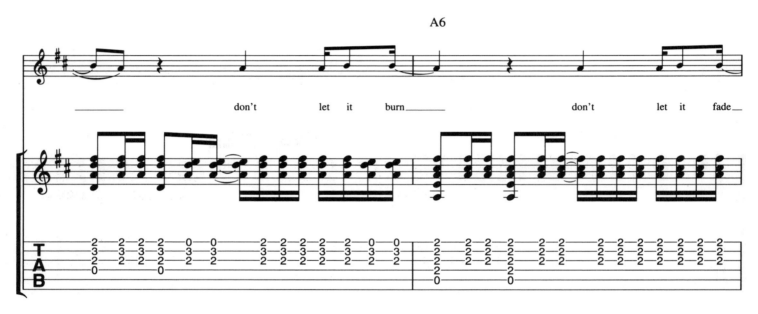

_____ don't let it burn_____ don't let it fade_____

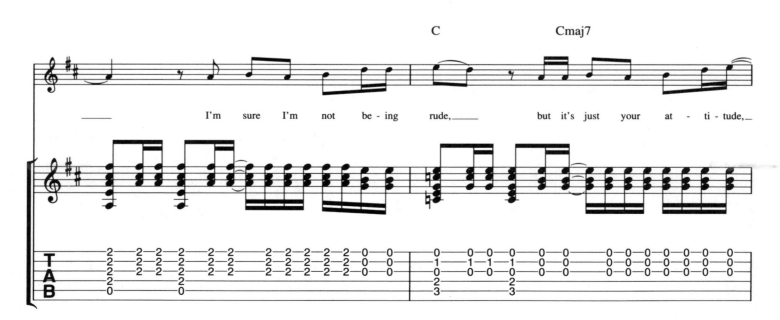

_____ I'm sure I'm not be - ing rude,_____ but it's just your at - ti - tude,_____

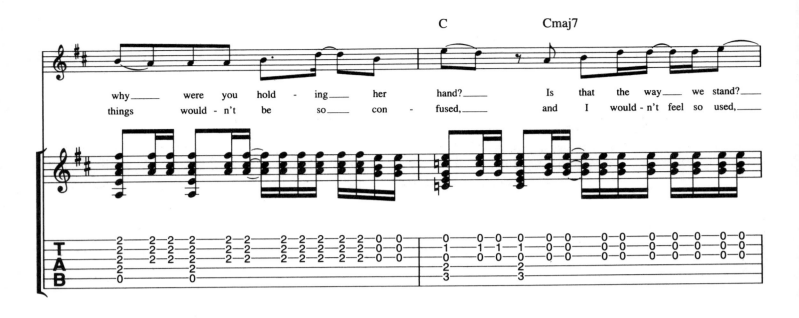

C
Cmaj7
G
it's tear - ing me a - part,
it's ru - in - ing ev - 'ry thing.
TAB
Verse
D
2. I swore,
I swore I would be true
if you could get by
Fig. 1 . . .
TAB
A6
and hon - ey, so did you,
so
try - ing not to lie,
TAB

why_____ were you hold - ing_____ her   hand?_____   Is   that   the   way____ we   stand?____
things   would - n't   be   so   con - fused,_____   and   I   would - n't   feel   so   used,

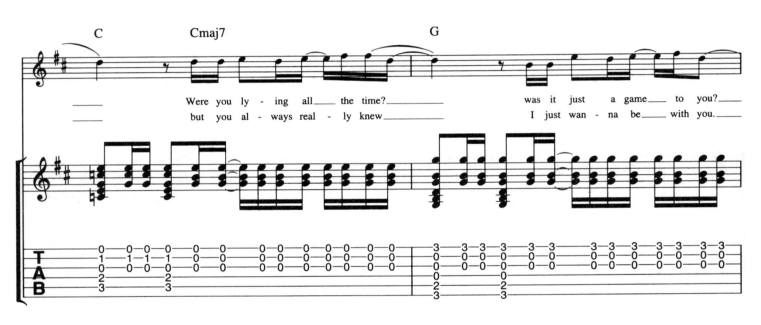

_____ }   Were   you   ly - ing   all____ the   time?____   was   it   just   a   game____   to   you?____
_____   but   you   al - ways   real - ly   knew____   I   just   wan - na   be____   with   you.____

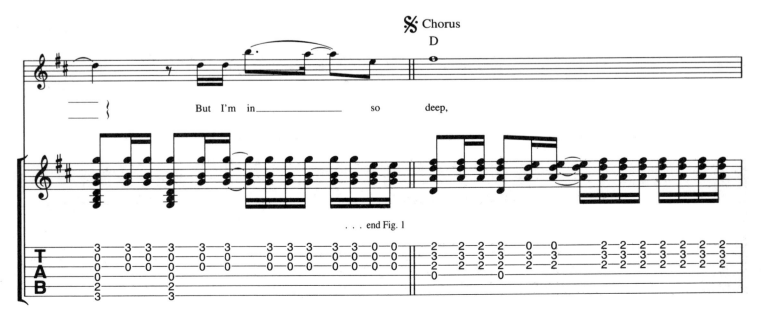

_____ {   But   I'm   in_____   so   deep,

. . . end Fig. 1

50

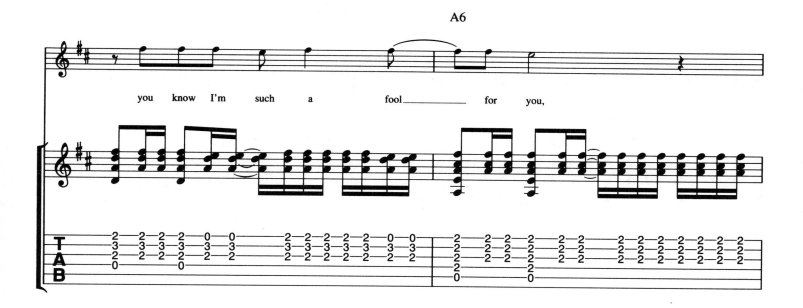

you know I'm such a   fool_____ for you,

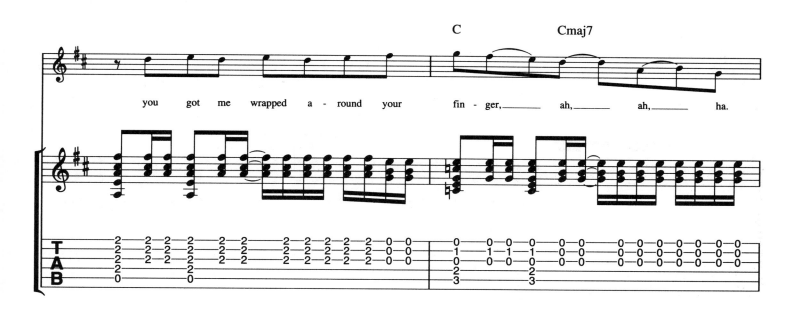

you got me wrapped a - round your   fin - ger,_____ ah,_____ ah,_____ ha.

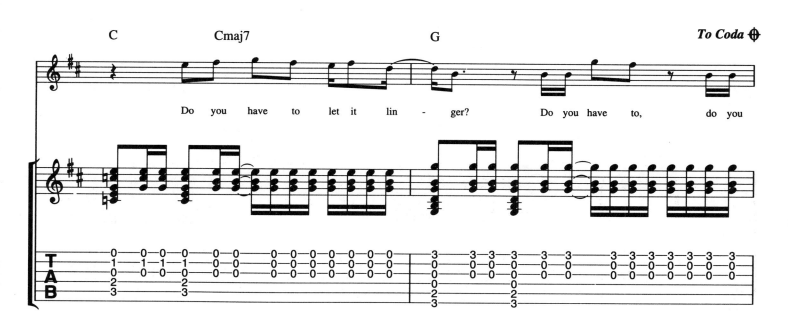

Do you have to let it lin - ger?   Do you have to,   do you

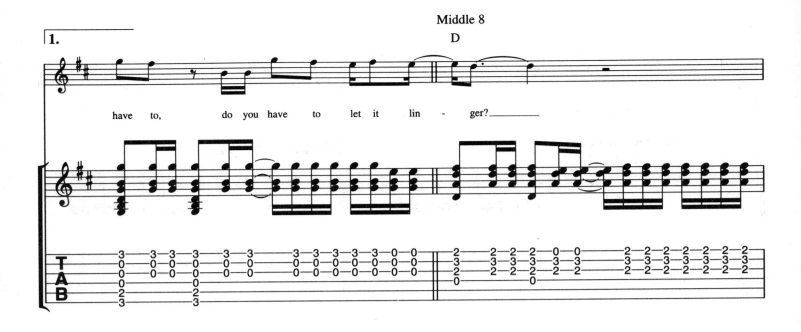

have to,   do you have   to   let it   lin - ger?_____

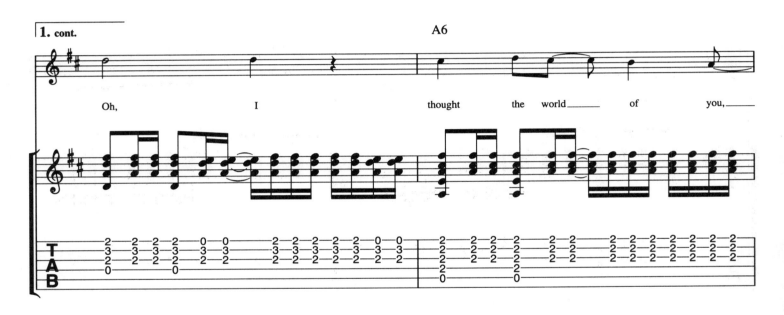

Oh,   I   thought   the   world_____   of   you,_____

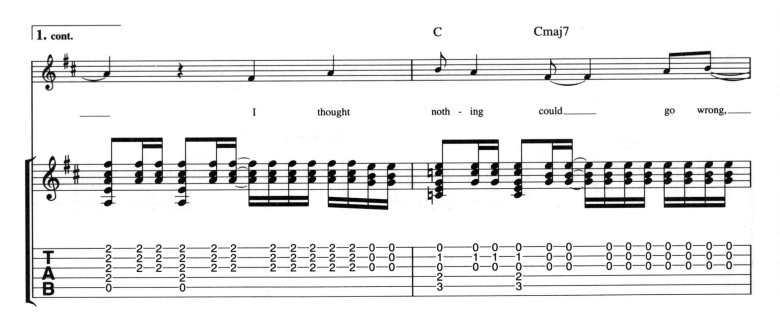

_____   I   thought   noth - ing   could_____   go   wrong,_____

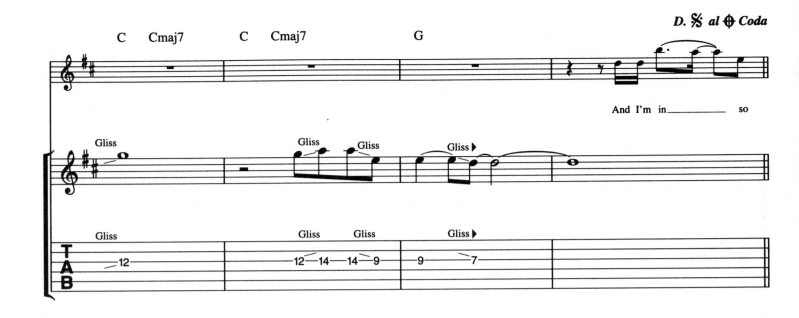

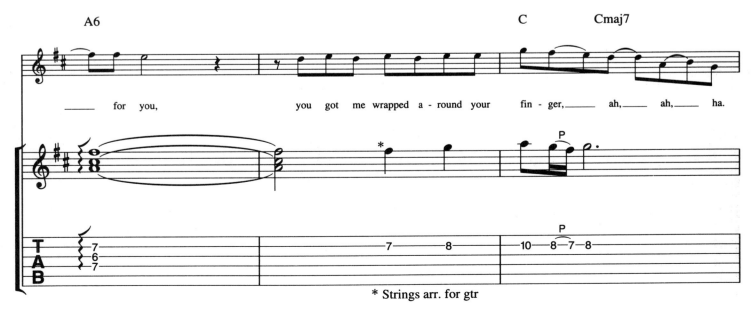

* Strings arr. for gtr

54

Do you have to let it lin - - ger? Do you have to, do you have to, do you have to let it lin -

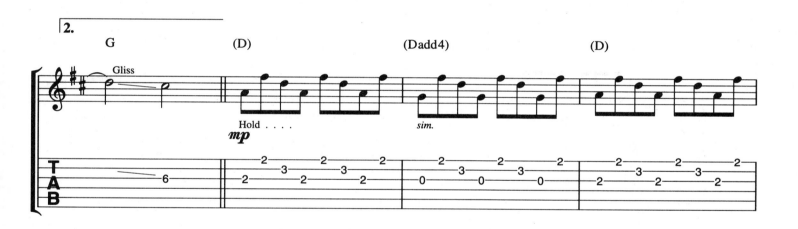

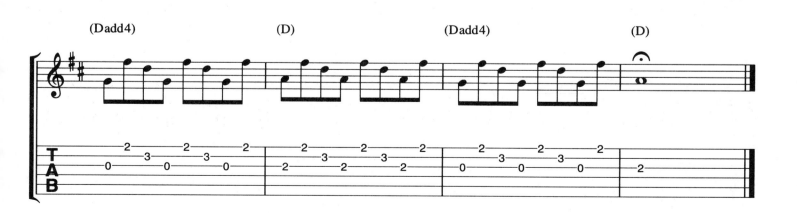

LOST IN YOU

Words & Music by Tim Wheeler

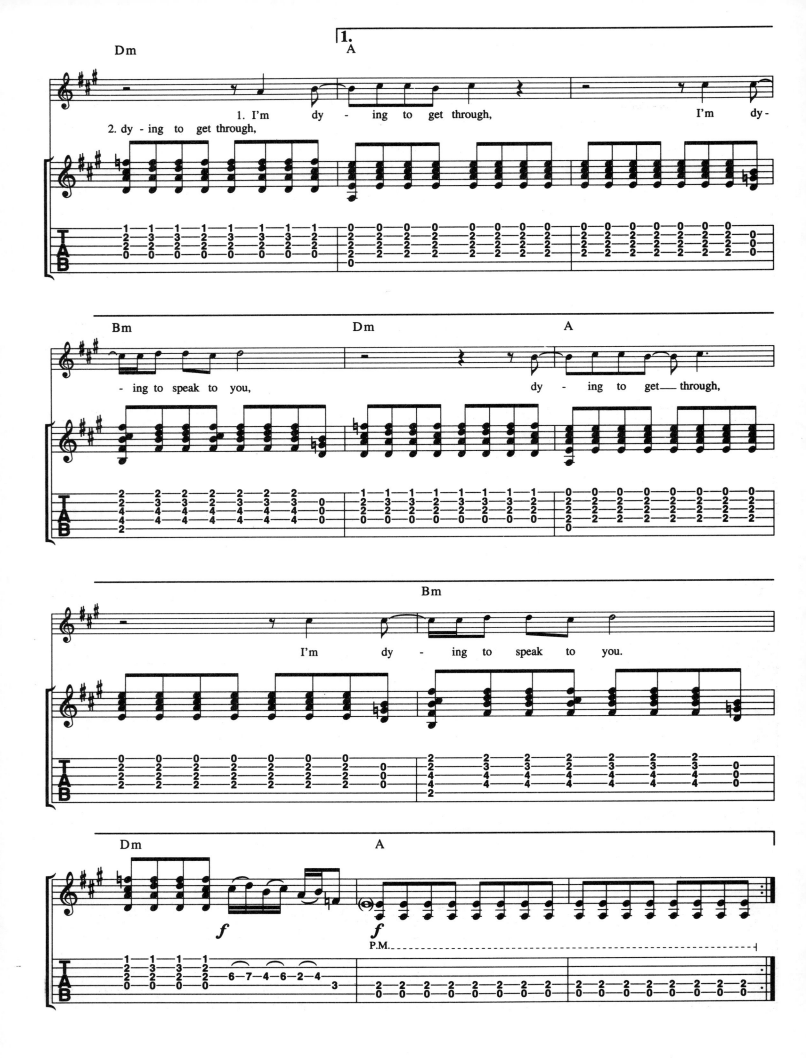

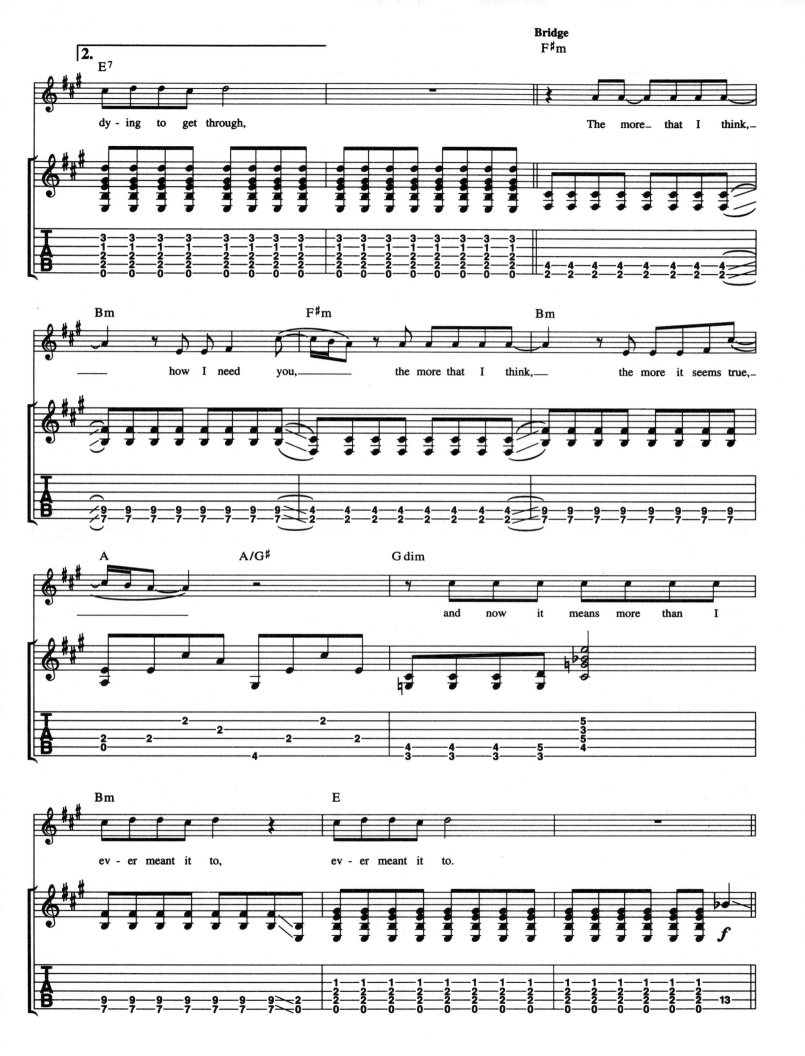

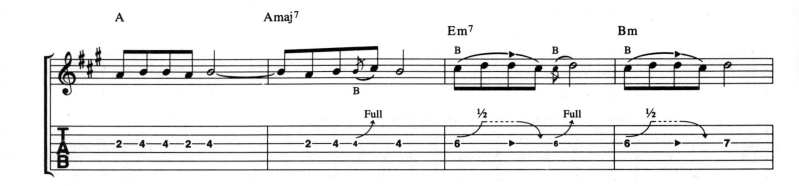

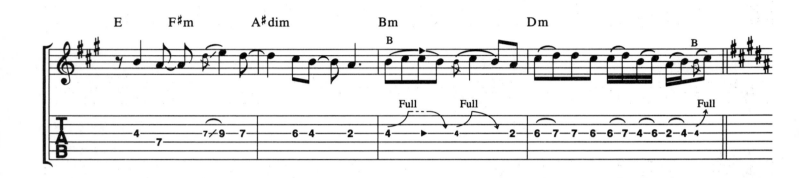

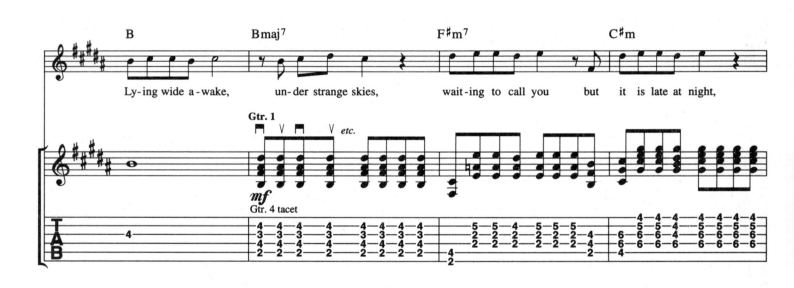

Ly-ing wide a-wake, under strange skies, wait-ing to call you but it is late at night,

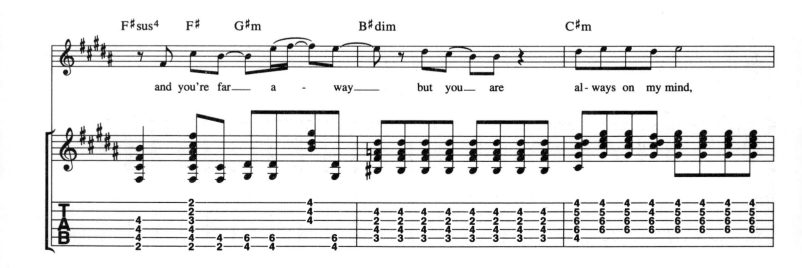

and you're far a-way but you are al-ways on my mind,

MICHELLE

Words & Music by John Lennon & Paul McCartney

ROMEO AND JULIET

Words & Music by Mark Knopfler

* Gtr. tuned to F B♭ F B♭ D F

* Alternatively, use G tuning and capo 3rd fret

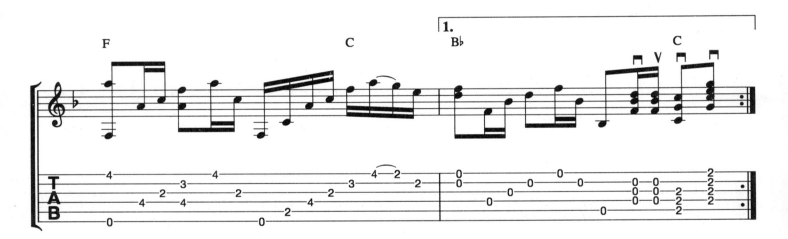

1. A love struck Ro - me - o   sings a street suss se - re - nade,___
See Block Lyrics for Verses 2&3

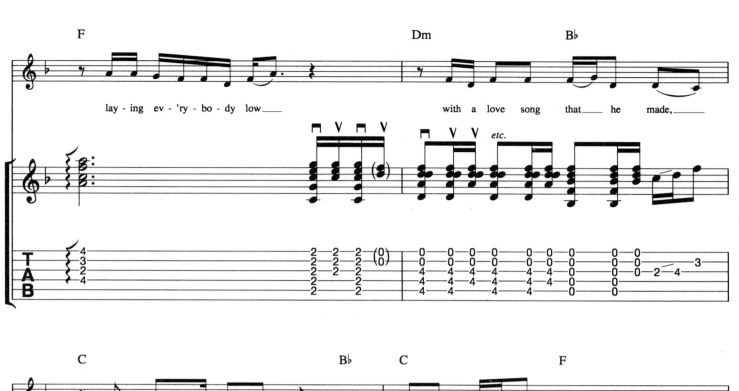

lay - ing ev - 'ry - bo - dy low____ with a love song that___ he made,____

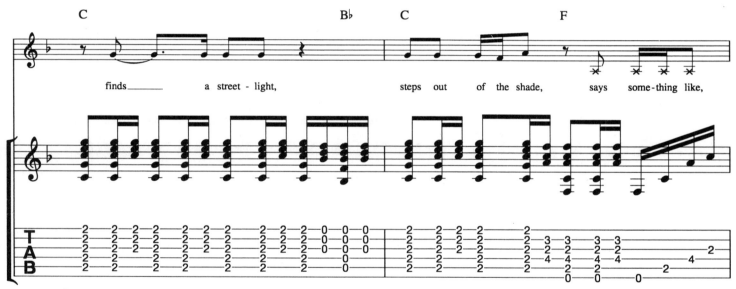

finds_____ a street - light, steps out of the shade, says some-thing like,

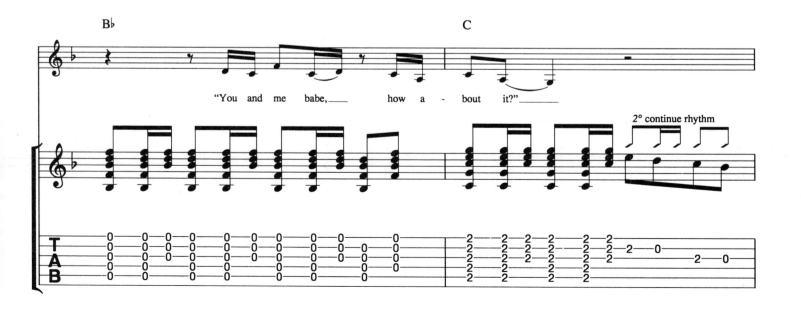

"You and me babe,____ how a - bout it?"_____

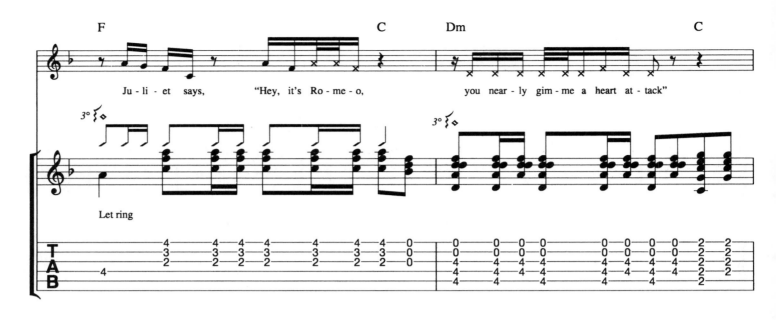

Ju - li - et says, "Hey, it's Ro - me - o, you near - ly gim - me a heart at - tack"

Let ring

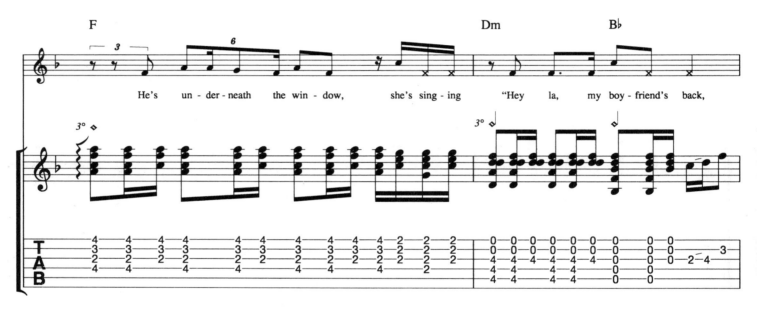

He's un - der - neath the win - dow, she's sing - ing "Hey la, my boy - friend's back,

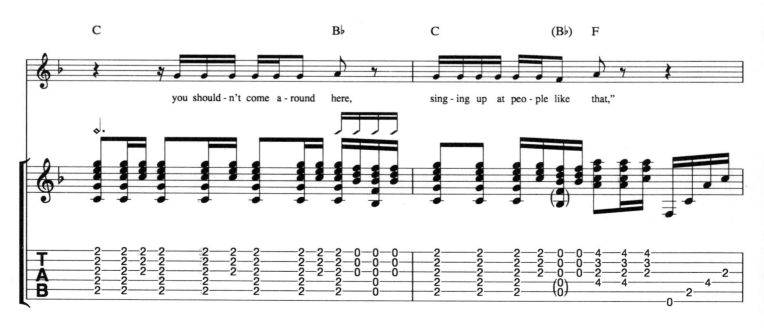

you should - n't come a - round here, sing - ing up at peo - ple like that,"

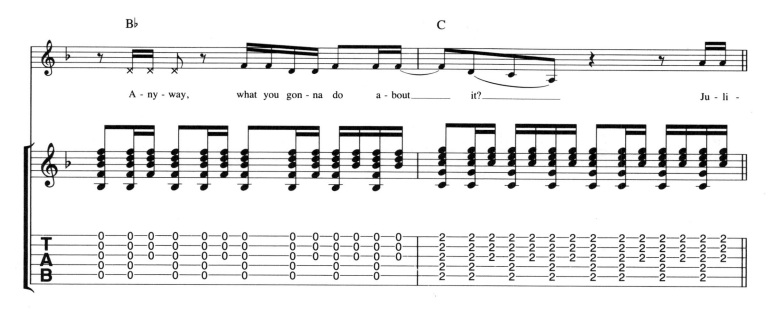

A - ny - way,   what you gon - na do a - bout_____ it?_____   Ju - li -

Chorus

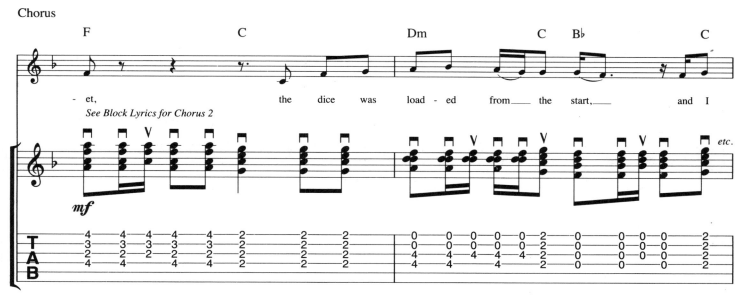

- et,   the dice was load - ed from___ the start,___   and I

See Block Lyrics for Chorus 2

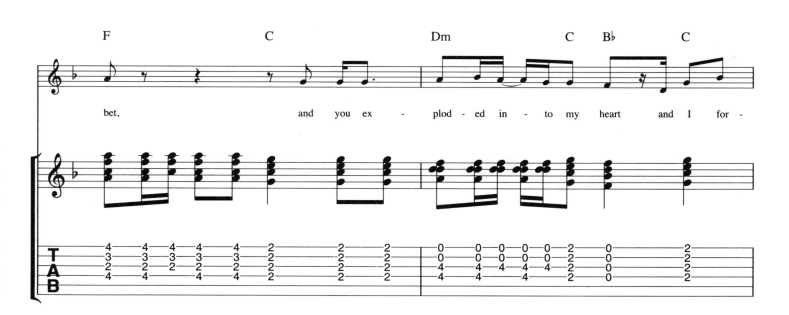

bet,   and you ex - plod - ed in - to my heart   and I for -

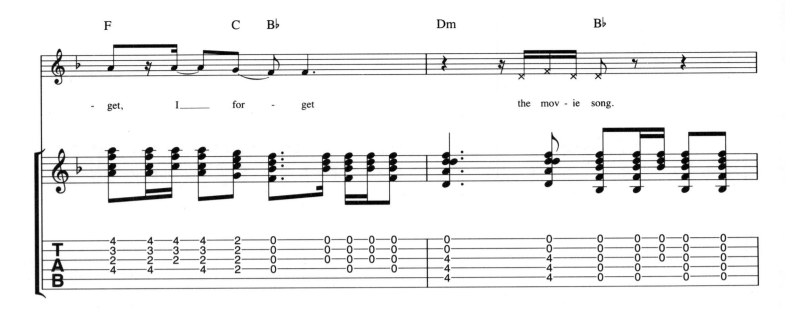

- get,   I____ for - get   the mov - ie song.

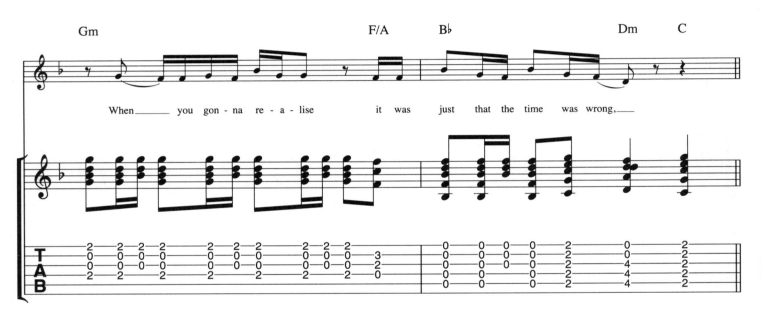

When____ you gon - na re - a - lise   it was   just   that the time   was wrong,____

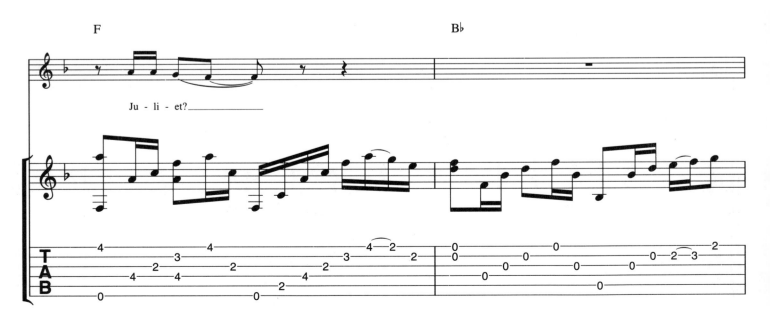

Ju - li - et?_____

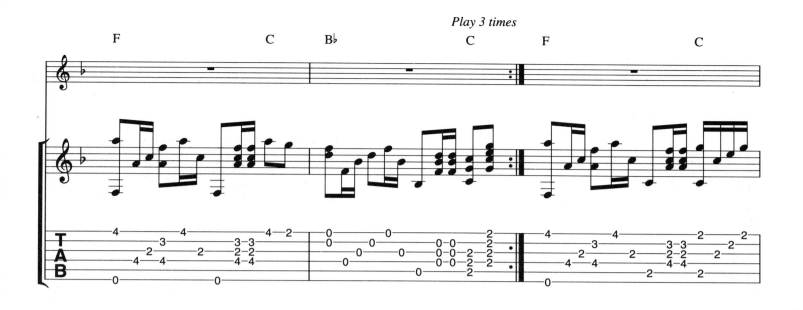

And a love - struck Ro - me - o___ sings a street a se - re - nade,___

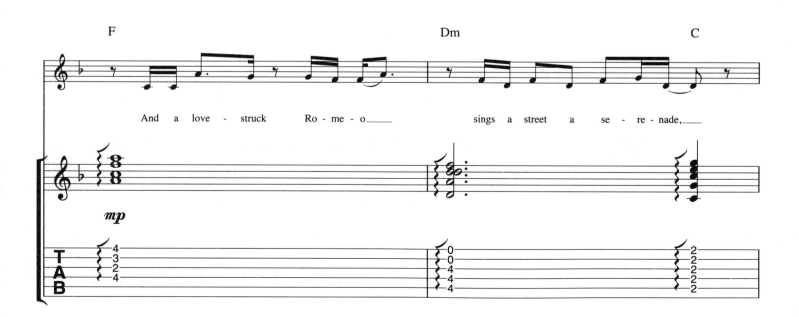

F   Dm   B♭

lay - ing ev - 'ry - bo - dy low,____ with a love song that____ he made,____

C   B♭   C   F

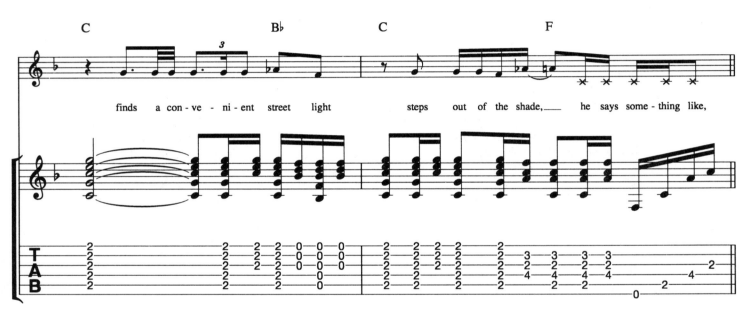

finds a con - ve - ni - ent street light steps out of the shade,____ he says some - thing like,

B♭   Cadd9

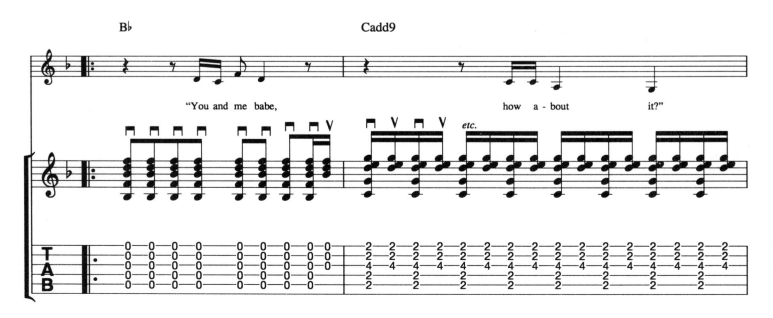

"You and me babe,   how a - bout   it?"

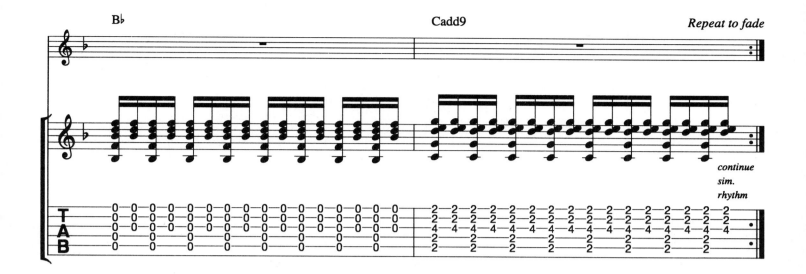

Verse 2
Came up on different streets
They both were streets of shame
Both dirty, both mean
Yes and the dream was just the same
And I dreamed your dream for you
And now your dream is real
How can you look at me as if I was
Just another one of your deals?

When you can fall for chains of silver
You can fall for chains of gold
You can fall for pretty strangers
And the promises they hold
You promised me everything
You promised me thick and thin, yeah
Now you just say 'Oh Romeo, yeah
You know I used to have a scene with him'

Chorus 2
Juliet, when we made love you used to cry
You said 'I love you like the stars above
I'll love you till I die'
There's a place for us, you know the movie song
When you gonna realise,
It was just that the time was wrong Juliet.

Verse 3
I can't do the talks
Like they talk on the T.V.
And I can't do a love song
Like the way it's meant to be
I can't do everything
But I'll do anything for you
I can't do anything
'cept be in love with you.

And all I do is miss you
And the way we used to be
All I do is keep the beat
And bad company
And all I do is kiss you
Through the bars of a rhyme
Julie, I'd do the stars with you
Anytime.

Chorus 3   As chorus 2

LOVE THE ONE YOU'RE WITH

Words & Music by Stephen A. Stills

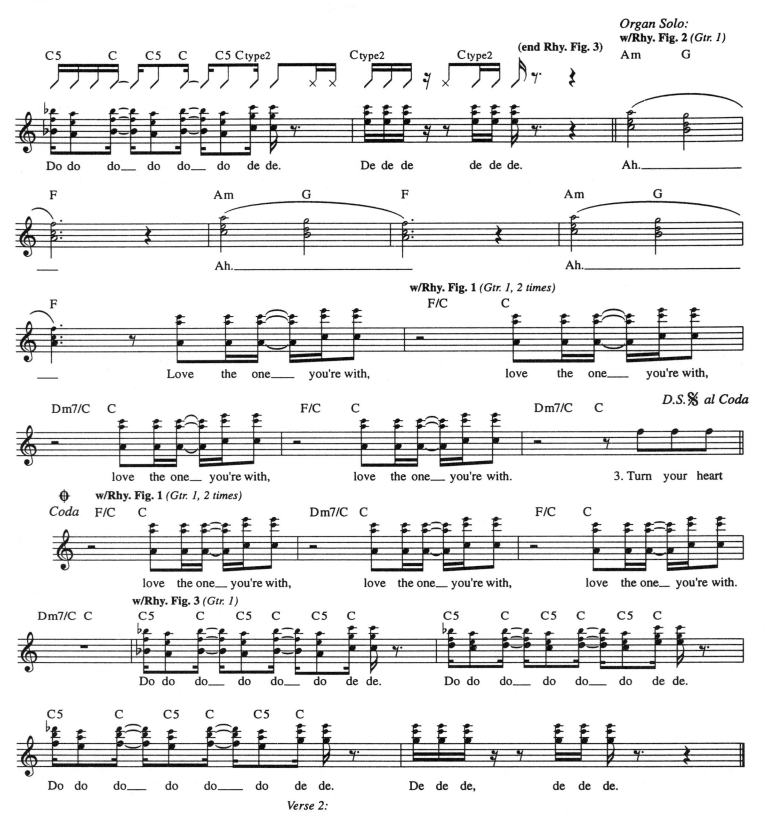

Verse 2:

Don't be angry, don't be sad,
But don't sit quiet over good times you had.
There's a girl right next to you,
And she's just waiting for something to do.
(To Chorus:)

Verse 3:

Turn your heartache right into joy,
She's a girl, and you're a boy.
Put it together, make it nice,
Ain't gonna need anymore advice.
(To Chorus:)

STAY

Words & Music by Bernard Butler

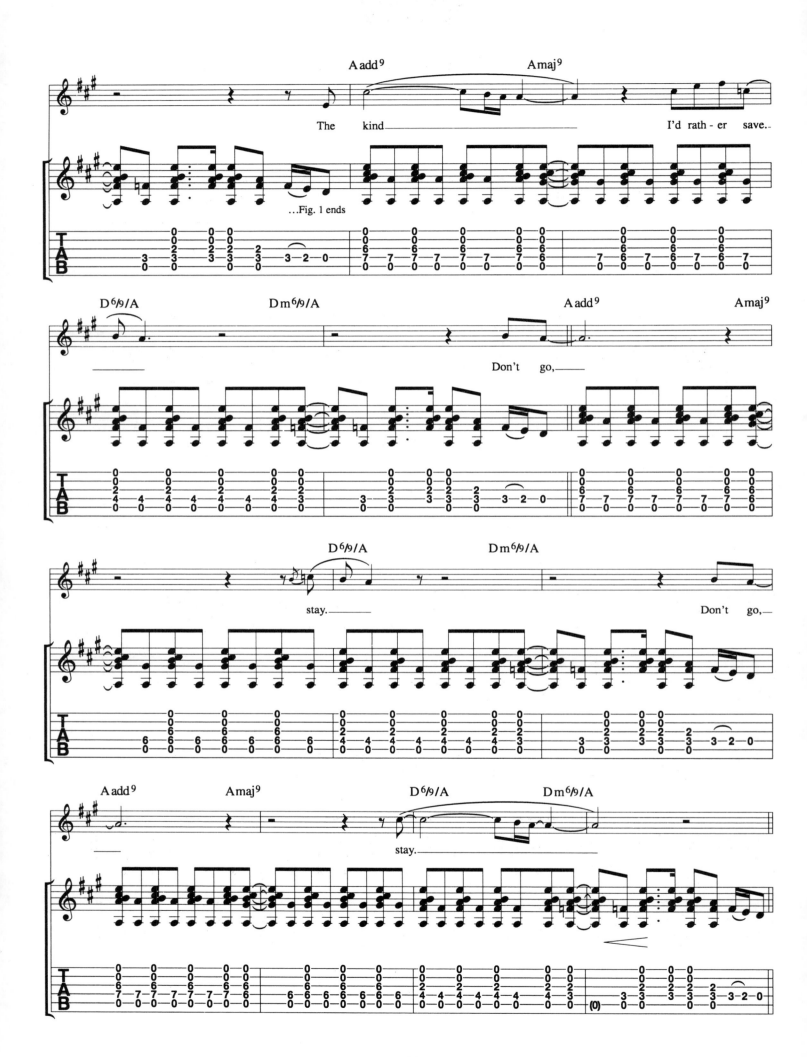

*adapted from electric guitar part (sounds 8va on recording)

Verse 3:
I know I've gotta move with the times
For you to be mine
For you to be mine
I've tried to believe what you say
But you won't change if you just stay.

SOMETHING CHANGED

Music by Pulp
Lyrics by Jarvis Cocker

Verse:

I wrote this song_____ two
See Block Lyrics for Verse 2

8 bars of first verse, strum and hold first chord only

hours be-fore we met,_____ I did-n't know_____

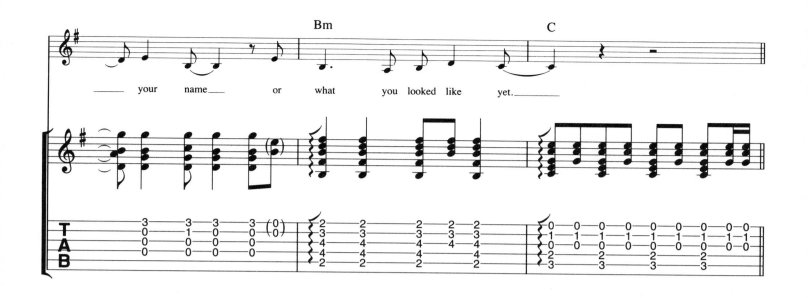

your name____ or what you looked like yet.____

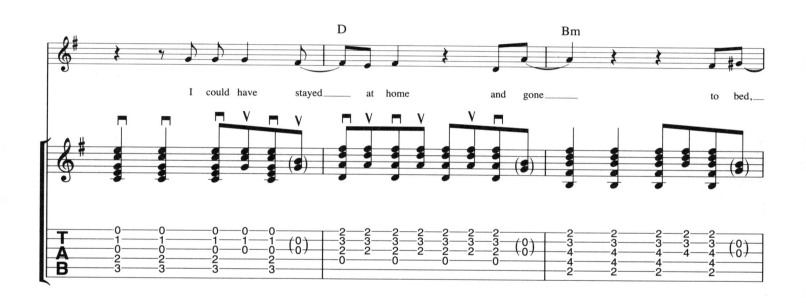

I could have stayed____ at home and gone____ to bed,____

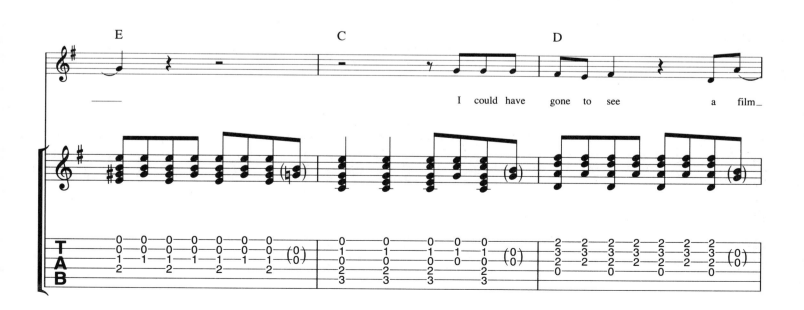

I could have gone to see a film____

83

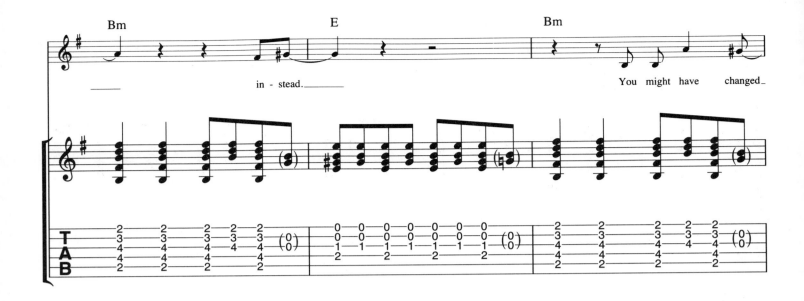

Chorus:

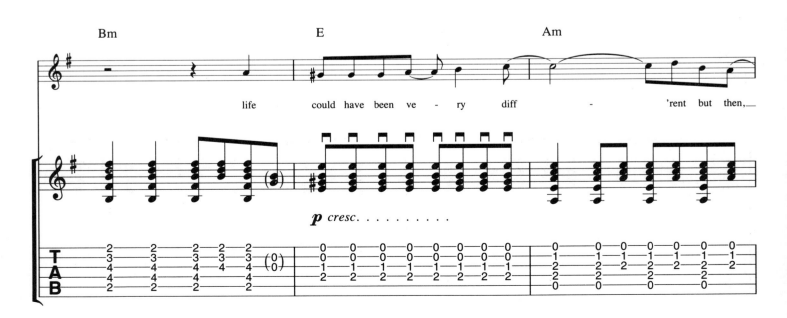

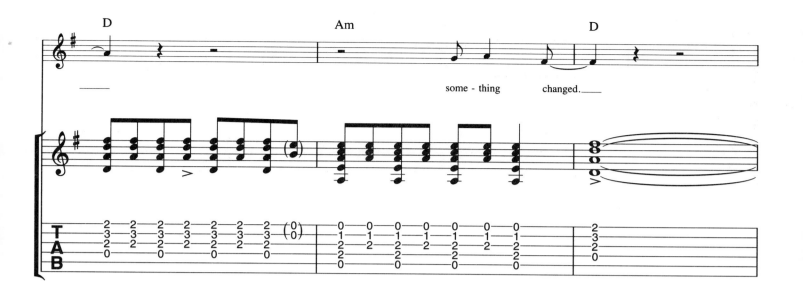

some - thing   changed.____

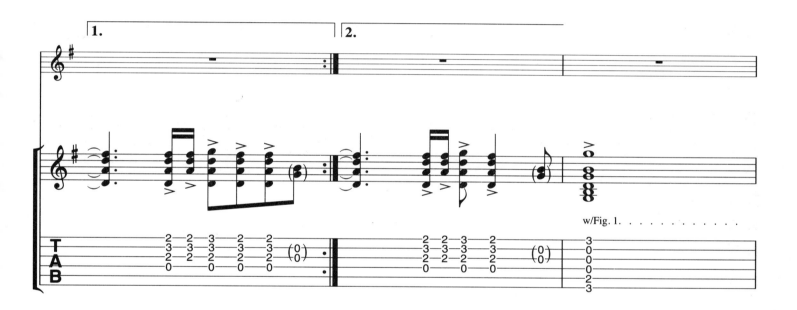

Solo:

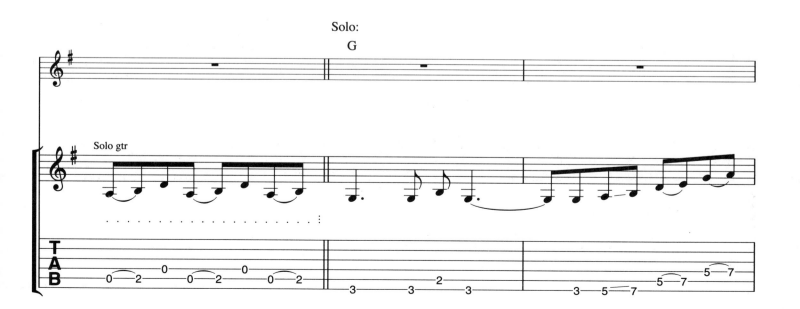

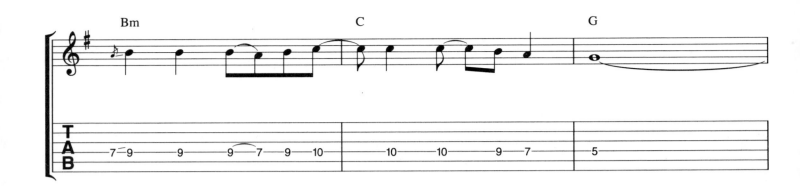

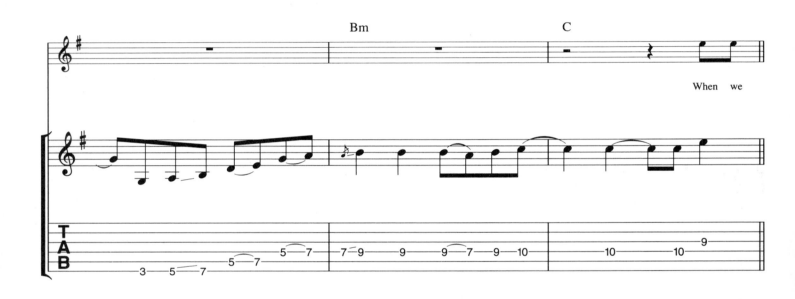

When we

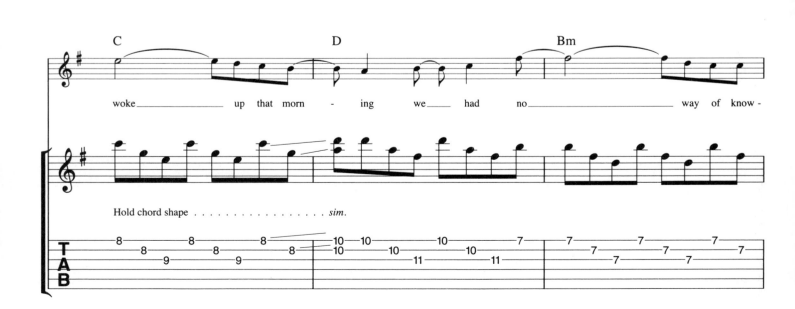

woke _____ up that morn - ing we ____ had no _____ way of know -

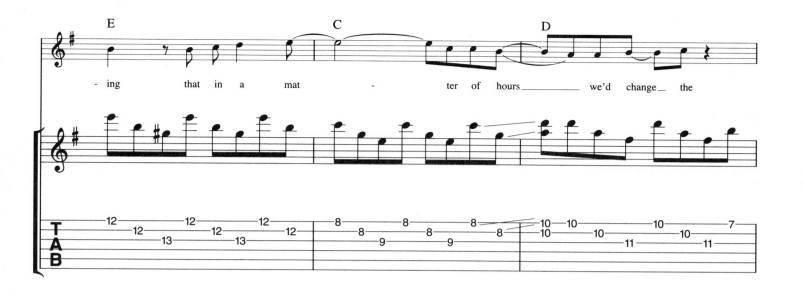

- ing   that   in   a   mat   -   ter of hours_____ we'd change_ the

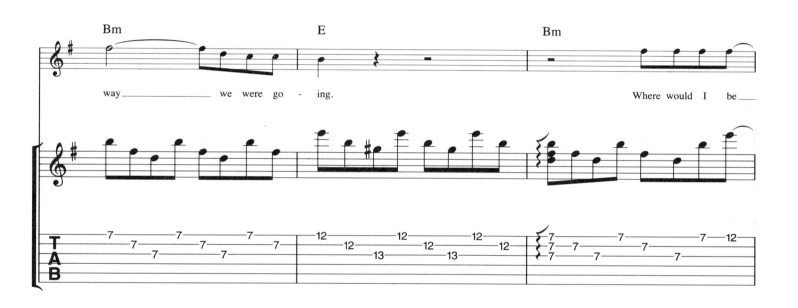

way_____ we   were   go - ing.   Where would I be___

_____ now   where would I be_____ now   if___ we'd ne -

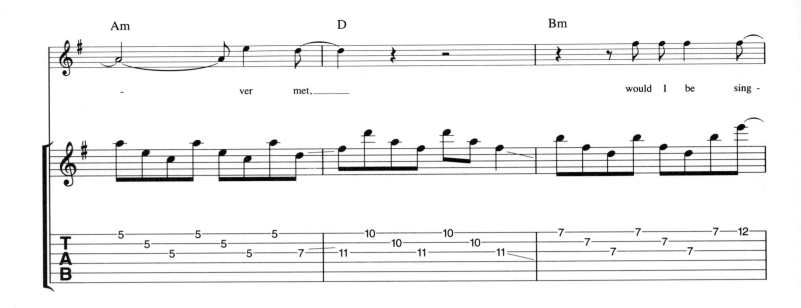

ver met,_____ would I be sing-

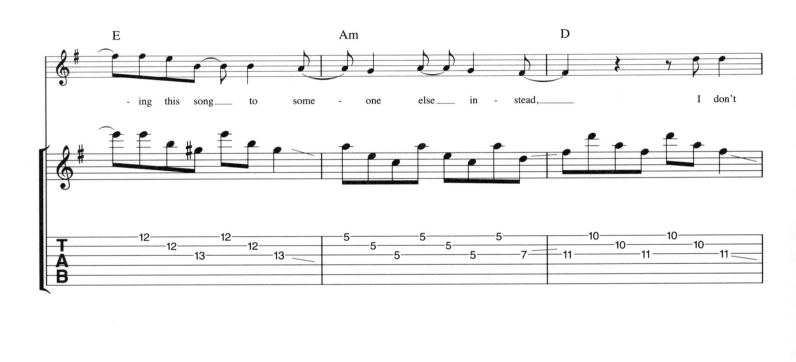

- ing this song_____ to some - one else_____ in - stead,_____ I don't

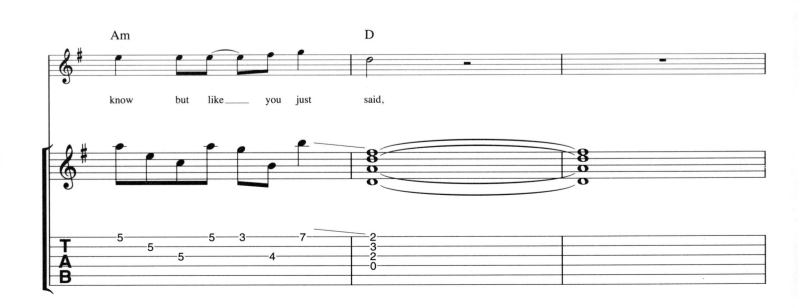

know but like_____ you just said,

some - thing   changed.

rall. . . . . .

Verse 2:   Do you believe
That there's someone up above?
Does he have a timetable
Directory acts of love?
Why did I write this song
On that one day?
Why did you touch my hand
And softly say?
Stop asking questions that don't matter anyway
Just give us a kiss to celebrate here today
Something changed.

SUZANNE

Words & Music by Leonard Cohen

1. Su - zanne
(Verses 2 & 3 see block lyric)

takes   you   down   to her   place   near   the   riv - er;   you can

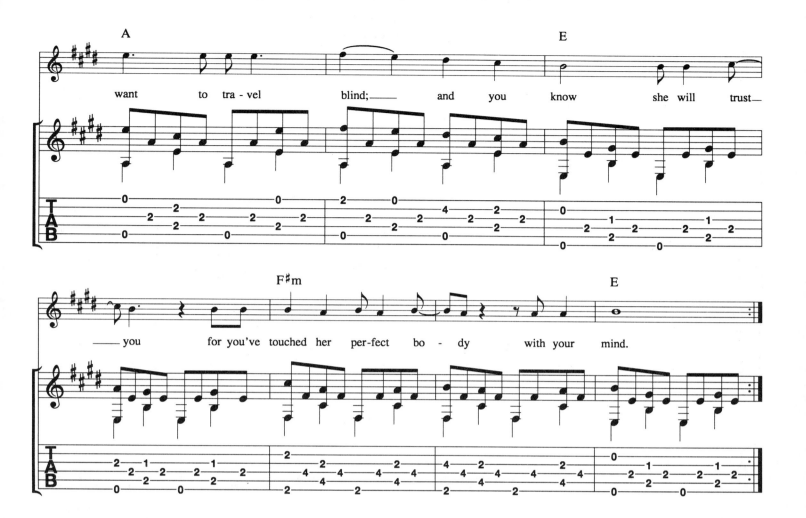

Verse 2:

And Jesus was a sailor
When he walked upon the water
And he spent a long time watching
From his lonely wooden tower.
And when he knew for certain
Only drowning men could see him
He said, "All men will be sailors then
Until the sea shall free them."
But he himself was broken
Long before the sky would open
Forsaken, almost human,
He sank beneath your wisdom like a stone.

And you want to travel with him
And you want to travel blind
And you think maybe you'll trust him
For he's touched your perfect body with his mind.

Verse 3:

Now Suzanne takes your hand
And she leads you to the river
She is wearing rags and feathers
From Salvation Army counters.
And the sun pours down like honey
On our lady of the harbour;
And she shows you where to look
Among the garbage and the flowers.
There are heroes in the seaweed,
There are children in the morning,
They are leaning out for love
And they will lean that way forever
While Suzanne holds the mirror.

And you want to travel with her
And you want to travel blind
And you know that you can trust her
For she's touched your perfect body with her mind.

TALK TONIGHT

Words & Music by Noel Gallagher

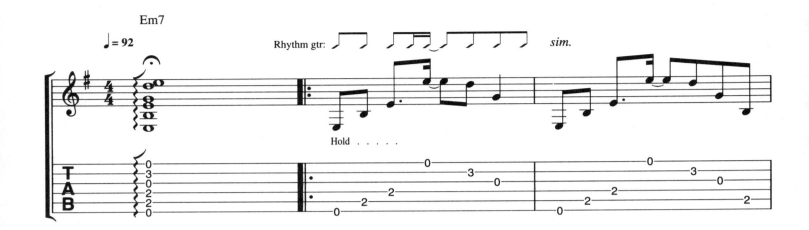

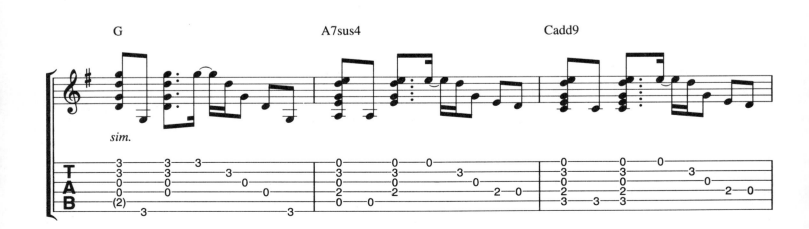

Verse:

Sit - ting on my own, chew - ing on a bone a thou - sand mil - lion miles

See Block Lyrics for Verse 2

Hold . . . . .

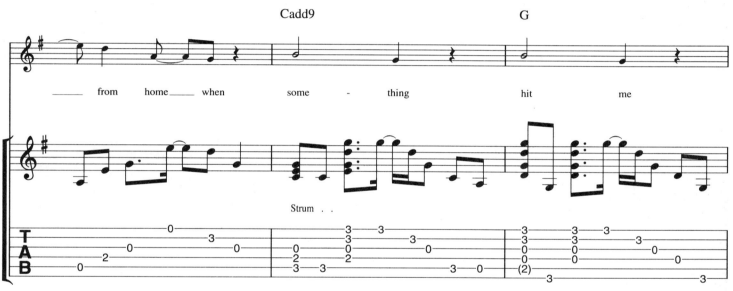

——— from home——— when some - thing hit me

Strum . .

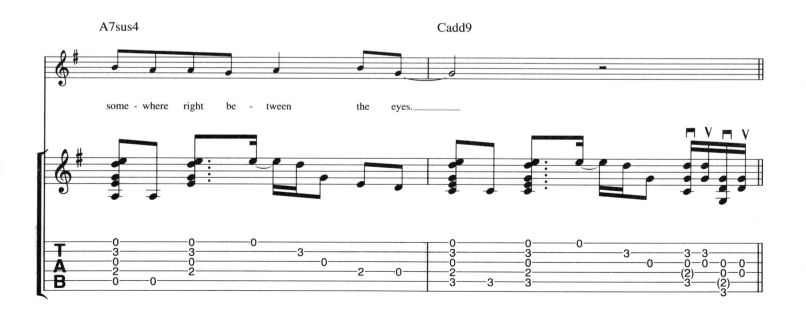

some - where right be - tween the eyes._____

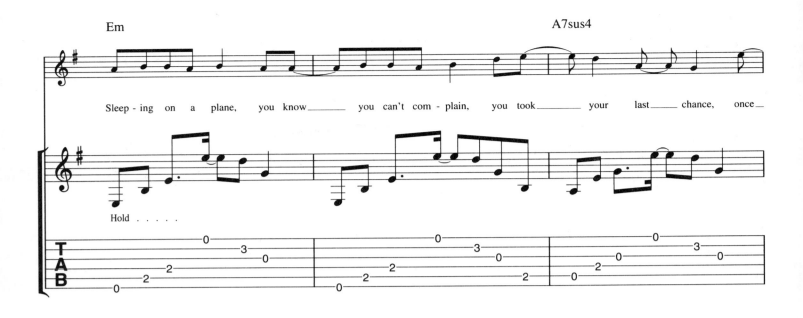

Sleep - ing on a plane, you know_____ you can't com - plain, you took_____ your last_____ chance, once

Hold . . . . .

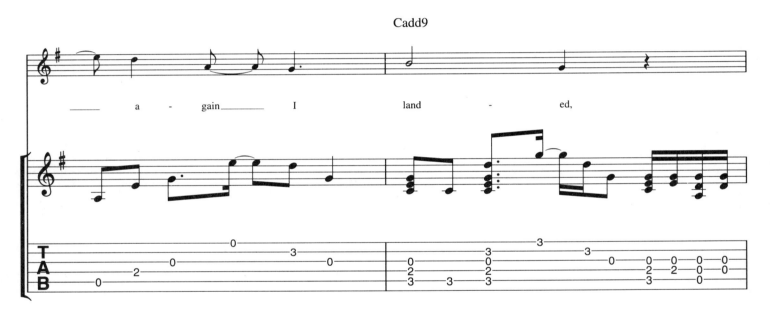

_____ a - gain_____ I land - ed,

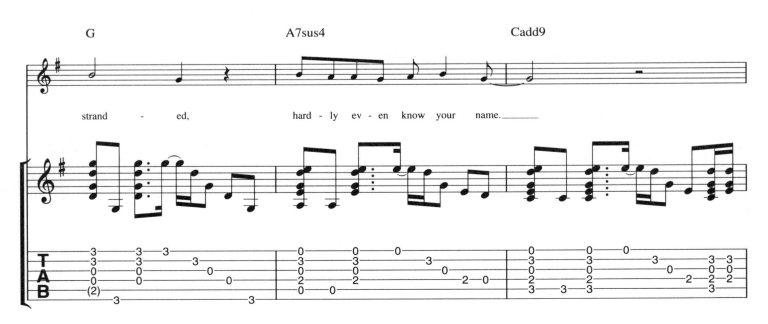

strand - ed, hard - ly ev - en know your name._____

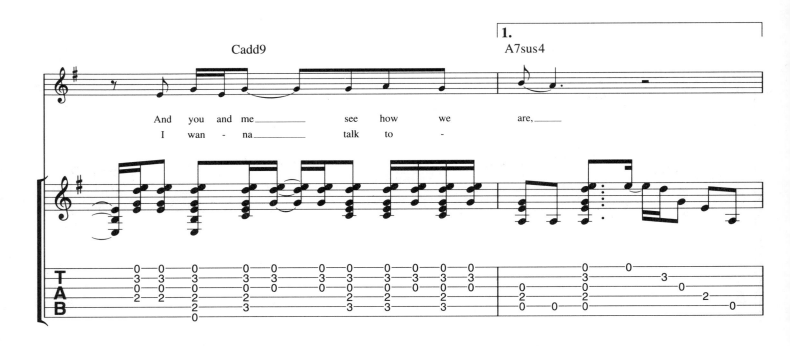

And you and me_____ see how we are,_____
I wan - na_____ talk to -

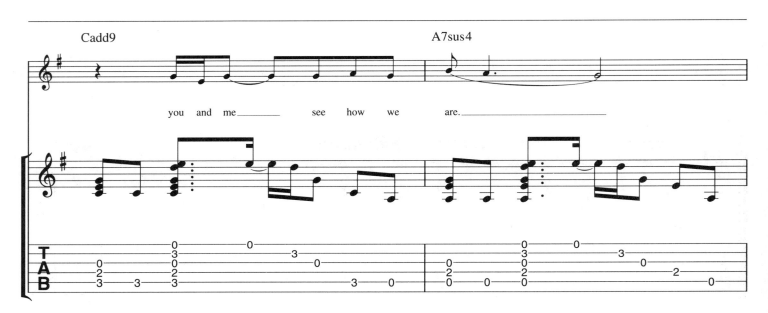

you and me_____ see how we are._____

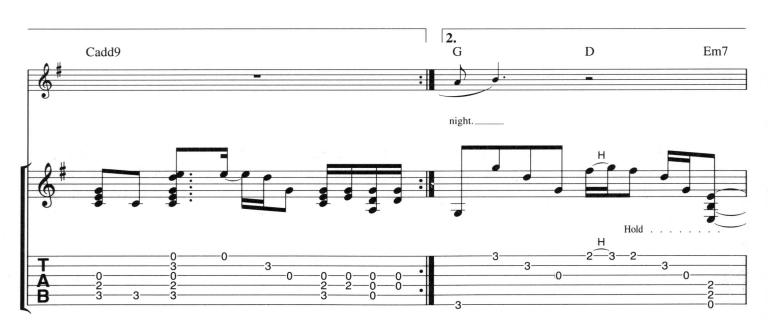

night._____

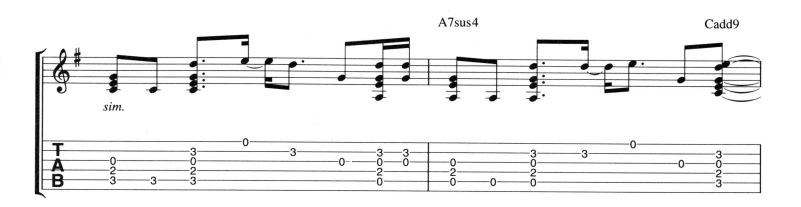

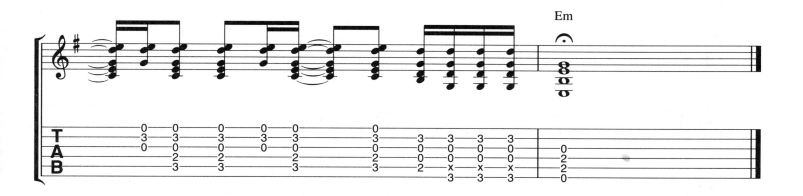

Verse 2:   All your dreams are made of strawberry lemonade
And you make sure I eat today
Take me walking
To where you played when you were young.

I'll never say that I won't ever make you cry
And this I'll say I don't know why
I know I'm leaving
But I'll be back another day.

TWO OF US

Words & Music by John Lennon & Paul McCartney

1. Two of us rid - ing no - where, spend - ing some - one's hard earned pay.
2. Two of us send - ing post - cards, writ - ing let - ters on my wall.
3.4. Two of us wear - ing rain - coats, stand - ing so - lo in the sun.

You and me Sun - day driv - ing, not ar - riv - ing, on our way back home.
You and me burn - ing match - es, lift - ing latch - es, on our way back home.
You and me chas - ing pa - per, get - ting no - where, on our way back home.

We're on our way

WHEN WE DANCE

Words & Music by Sting

110

WHEN YOU'RE GONE

Words & Music by Dolores O'Riordan

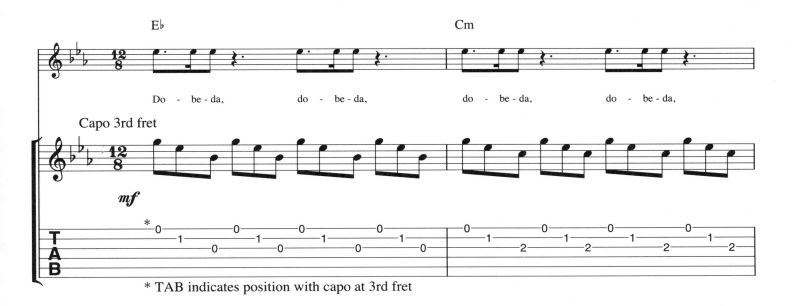

Do - be - da,   do - be - da,   do - be - da,   do - be - da,

Capo 3rd fret

mf

* TAB indicates position with capo at 3rd fret

do - be - da,   do - be - da,   do - be - da,   do - be - da.

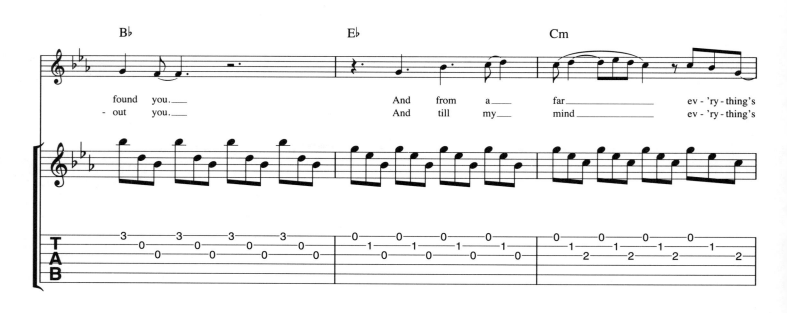

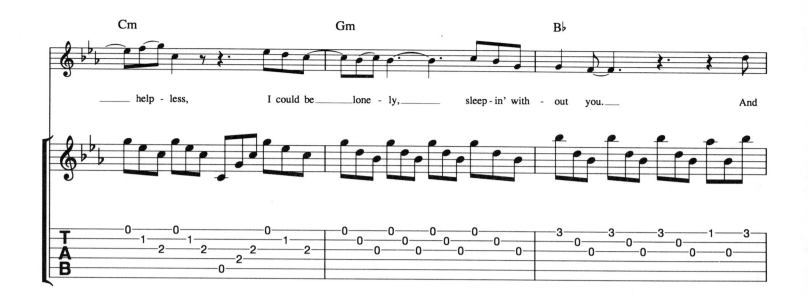

help - less,   I could be ____ lone - ly,   sleep - in' with - out you. ____   And

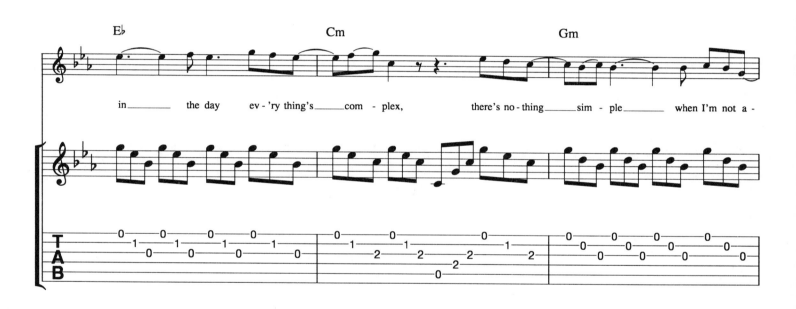

in ____ the day   ev - 'ry thing's ____ com - plex,   there's no - thing ____ sim - ple ____ when I'm not a -

Chorus

round   you. ____   But I   miss   you   when   you're   gone, ____

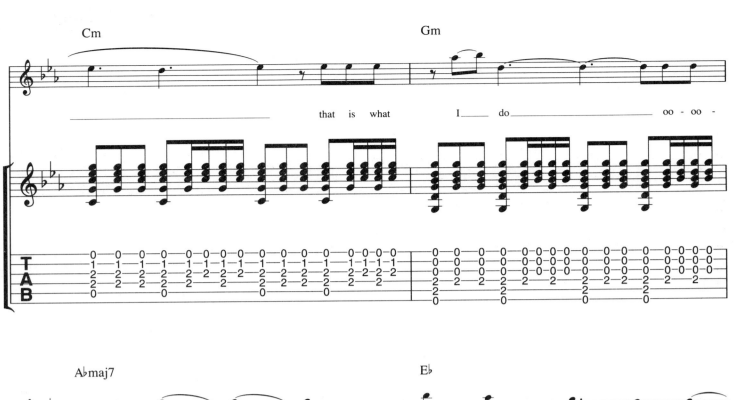

that is what I do oo - oo -

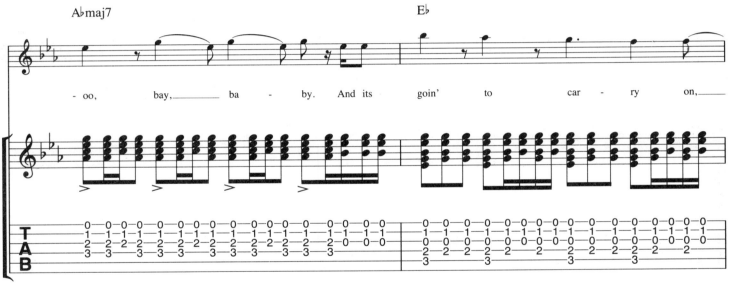

- oo, bay, ba - by. And its goin' to car - ry on,

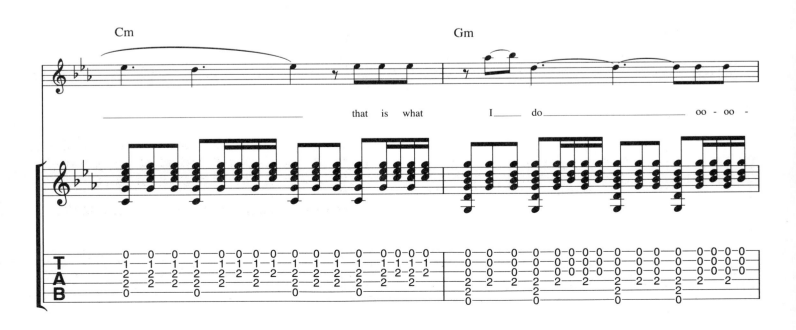

that is what I do oo - oo -

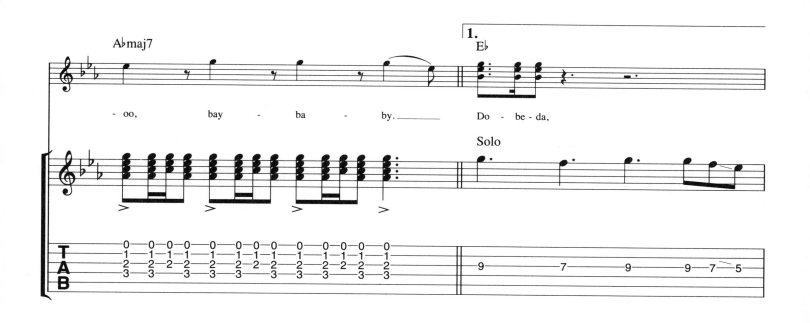

-oo, bay - ba - by. ____ Do - be - da,

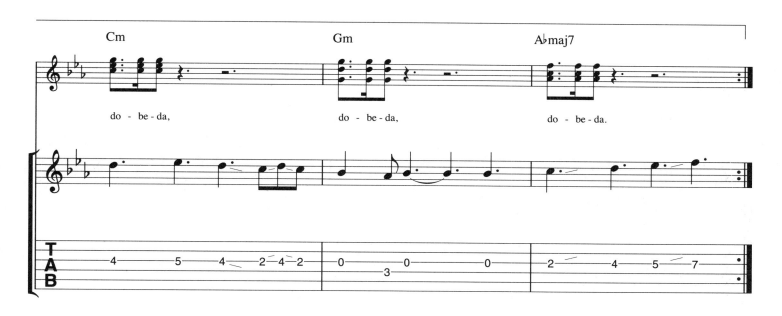

do - be - da, do - be - da, do - be - da.

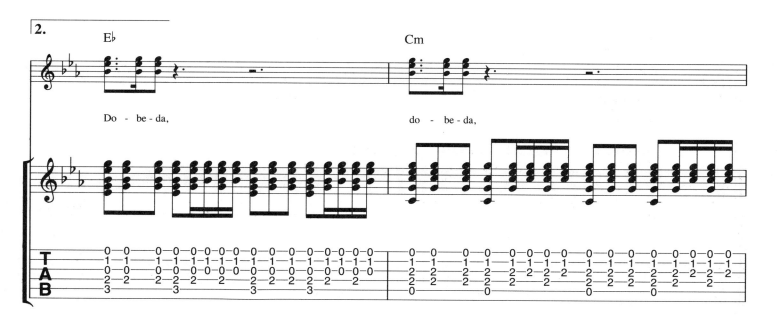

Do - be - da, do - be - da,

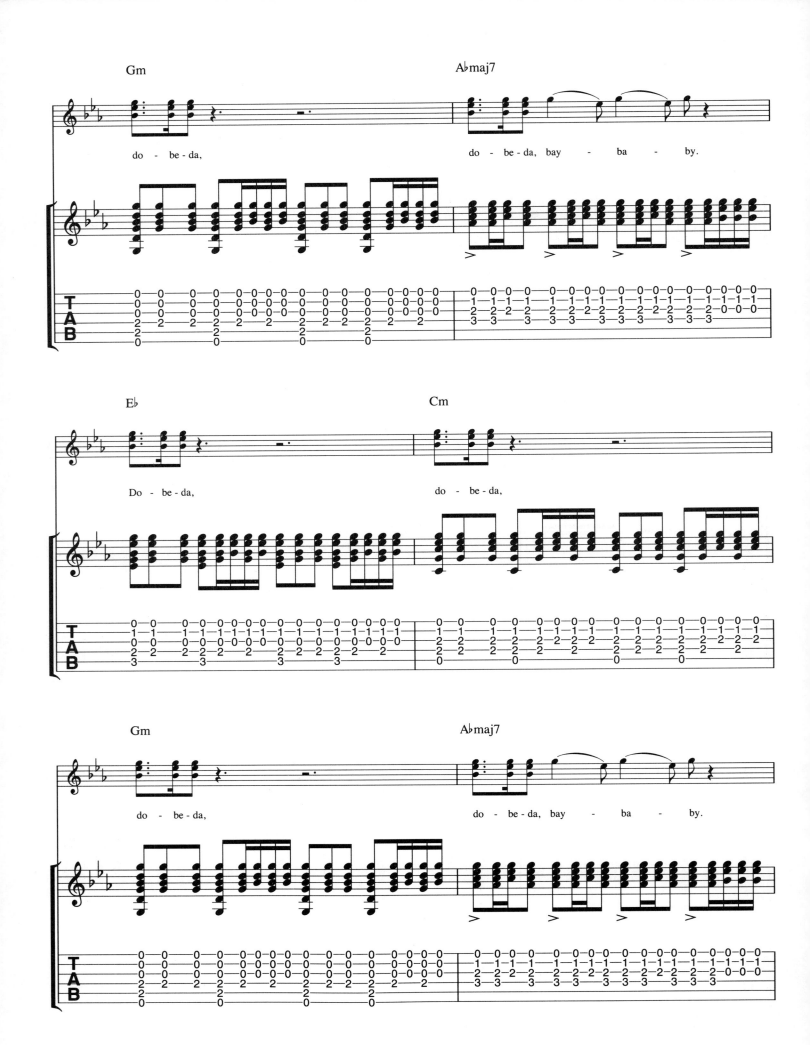

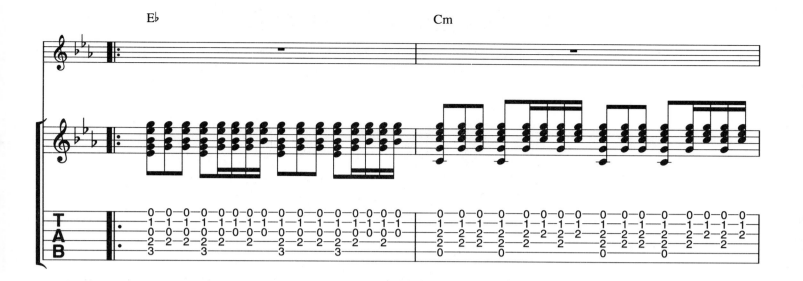

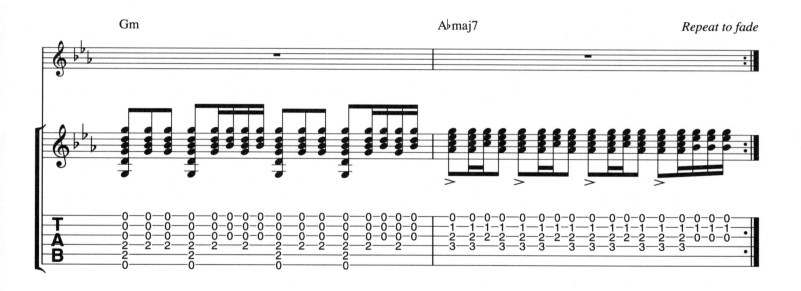

YOU'VE GOT TO HIDE YOUR LOVE AWAY

Words & Music by John Lennon & Paul McCartney

* For C chord, hammer from open D ④ to 2nd fret E simultaneously with the rest of chord.

For D chord, hammer from open G ③ to 2nd fret A.

YOU LIGHT THE FIRE

Words & Music by Bernard Butler

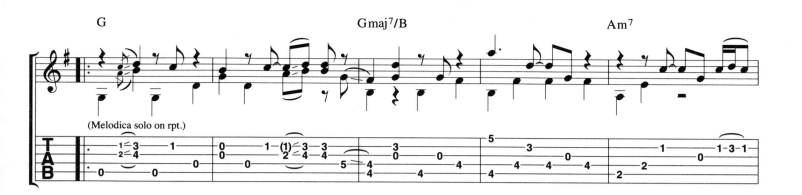

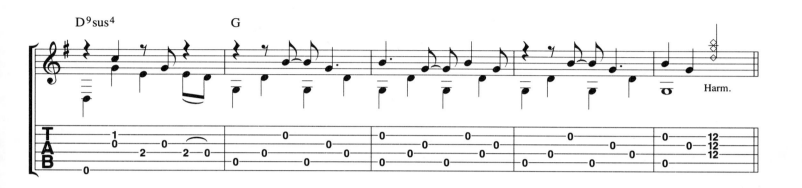

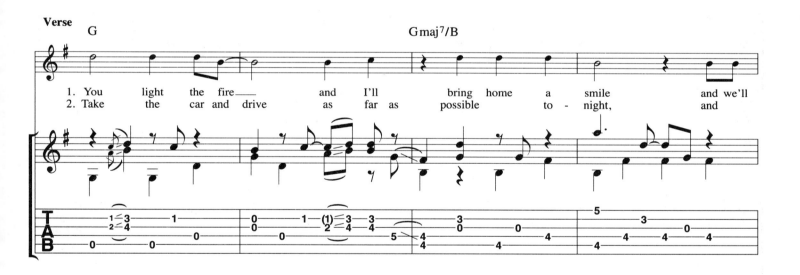

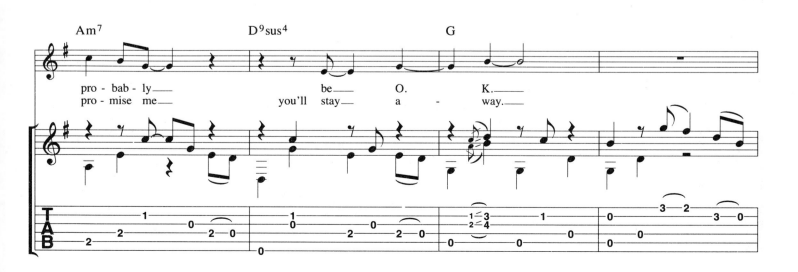

How long un - til you re - cov - er,_____ all the
How long un - til you re - cov - er,_____ and the

me - mo - ries you threw a - way?
man you broke_ walks a - way?

D.C. al Coda

Coda

123

3. (So) you light the fire—— and I'll bring home a smile and we'll pro - bab - ly—— be O. K.——

PRÉSENTATION DE LA TABLATURE DE GUITARE

Il existe trois façons différentes de noter la musique pour guitare : à l'aide d'une portée musicale, de tablatures ou de barres rythmiques

Les BARRES RYTHMIQUES sont indiquées au-dessus de la portée. Jouez les accords dans le rythme indiqué. Les notes rondes indiquent des notes réciles.

La PORTÉE MUSICALE indique les notes et rythmes et est divisée en mesures. Cette division est représentée par des lignes. Les notes sont : do, ré, mi, fa, sol, la, si.

La PORTÉE EN TABLATURE est une représentation graphique des touches de guitare. Chaque ligne horizontale correspond à une corde et chaque chiffre correspond à une case.

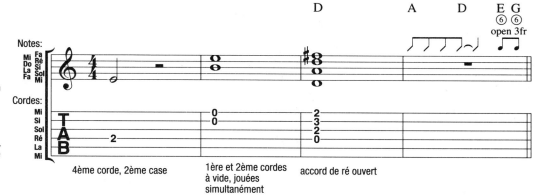

4ème corde, 2ème case

1ère et 2ème cordes à vide, jouées simultanément

accord de ré ouvert

Notation Spéciale De Guitare : Définitions

TIRÉ DEMI-TON : Jouez la note et tirez la corde afin d'élever la note d'un demi-ton (étape à moitié).

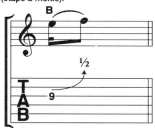

TIRÉ PLEIN : Jouez la note et tirez la corde afin d'élever la note d'un ton entier (étape entière).

TIRÉ D'AGRÉMENT : Jouez la note et tirez la corde comme indiqué. Jouez la première note aussi vite que possible.

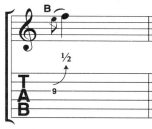

TIRÉ QUART DE TON : Jouez la note et tirez la corde afin d'élever la note d'un quart de ton.

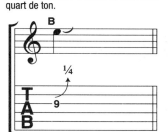

TIRÉ ET LÂCHÉ : Jouez la note et tirez la corde comme indiqué, puis relâchez, afin d'obtenir de nouveau la note de départ.

TIRÉ ET REJOUÉ : Jouez la note et tirez la corde comme indiqué puis rejouez la corde où le symbole apparaît.

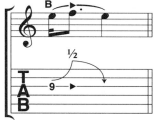

PRÉ-TIRÉ : Tirez la corde comme indiqué puis jouez cette note.

PRÉ-TIRÉ ET LÂCHÉ : Tirez la corde comme indiqué. Jouez la note puis relâchez la corde afin d'obtenir le ton de départ.

HAMMER-ON: Jouez la première note (plus basse) avec un doigt puis jouez la note plus haute sur la même corde avec un autre doigt, sur le manche mais sans vous servir du médiator.

PULL-OFF: Positionnez deux doigts sur les notes à jouer. Jouez la première note et sans vous servir du médiator, dégagez un doigt pour obtenir la deuxième note, plus basse.

GLISSANDO : Jouez la première note puis faites glisser le doigt le long du manche pour obtenir la seconde note qui, elle, n'est pas jouée.

GLISSANDO ET REJOUÉ : Identique au glissando à ceci près que la seconde note est jouée.

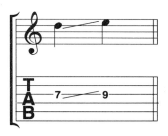

HARMONIQUES NATURELLES : Jouez la note tandis qu'un doigt effleure la corde sur le manche correspondant à la case indiquée.

PICK SCRAPE (SCRATCH) : On fait glisser le médiator le long de la corde, ce qui produit un son éraillé.

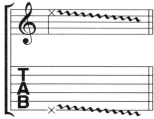

ÉTOUFFÉ DE LA PAUME : La note est partiellement étouffée par la main (celle qui se sert du médiator). Elle effleure la (les) corde(s) juste au-dessus du chevalet.

CORDES ÉTOUFFÉES : Un effet de percussion produit en posant à plat la main sur le manche sans relâcher, puis en jouant les cordes avec le médiator.

NOTE: La vitesse des tirés est indiquée par la notation musicale et le tempo.

ERLÄUTERUNG ZUR TABULATURSCHREIBWEISE

Es gibt drei Möglichkeiten, Gitarrenmusik zu notieren: im klassichen Notensystem, in Tabulaturform oder als rhythmische Akzente

RHYTHMISCHE AKZENTE werden über dem Notensystem notiert. Geschlagene Akkorde werden rhythmisch dargestellt. Ausgeschriebene Noten stellen Einzeltöne dar.

Im **NOTENSYSTEM** werden Tonhöhe und rhythmischer Verlauf festgelegt; es ist durch Taktstriche in Takte unterteilt. Die Töne werden nach den ersten acht Buchstaben des Alphabets benannt.
Beachte: "B" in der anglo-amerkanischen Schreibweise entspricht dem deutschen "H"!

DIE TABULATUR ist die optische Darstellung des Gitarrengriffbrettes. Jeder horizontalen Linie ist eine bestimmte Saite zugeordnet, jede Zahl bezeichnet einen Bund.

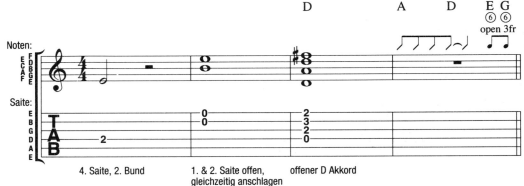

4. Saite, 2. Bund   1. & 2. Saite offen, gleichzeitig anschlagen   offener D Akkord

Erklärungen zur speziellen Gitarennotation

HALBTON-ZIEHER: Spiele die Note und ziehe dann um einen Halbton höher (Halbtonschritt).

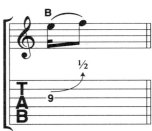

GANZTON-ZIEHER: Spiele die Note und ziehe dann einen Ganzton höher (Ganztonschritt).

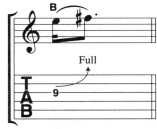

ZIEHER MIT VORSCHLAG: Spiele die Note und ziehe wie notiert. Spiele die erste Note so schnell wie möglich.

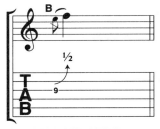

VIERTELTON-ZIEHER: Spiele die Note und ziehe dann einen Viertelton höher (Vierteltonschritt).

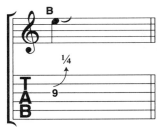

ZIEHEN UND ZURÜCKGLEITEN: Spiele die Note und ziehe wie notiert; lasse den Finger dann in die Ausgangsposition zurückgleiten. Dabei wird nur die erste Note angeschlagen.

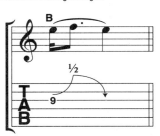

ZIEHEN UND NOCHMALIGES ANSCHLAGEN: Spiele die Note und ziehe wie notiert, schlage die Saite neu an, wenn das Symbol "▶" erscheint und lasse den Finger dann zurückgleiten.

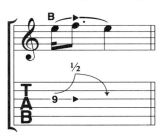

ZIEHER VOR DEM ANSCHLAGEN: Ziehe zuerst die Note wie notiert; schlage die Note dann an.

ZIEHER VOR DEM ANSCHLAGEN MIT ZURÜCKGLEITEN: Ziehe die Note wie notiert; schlage die Note dann an und lasse den Finger auf die Ausgangslage zurückgleiten.

AUFSCHLAGTECHNIK: Schlage die erste (tiefere) Note an; die höhere Note (auf der selben Saite) erklingt durch kräftiges Aufschlagen mit einem anderen Finger der Griffhand.

ABZIEHTECHNIK: Setze beide Finger auf die zu spielenden Noten und schlage die erste Note an. Ziehe dann (ohne nochmals anzuschlagen) den oberen Finger der Griffhand seitlich - abwärts ab, um die zweite (tiefere) Note zum klingen zu bringen.

GLISSANDOTECHNIK: Schlage die erste Note an und rutsche dann mit dem selben Finger der Griffhand aufwärts oder abwärts zur zweiten Note. Die zweite Note wird nicht angeschlagen.

GLISSANDOTECHNIK MIT NACHFOLGENDEM ANSCHLAG: Gleiche Technik wie das gebundene Glissando, jedoch wird die zweite Note angeschlagen.

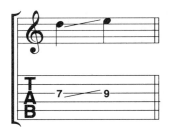

NATÜRLICHES FLAGEOLETT: Berühre die Saite über dem angegebenen Bund leicht mit einem Finger der Griffhand. Schlage die Saite an und lasse sie frei schwingen.

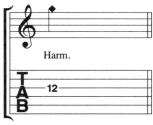

PICK SCRAPE: Fahre mit dem Plektrum nach unten über die Saiten - klappt am besten bei umsponnenen Saiten.

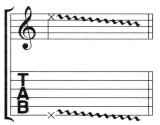

DÄMPFEN MIT DER SCHLAGHAND: Lege die Schlaghand oberhalb der Brücke leicht auf die Saite(n).

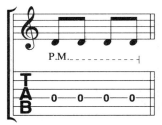

DÄMPFEN MIT DER GRIFFHAND: Du erreichst einen percussiven Sound, indem du die Griffhand leicht über die Saiten legst (ohne diese herunterzudrücken) und dann mit der Schlaghand anschlägst.

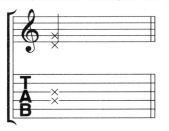

AMMERKUNG: Das Tempo der Zieher und Glissandos ist abhängig von der rhythmischen Notation und dem Grundtempo.

SPIEGAZIONI DI TABLATURA PER CHITARRA

La musica per chitarra può essere annotata in tre diversi modi: sul pentagramma, in tablatura e in taglio ritmico

IL TAGLIO RITMICO è scritto sopra il pentagramma. Percuotere le corde al ritmo indicato Le teste arrotondate delle note indicano note singole.

IL PENTAGRAMMA MUSICALE mostra toni e ritmo ed è divisa da linee in settori. I toni sono indicati con le prime sette lettere dell'alfabeto.

LA TABLATURA rappresenta graficamente la tastiera della chitarra. Ogni linea orizzontale rappresenta una corda, ed ogni corda rappresenta un tasto.

4° corda, 2° tasto   1° e 2° corda aperte, suonate insieme   accordo D aperto

Definizioni Per Annotazioni Speciali Per Chitarra

SEMI-TONO CURVATO: percuotere la nota e curvare di un semitono (1/2 passo).

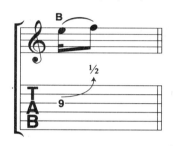

TONO CURVATO: Percuotere la nota e curvare di un tono (passo intero).

NOTA BREVE, CURVATA: percuotere la nota e curvare come indicato. Suonare la prima nota il più velocemente possibile.

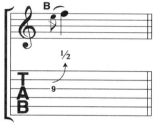

QUARTO DI TONO, CURVATO: Percuotere la nota e curvare di un quarto di passo.

CURVA E LASCIA: Percuotere la nota e curvare come indicato, quindi rilasciare indietro alla nota originale.

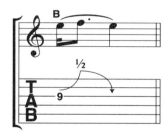

CURVA E RIPERCUOTI: Percuotere la nota e curvare come indicato poi ripercuotere la corda nel punto del simbolo.

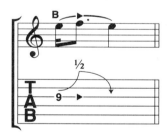

PRE-CURVA: Curvare la nota come indicato e quindi percuoterla.

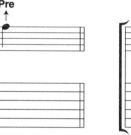

PRE-CURVA E RILASCIO: Curvare la nota come indicato. Colpire e rilasciare la nota indietro alla tonalità indicata.

MARTELLO-COLPISCI: Colpire la prima nota (in basso) con un dito; quindi suona la nota più alta (sulla stessa corda) con un altro dito, toccandola senza pizzicare.

TOGLIERE: Posizionare entrambe le dita sulla nota da suonare. Colpire la prima nota e, senza pizzicare, togliere le dita per suonare la seconda nota (più in basso).

LEGATO SCIVOLATO (GLISSATO): Colpire la prima nota e quindi far scivolare lo stesso dito della mano della tastiera su o giù alla seconda nota. La seconda nota non viene colpita.

CAMBIO SCIVOLATO (GLISSARE E RICOLPIRE): Uguale al legato - scivolato eccetto che viene colpita la seconda nota.

ARMONICA NATURALE: Colpire la nota mentre la mano della tastiera tocca leggermente la corda direttamente sopra il tasto indicato.

PIZZICA E GRAFFIA: Il limite del pizzicato è tirato su (o giù) lungo la corda, producendo un suono graffiante.

SORDINA CON IL PALMO: La nota è parzialmente attenuata dalla mano del pizzicato toccando la corda (le corde) appena prima del ponte.

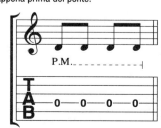

CORDE SMORZATE: Un suono di percussione viene prodotto appoggiando la mano della tastiera attraverso la corda (le corde) senza premere, e colpendole con la mano del pizzicato.

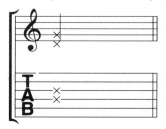

NOTA: La velocità di ogni curvatura è indicata dalle annotazioni musicali e dal tempo.

Part 3
90's HITS

GUITAR TABLATURE EXPLAINED

Guitar music can be notated three different ways: on a musical stave, in tablature, and in rhythm slashes

RHYTHM SLASHES are written above the stave. Strum chords in the rhythm indicated. Round noteheads indicate single notes.

THE MUSICAL STAVE shows pitches and rhythms and is divided by lines into bars. Pitches are named after the first seven letters of the alphabet.

TABLATURE graphically represents the guitar fingerboard. Each horizontal line represents a string, and each number represents a fret.

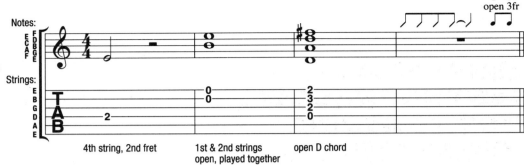

4th string, 2nd fret   1st & 2nd strings open, played together   open D chord

Definitions for special guitar notation

SEMI-TONE BEND: Strike the note and bend up a semi-tone (1/2 step).

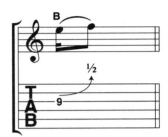

WHOLE-TONE BEND: Strike the note and bend up a whole-tone (whole step).

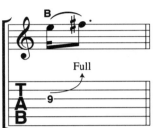

GRACE NOTE BEND: Strike the note and bend as indicated. Play the first note as quickly as possible.

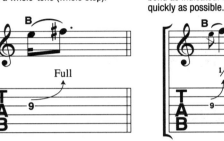

QUARTER-TONE BEND: Strike the note and bend up a 1/4 step.

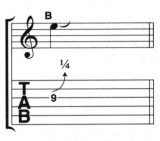

BEND & RELEASE: Strike the note and bend up as indicated, then release back to the original note.

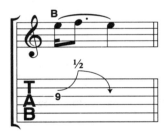

COMPOUND BEND & RELEASE: Strike the note and bend up and down in the rhythm indicated.

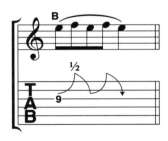

PRE-BEND: Bend the note as indicated, then strike it.

PRE-BEND & RELEASE: Bend the note as indicated. Strike it and release the note back to the original pitch.

UNISON BEND: Strike the two notes simultaneously and bend the lower note up to the pitch of the higher.

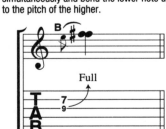

BEND & RESTRIKE: Strike the note and bend as indicated then restrike the string where the symbol occurs.

BEND, HOLD AND RELEASE: Same as bend and release but hold the bend for the duration of the tie.

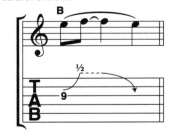

BEND AND TAP: Bend the note as indicated and tap the higher fret while still holding the bend.

VIBRATO: The string is vibrated by rapidly bending and releasing the note with the fretting hand.

HAMMER-ON: Strike the first (lower) note with one finger, then sound the higher note (on the same string) with another finger by fretting it without picking.

PULL-OFF: Place both fingers on the notes to be sounded, Strike the first note and without picking, pull the finger off to sound the second (lower) note.

LEGATO SLIDE (GLISS): Strike the first note and then slide the same fret-hand finger up or down to the second note. The second note is not struck.

NOTE: The speed of any bend is indicated by the music notation and tempo.

SHIFT SLIDE (GLISS & RESTRIKE): Same as legato slide, except the second note is struck.

TRILL: Very rapidly alternate between the notes indicated by continuously hammering on and pulling off.

TAPPING: Hammer ("tap") the fret indicated with the pick-hand index or middle finger and pull off to the note fretted by the fret hand.

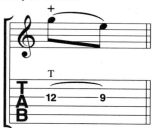

PICK SCRAPE: The edge of the pick is rubbed down (or up) the string, producing a scratchy sound.

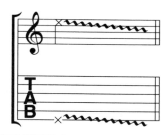

MUFFLED STRINGS: A percussive sound is produced by laying the fret hand across the string(s) without depressing, and striking them with the pick hand.

NATURAL HARMONIC: Strike the note while the fret-hand lightly touches the string directly over the fret indicated.

PINCH HARMONIC: The note is fretted normally and a harmonic is produced by adding the edge of the thumb or the tip of the index finger of the pick hand to the normal pick attack.

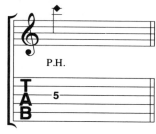

HARP HARMONIC: The note is fretted normally and a harmonic is produced by gently resting the pick hand's index finger directly above the indicated fret (in parentheses) while the pick hand's thumb or pick assists by plucking the appropriate string.

PALM MUTING: The note is partially muted by the pick hand lightly touching the string(s) just before the bridge.

RAKE: Drag the pick across the strings indicated with a single motion.

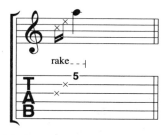

TREMOLO PICKING: The note is picked as rapidly and continuously as possible.

ARPEGGIATE: Play the notes of the chord indicated by quickly rolling them from bottom to top.

SWEEP PICKING: Rhythmic downstroke and/or upstroke motion across the strings.

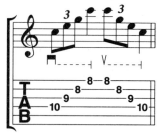

VIBRATO DIVE BAR AND RETURN: The pitch of the note or chord is dropped a specific number of steps (in rhythm) then returned to the original pitch.

VIBRATO BAR SCOOP: Depress the bar just before striking the note, then quickly release the bar.

VIBRATO BAR DIP: Strike the note and then immediately drop a specific number of steps, then release back to the original pitch.

Additional musical definitions

(accent)	•	Accentuate note (play it louder).
(accent)	•	Accentuate note with great intensity.
(staccato)	•	Shorten time value of note.
	•	Downstroke
V	•	Upstroke

D.%. al Coda

D.C. al Fine

tacet

- Go back to the sign (%), then play until the bar marked *To Coda* ⊕ then skip to the section marked ⊕ *Coda*.

- Go back to the beginning of the song and play until the bar marked *Fine* (end).

- Instrument is silent (drops out).

- Repeat bars between signs.

1.	2.

- When a repeated section has different endings, play the first ending only the first time and the second ending only the second time.

NOTE: Tablature numbers in parentheses mean: 1. The note is sustained, but a new articulation (such as hammer on or slide) begins.
2. A note may be fretted but not necessarily played.

AUSTRALIA

Music by James Dean Bradfield & Sean Moore
Lyrics by Nicky Wire

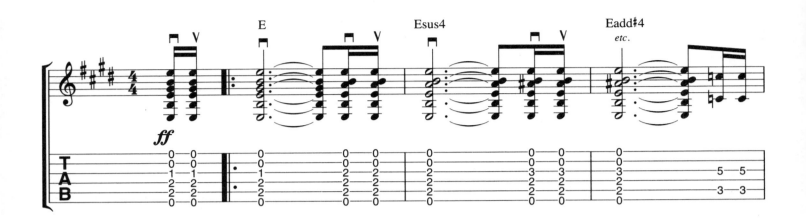

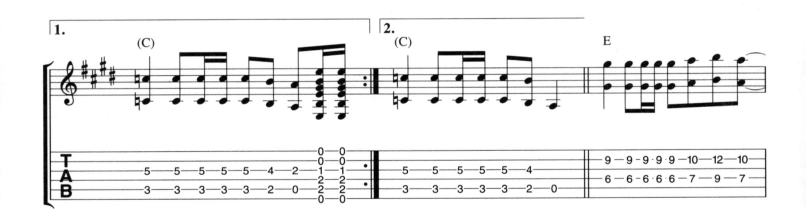

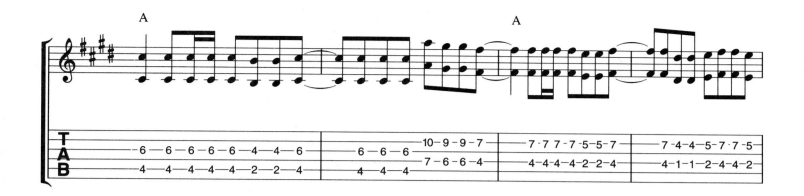

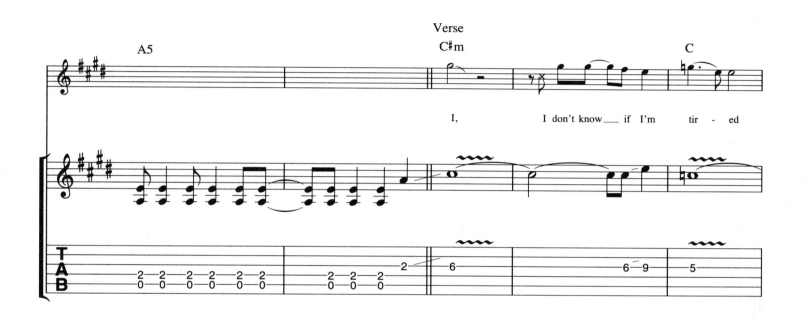

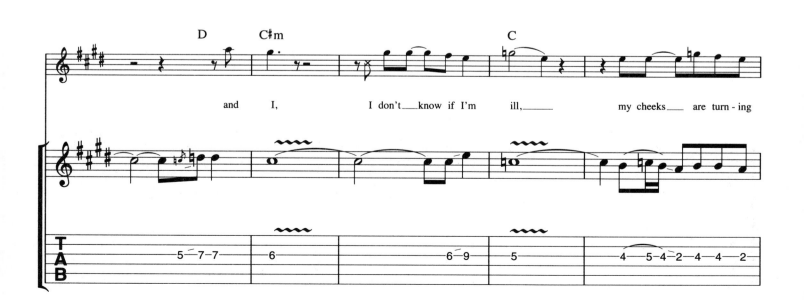

yel - low, I think I'll____ take a - no - ther____ pill.____

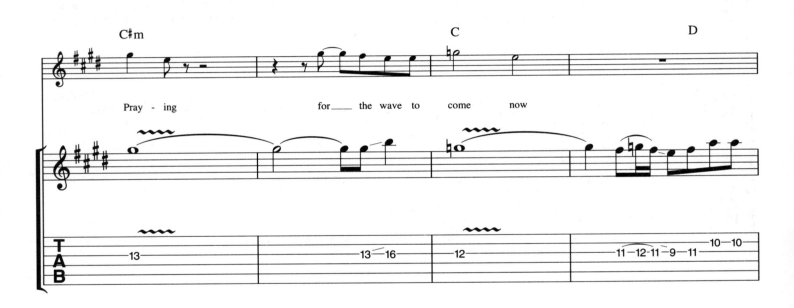

Pray - ing   for____ the wave to   come   now

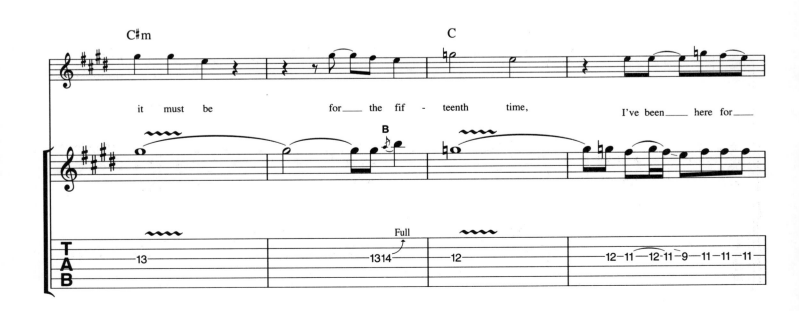

it   must be   for____ the fif - teenth time,   I've been____ here for____

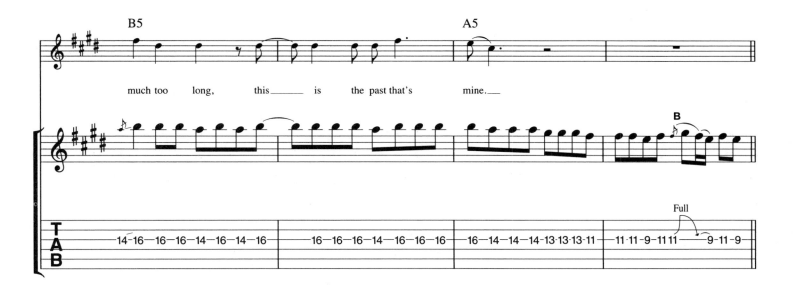

much too long, this＿ is the past that's mine.＿

Chorus

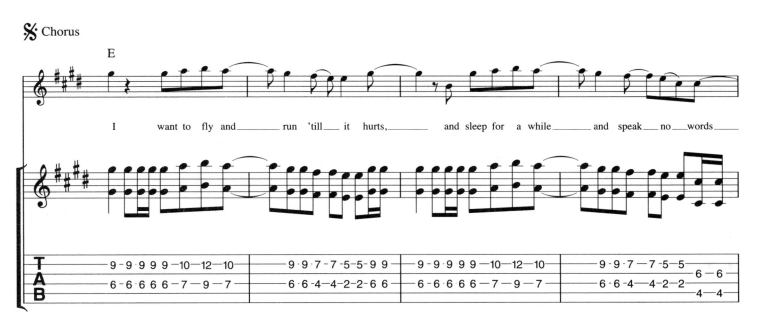

I want to fly and＿ run 'till＿ it hurts,＿ and sleep for a while＿ and speak＿ no＿ words＿

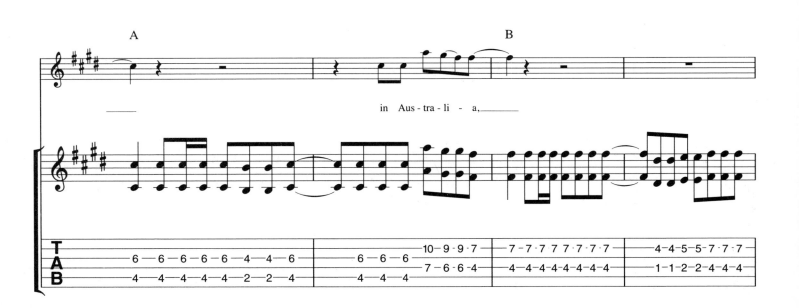

in Aus - tra - li - a,＿

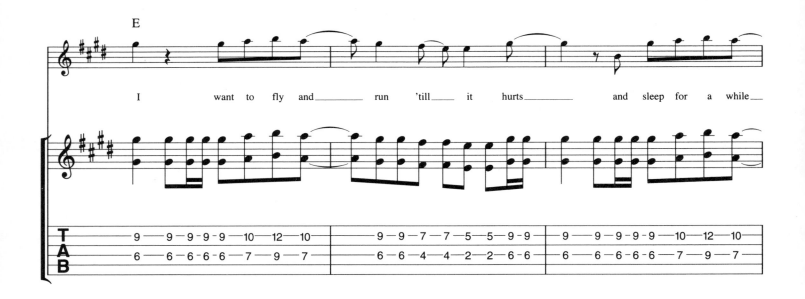

I want to fly and_____ run 'till____ it hurts_____ and sleep for a while____

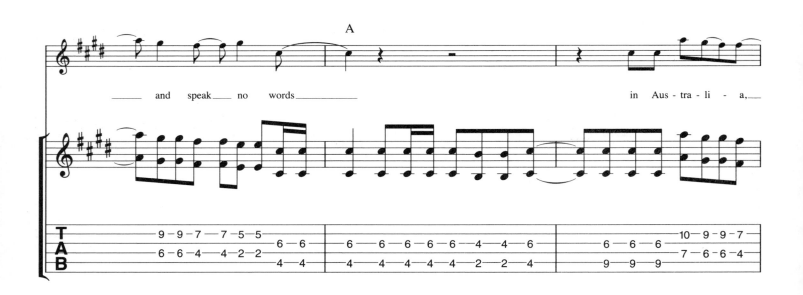

_____ and speak____ no words_____ in Aus - tra - li - a,____

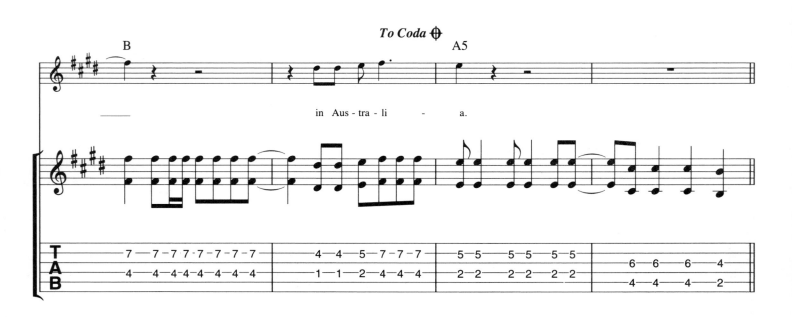

_____ in Aus - tra - li - a.

Solo

A pray - ing   for the wave to   come now

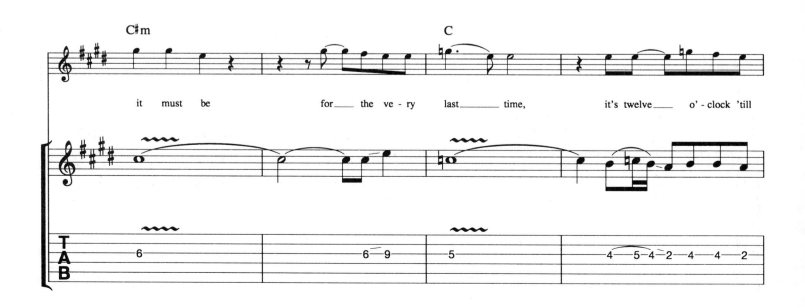

it must be   for the ve - ry last time,   it's twelve o' - clock 'till

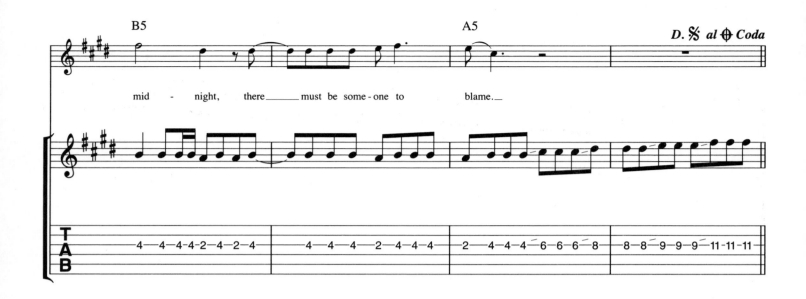

mid - night, there____ must be some - one to blame.____

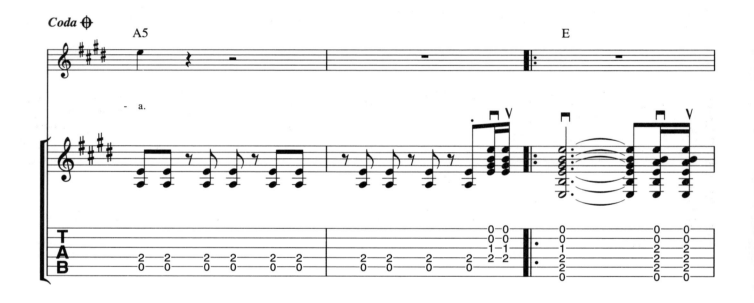

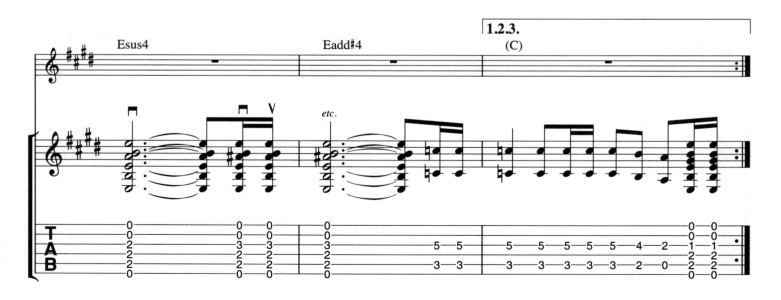

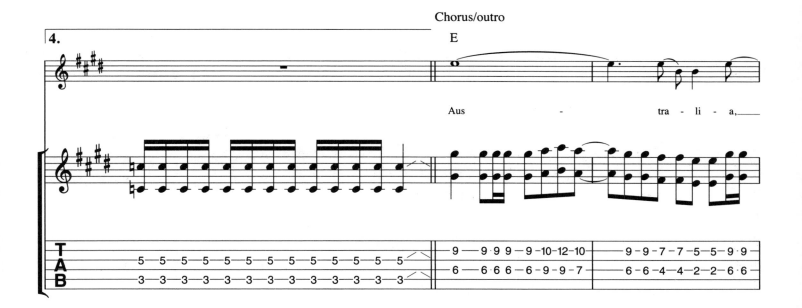

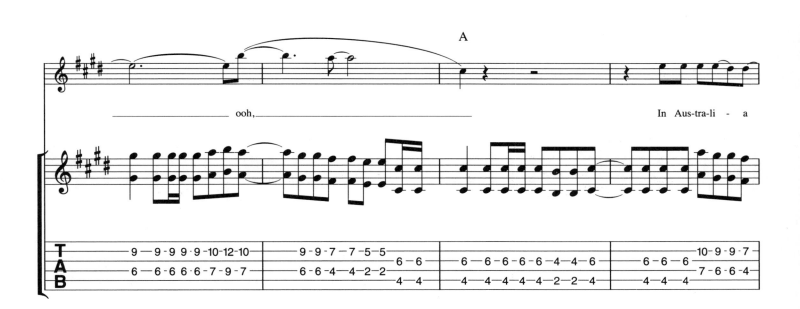

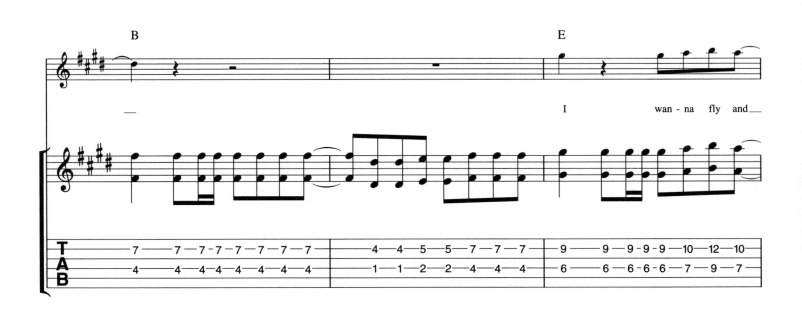

run 'till it hurts and sleep for a while and speak no words

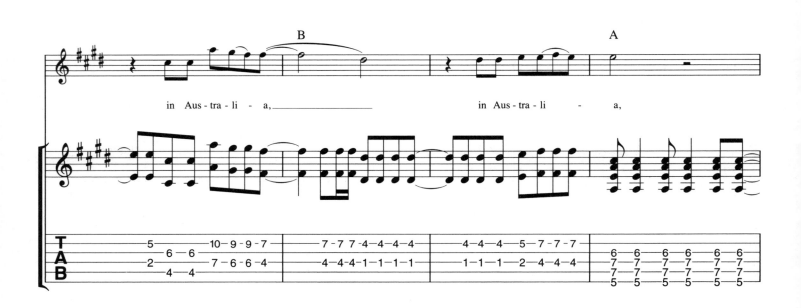

in Aus-tra-li - a, in Aus-tra-li - a,

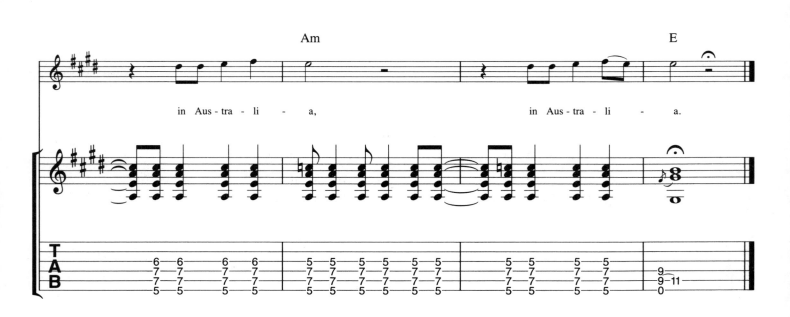

in Aus-tra-li - a, in Aus-tra-li - a.

CAST NO SHADOW

Words & Music by Noel Gallagher

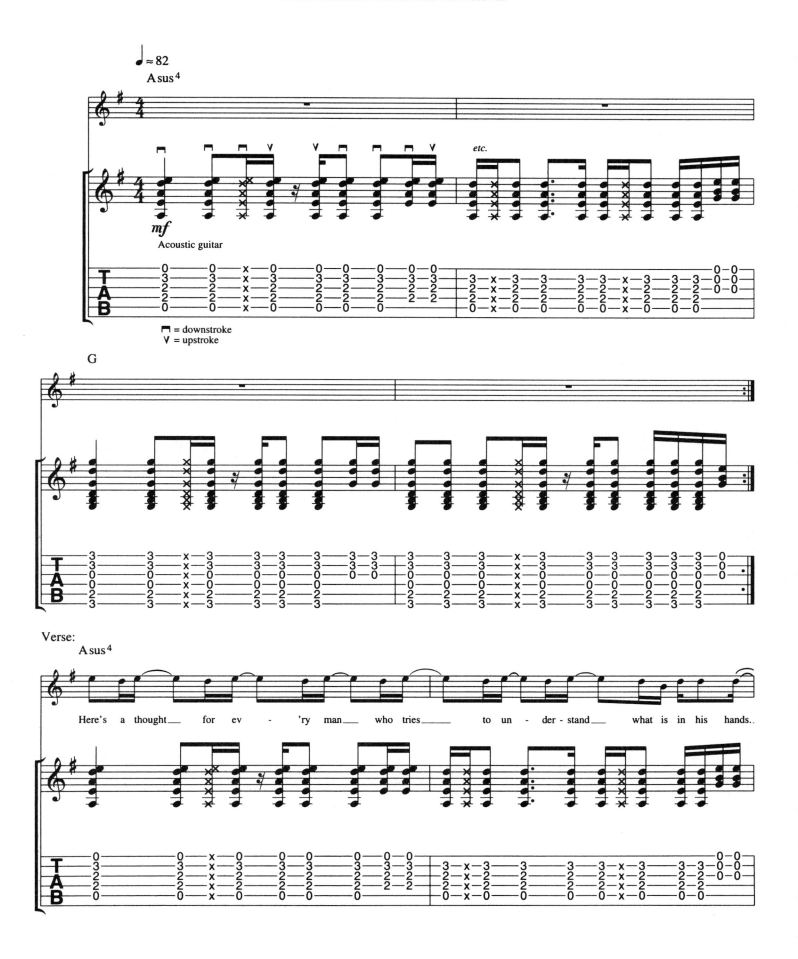

Verse:

Here's a thought___ for ev - 'ry man___ who tries___ to un - der - stand___ what is in his hands..

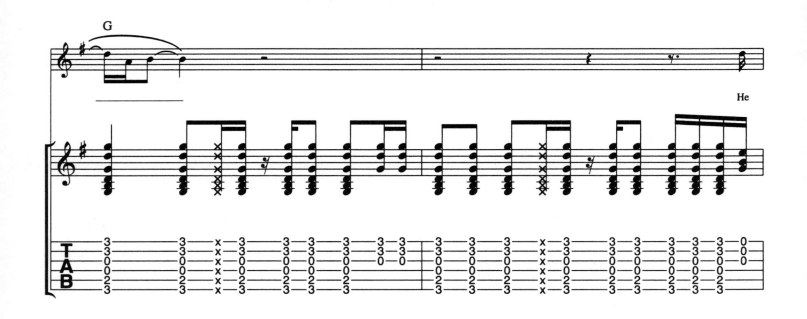

He

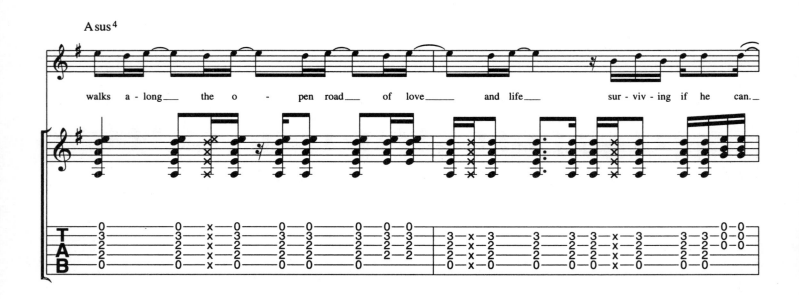

walks a - long___ the o - pen road___ of love___ and life___ sur - viv - ing if he can.___

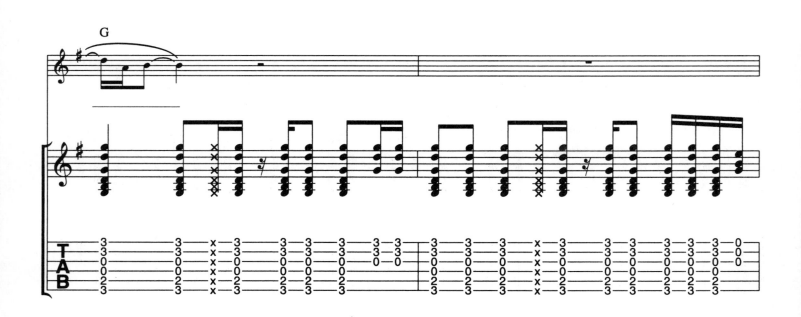

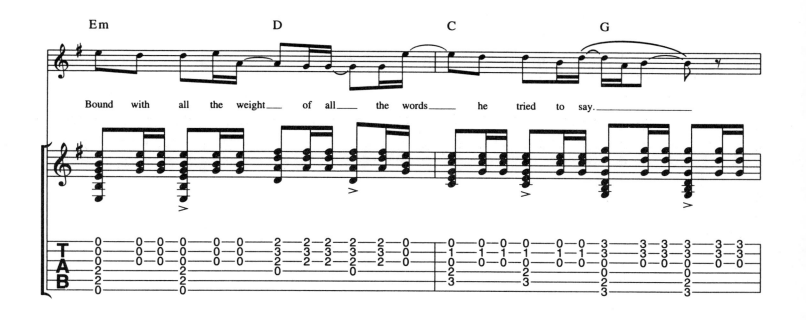

Bound with all the weight___ of all___ the words___ he tried to say.___

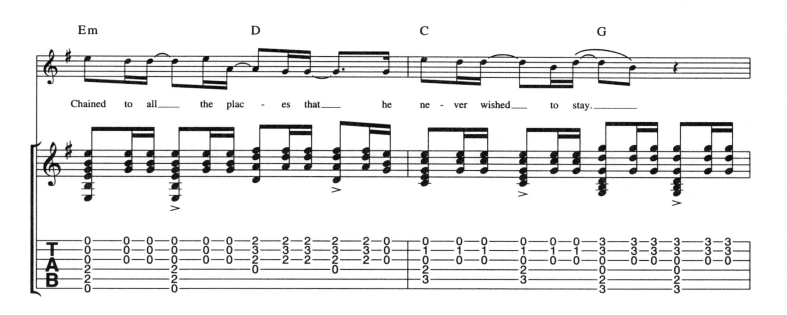

Chained to all___ the plac - es that___ he ne - ver wished___ to stay.___

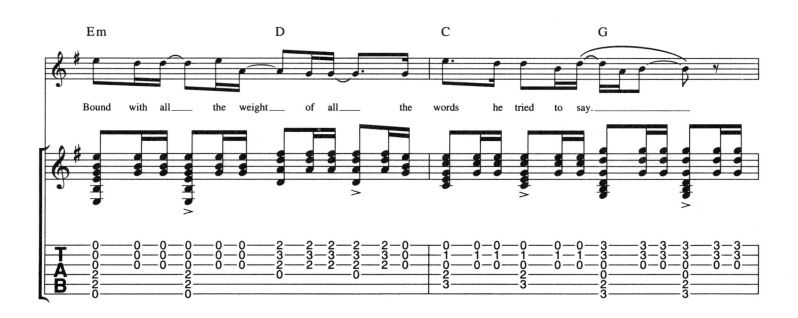

Bound with all___ the weight___ of all___ the words he tried to say.___

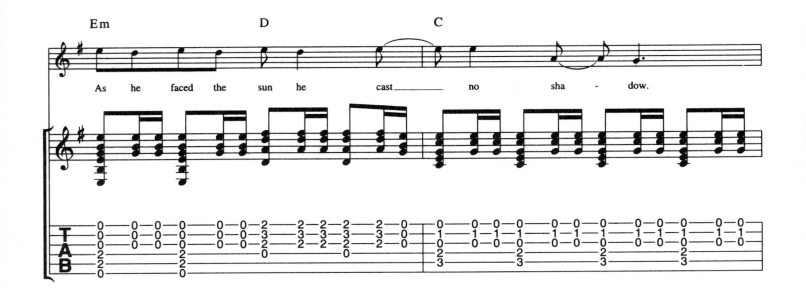

As he faced the sun he cast_____ no sha - dow.

Chorus:
G

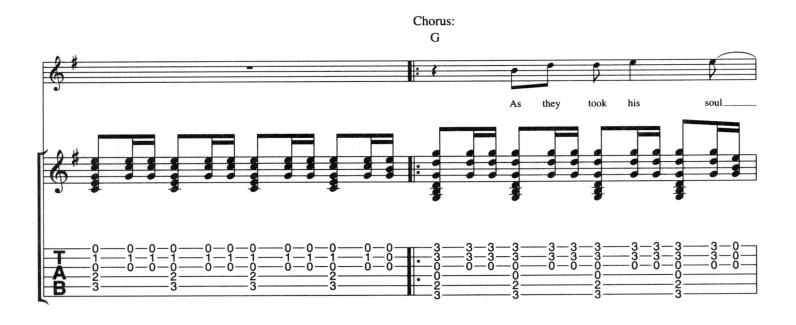

As they took his soul_____

Asus⁴   C

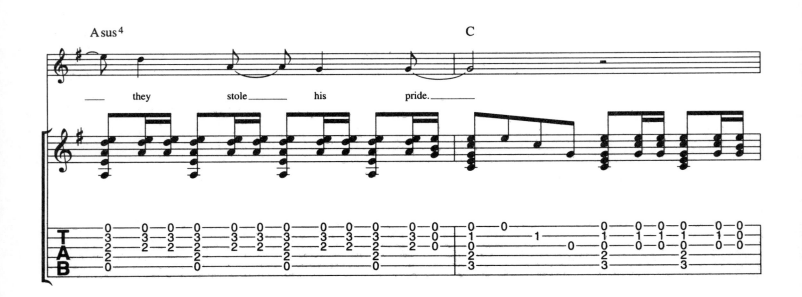

_____ they stole_____ his pride._____

18

As he faced the sun he cast

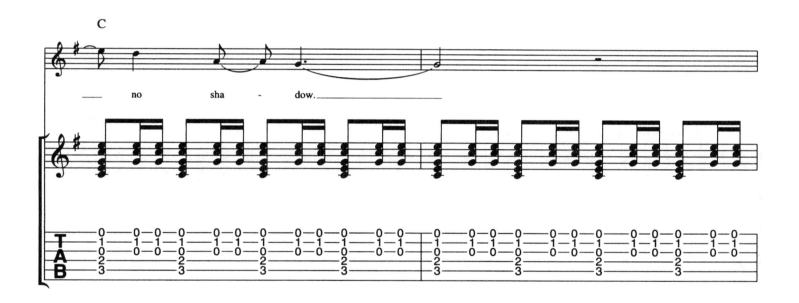

— no sha - dow.

(Asus⁴)

D.C. al ⊕ Coda
(with all repeats)

⊕ *Coda*

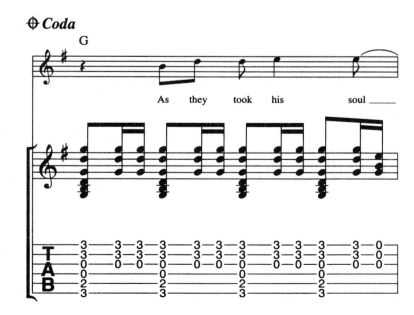

As they took his soul

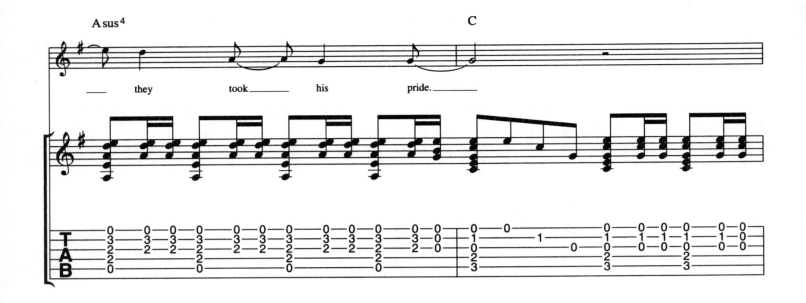

they took his pride.

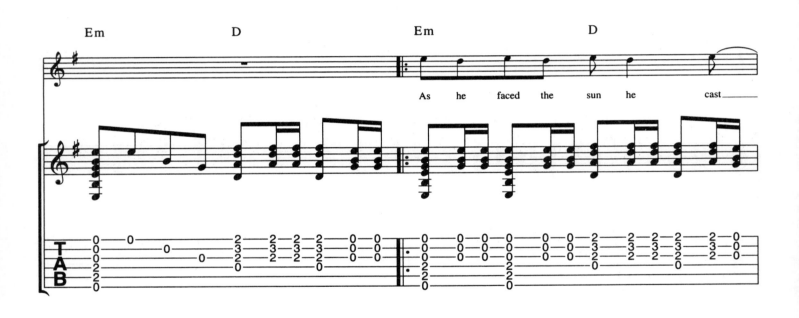

As he faced the sun he cast

1,2,3.

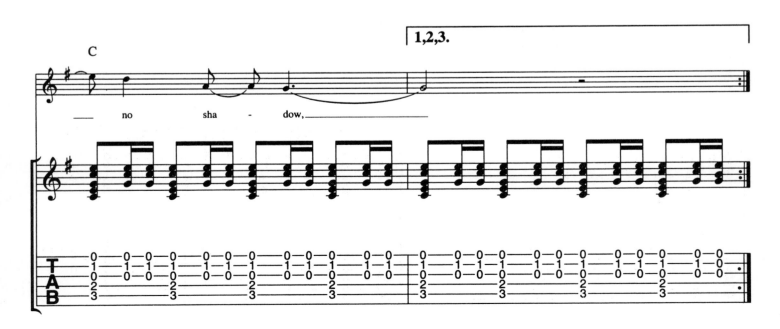

no sha - dow,

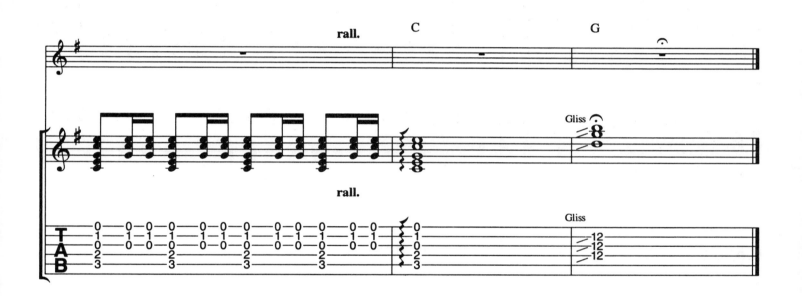

FREE TO DECIDE

Words & Music by Dolores O'Riordan

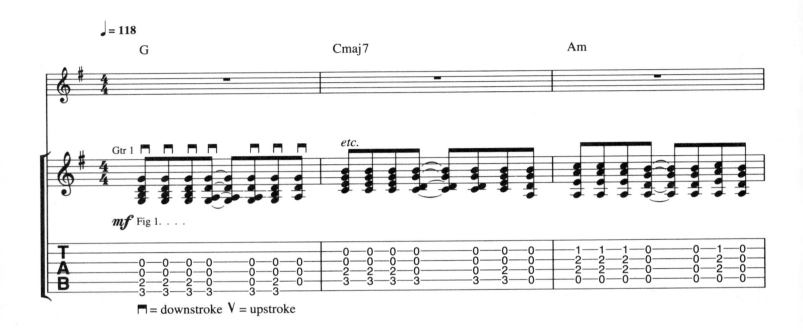

□ = downstroke V = upstroke

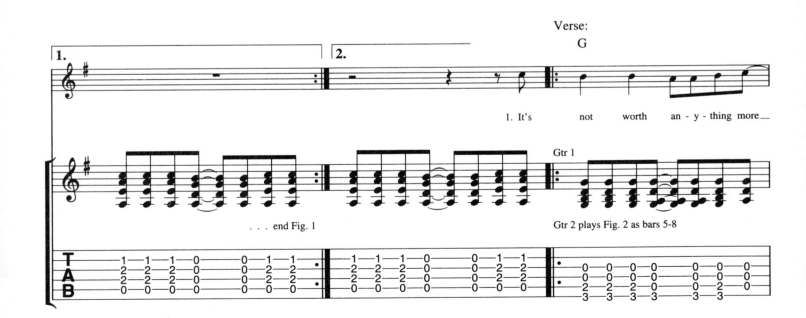

than this at all. _____ I

live as I choose ____ or I will not live at ____ all. _____ So re-

Gtr 2

Fig. 2 . . . . end Fig. 2

Gtr 1 continues *sim.* (as bars 1–4)

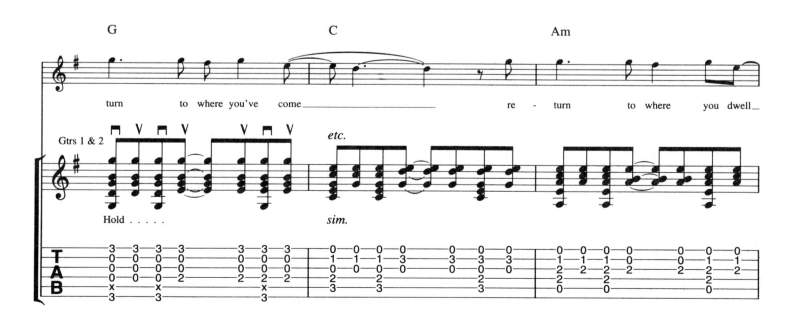

turn to where you've come _____ re - turn to where you dwell ____

Gtrs 1 & 2

etc.

Hold . . . . . *sim.*

23

be - cause har - rass - ment's not___ my for - té   but you do

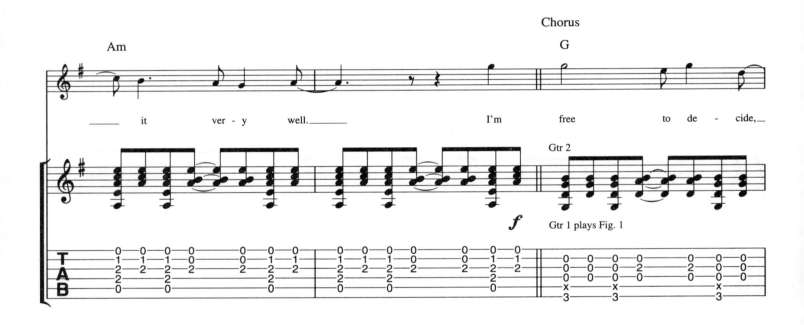

___ it ver - y well.___   I'm free to de - cide,___

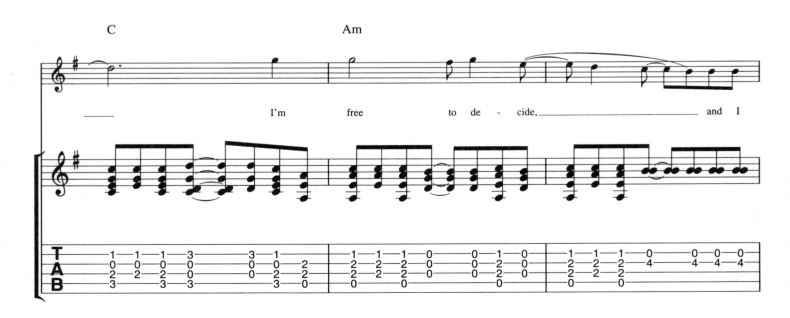

___ I'm free to de - cide,___   and I

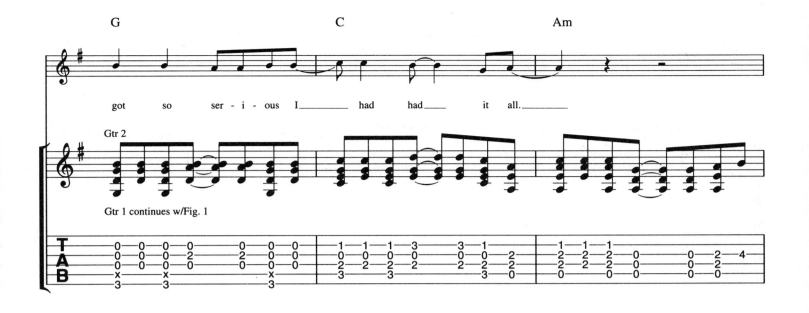

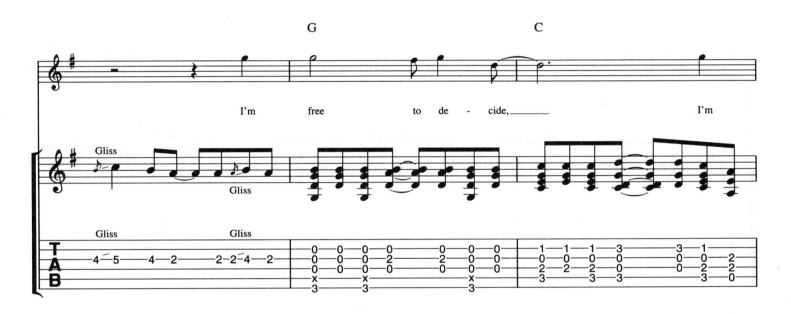

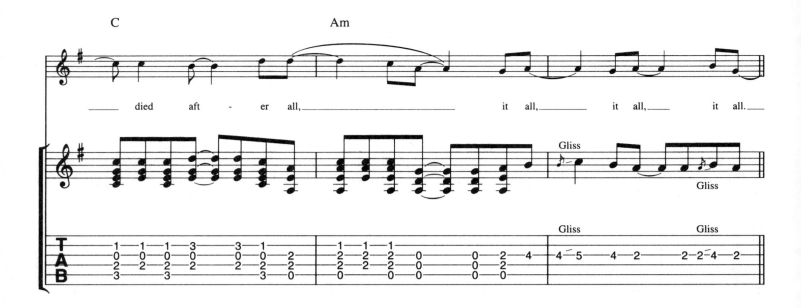

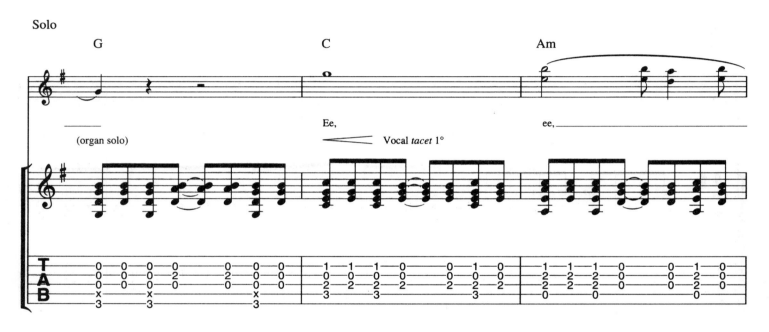

Solo

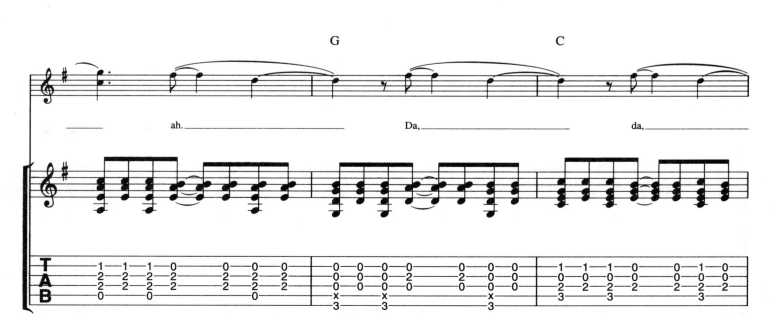

26

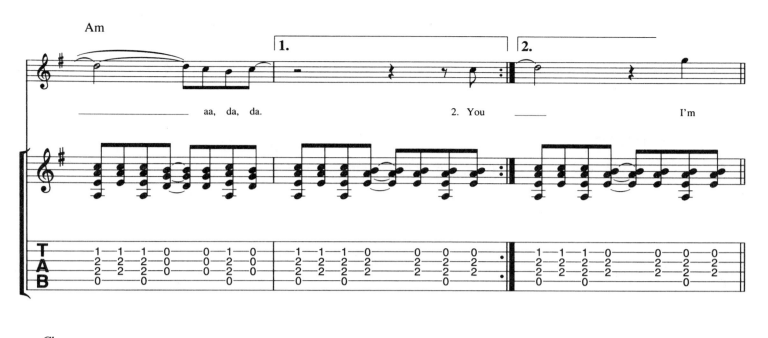

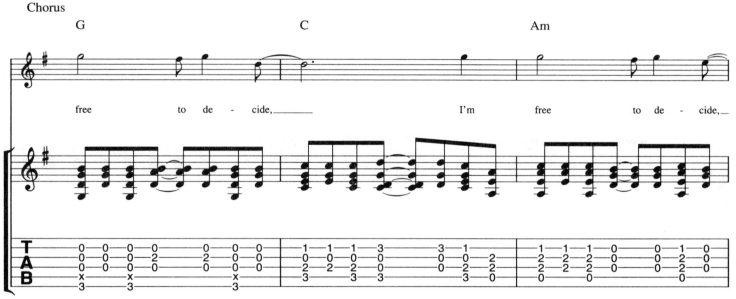

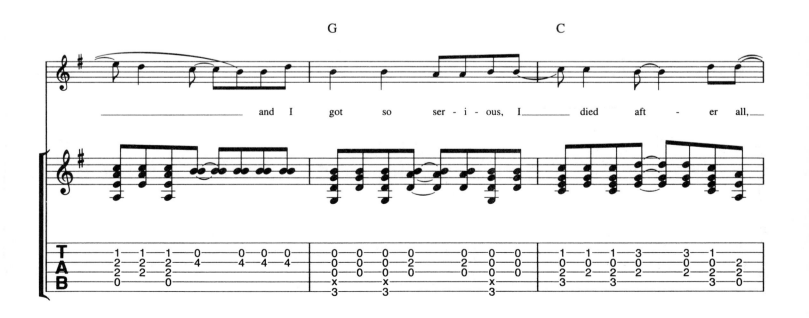

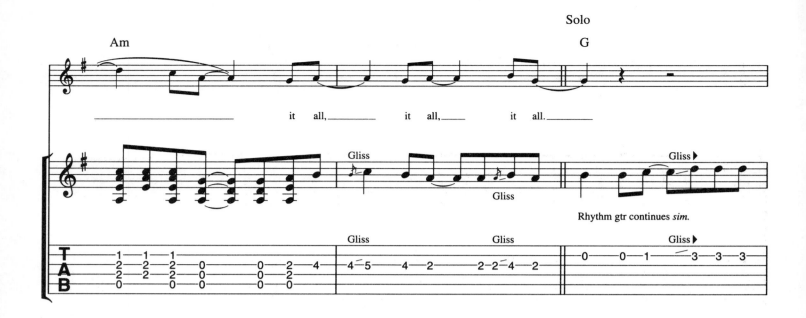

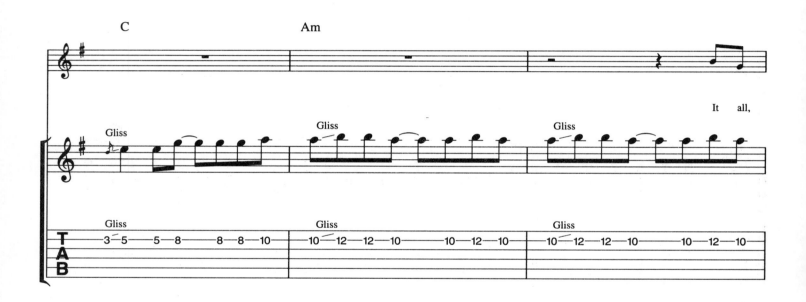

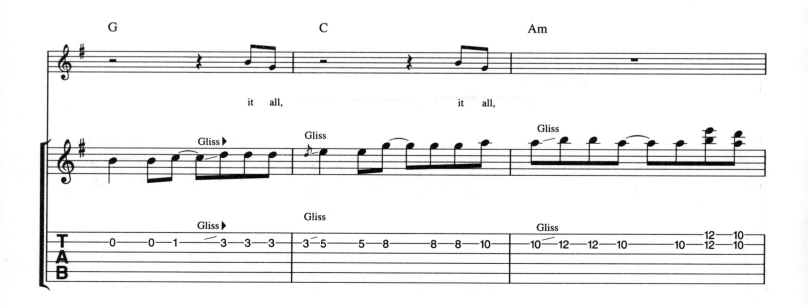

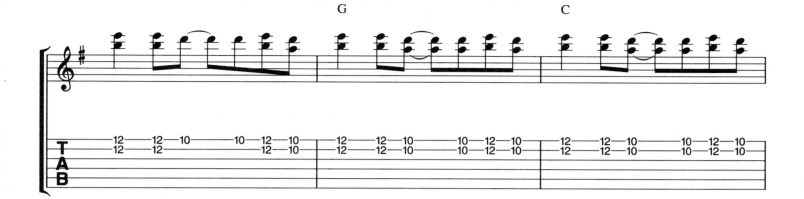

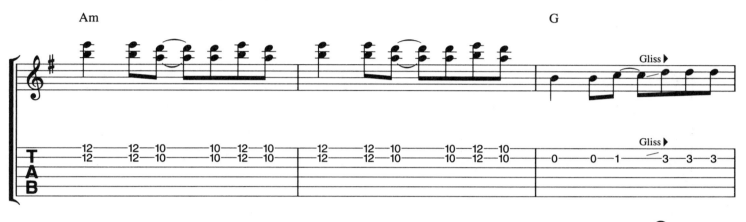

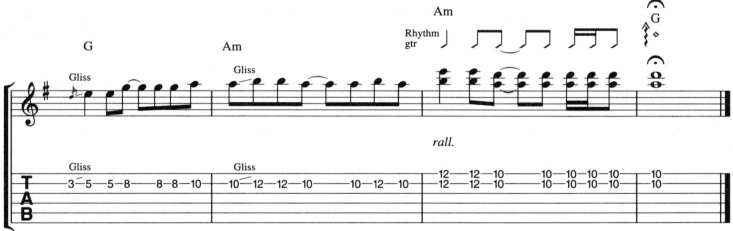

Verse 2   You must have nothing more with your time to do
There's a war in Russia and Sarajevo too
So to hell with what you're thinking
And to hell with your narrow mind
You're so distracted from the real thing
You should leave your life behind, behind.

'Cos I'm free *etc.*

FRIDAY STREET

Words & Music by Paul Weller

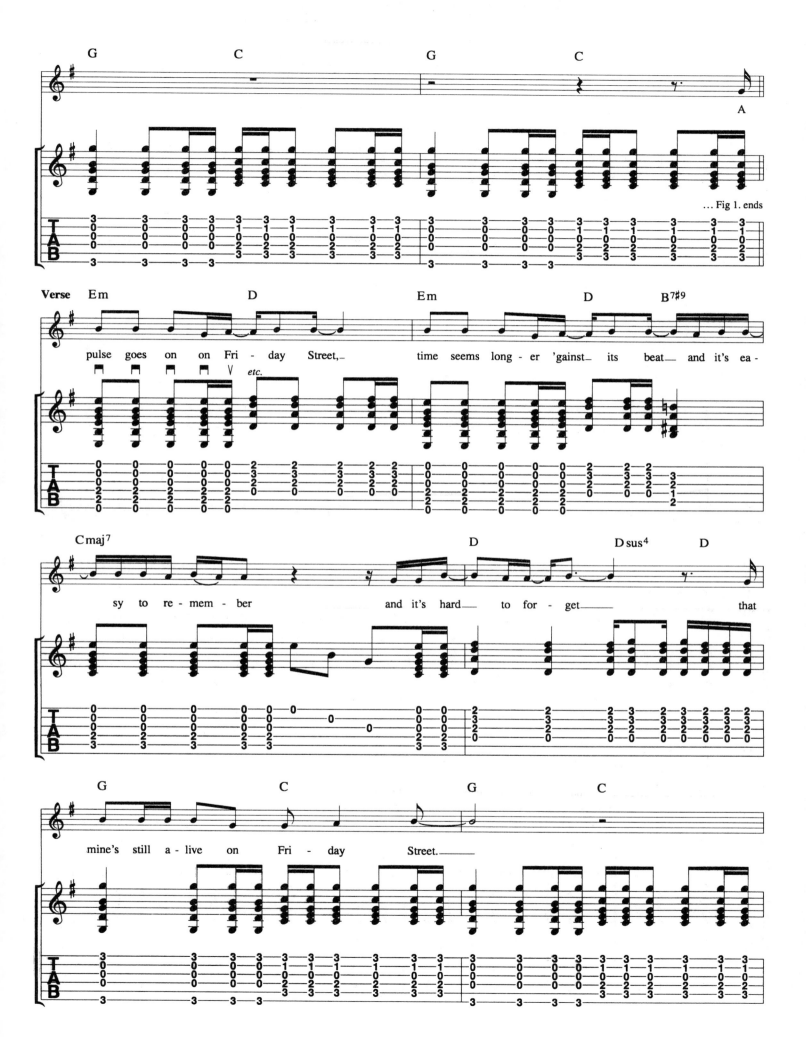

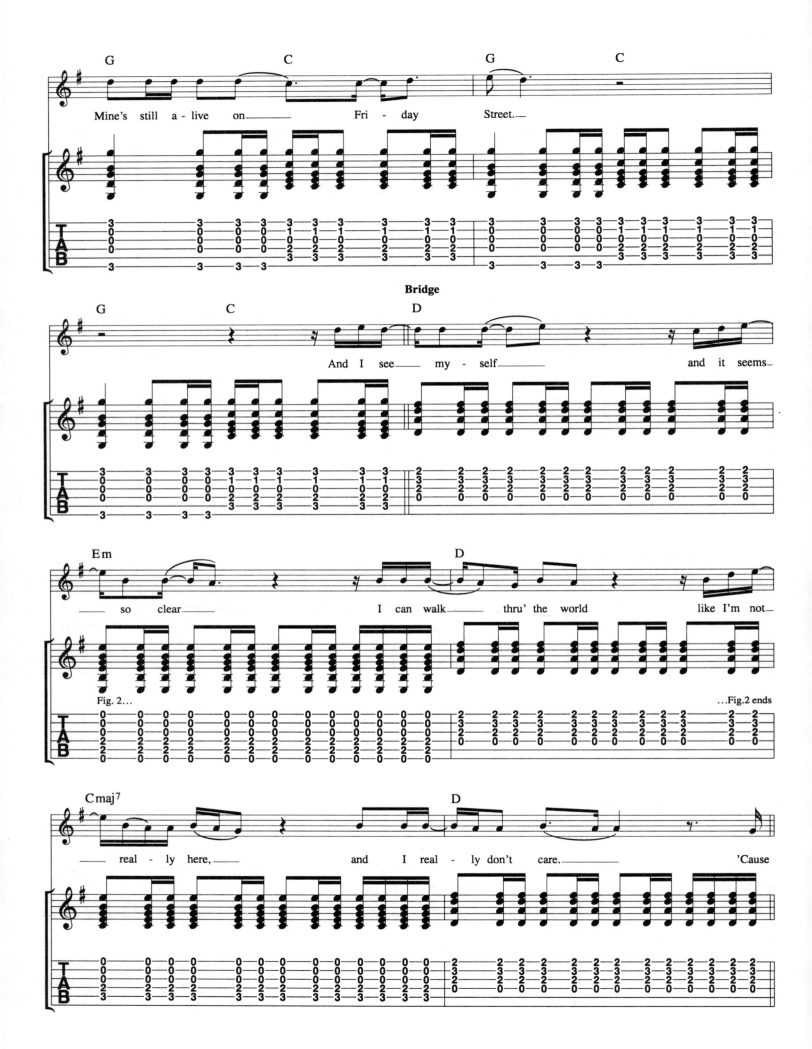

GOLDFINGER

Words & Music by Tim Wheeler

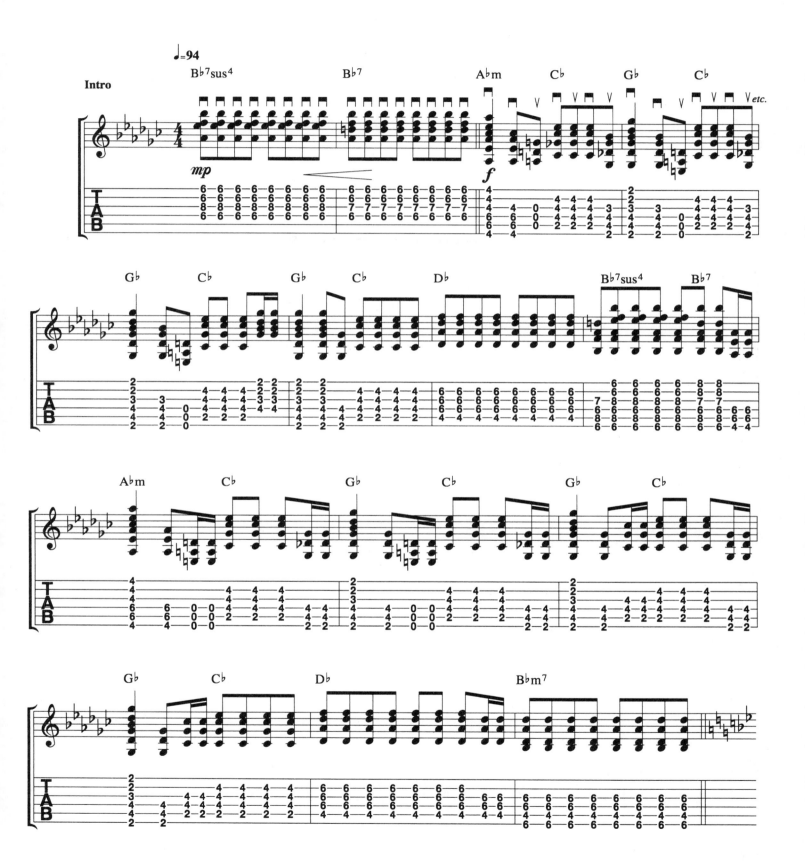

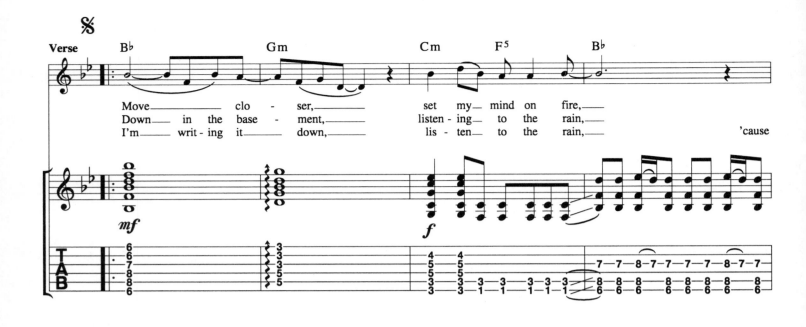

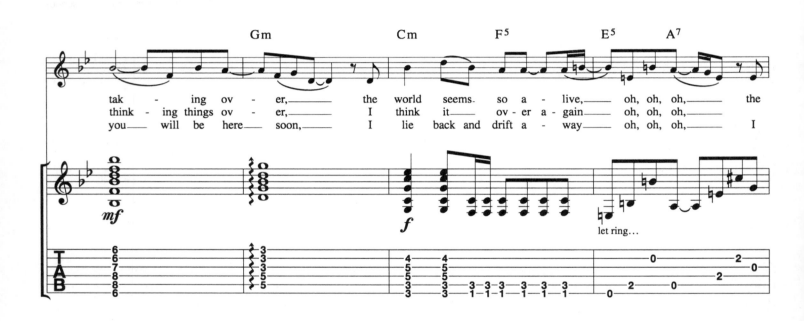

37

HUSH

Words & Music by Joe South

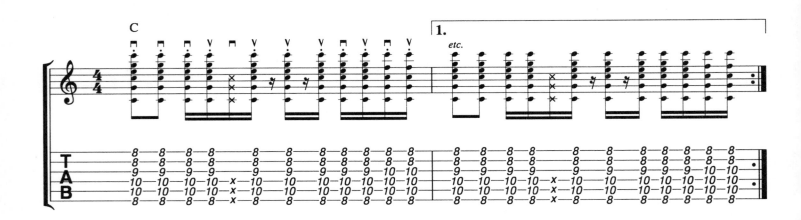

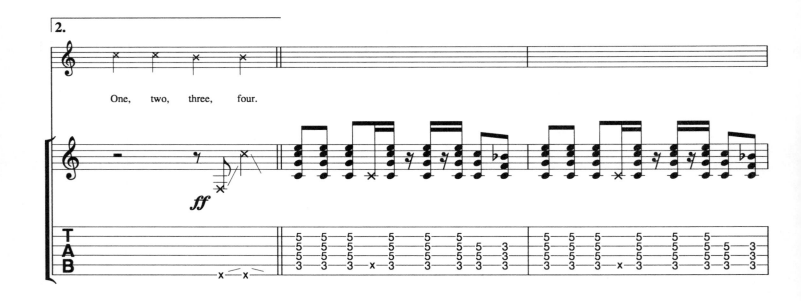

One, two, three, four.

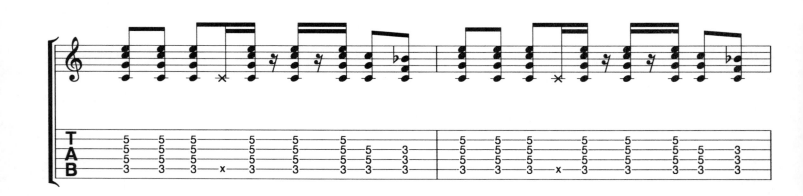

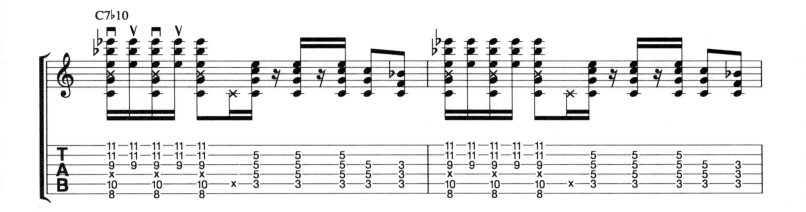

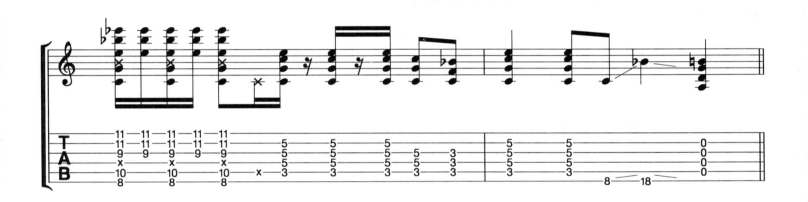

1.

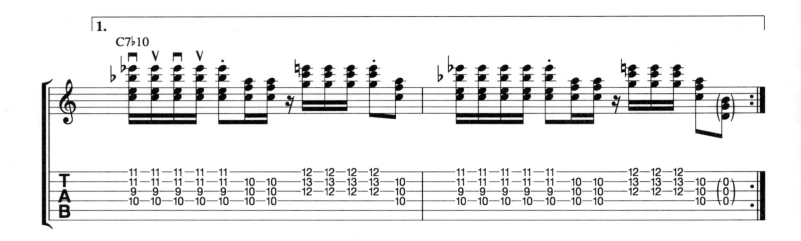

2.

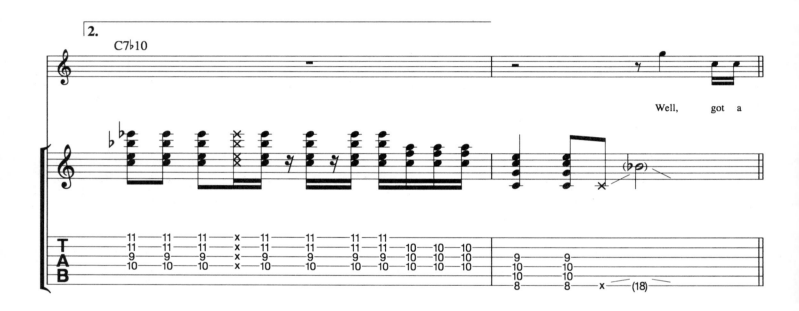

Well,　　got a

Verse
C

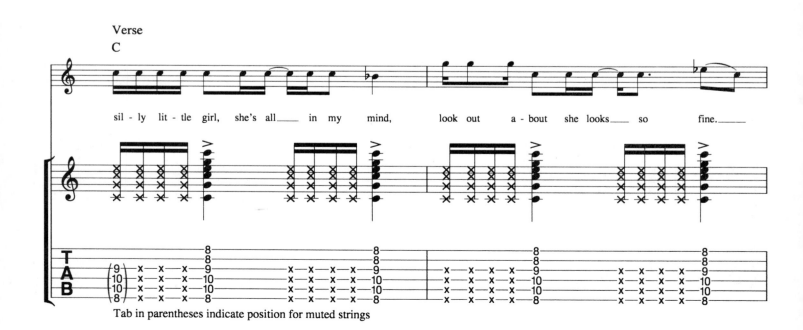

sil - ly lit - tle girl, she's all___ in my mind,　look out a - bout she looks___ so　fine.___

Tab in parentheses indicate position for muted strings

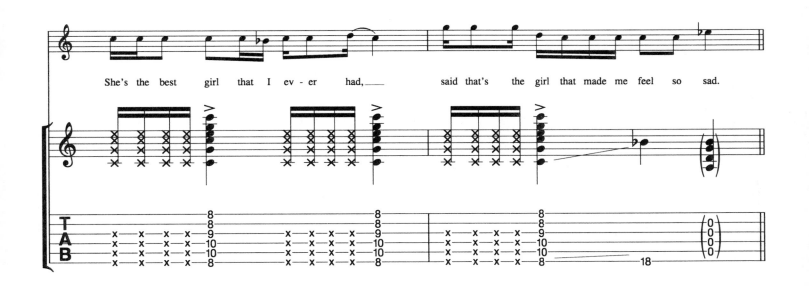

She's the best girl that I ev-er had, _____ said that's the girl that made me feel so sad.

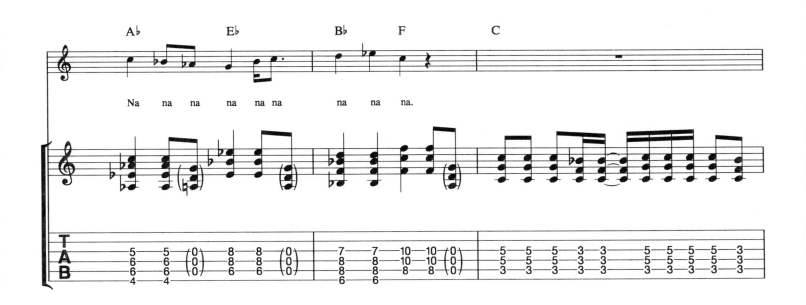

Ab   Eb   Bb   F   C

Na na na na na na na na na.

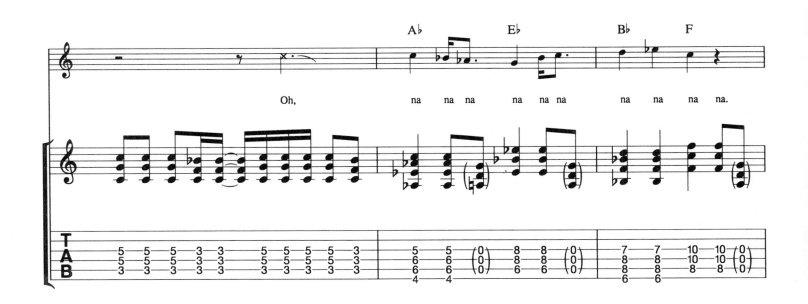

Ab   Eb   Bb   F

Oh, na na na na na na na na na na.

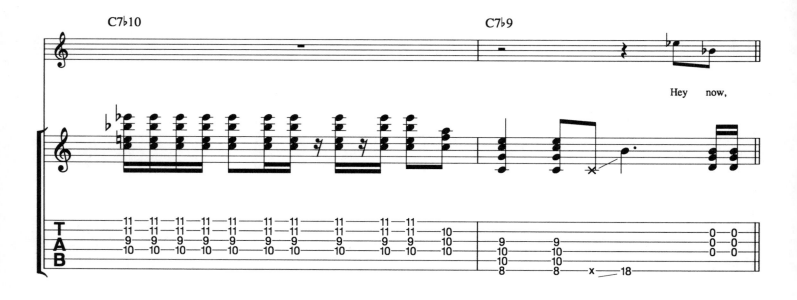

Hey now,

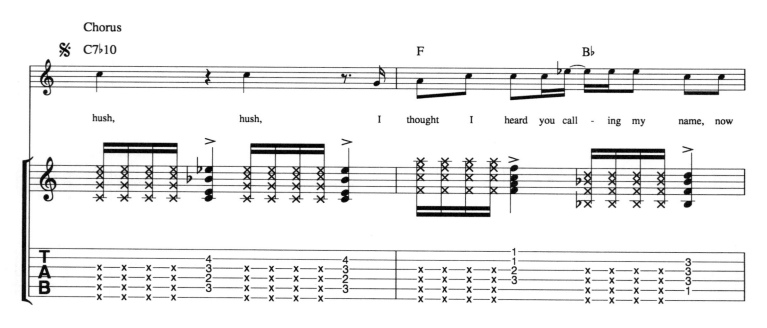

Chorus

hush, hush, I thought I heard you call - ing my name, now

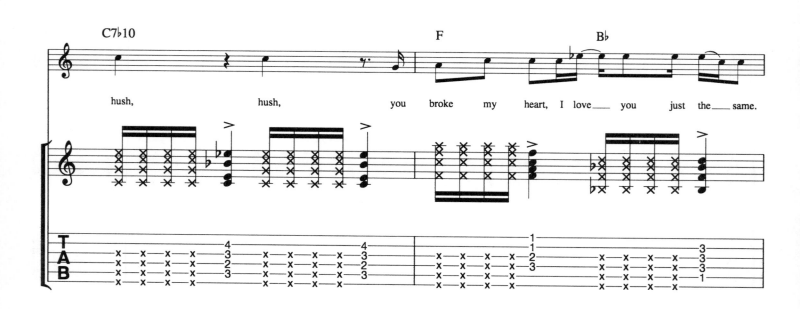

hush, hush, you broke my heart, I love____ you just the____ same.

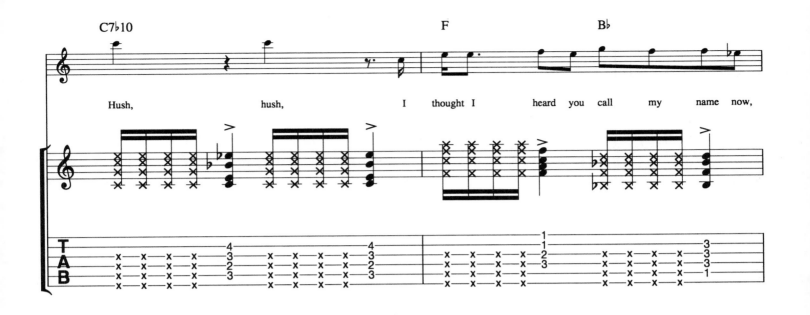

Hush,   hush,   I thought I heard you call my name now,

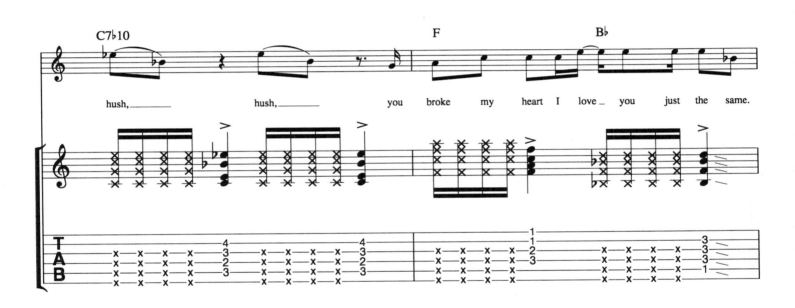

hush,_____   hush,_____   you broke my heart I love__ you just the same.

Spoken: Early in the morning.   Late in the evening.   Oh, gotta believe me honey.   Oh, do you want to believe me.

On 𝄋 . . . .

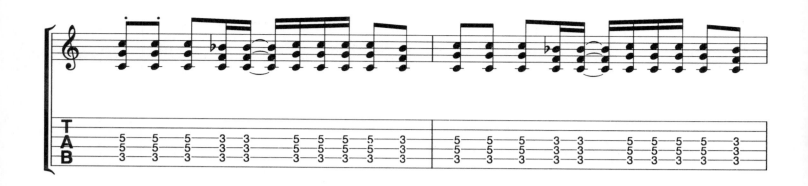

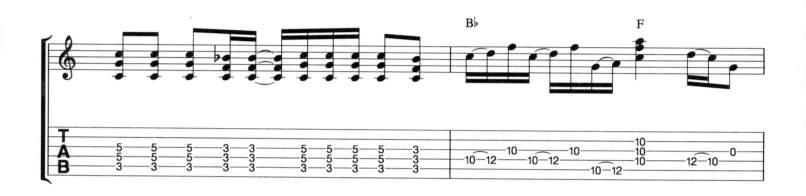

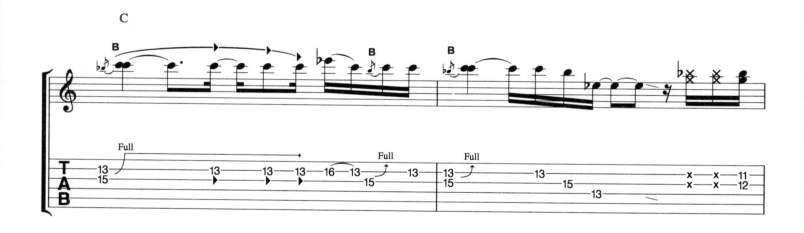

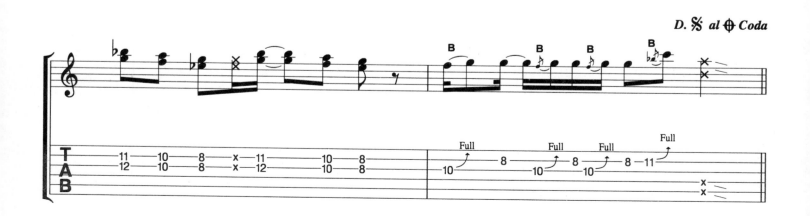

46

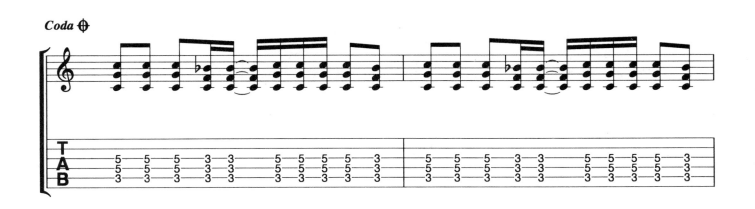

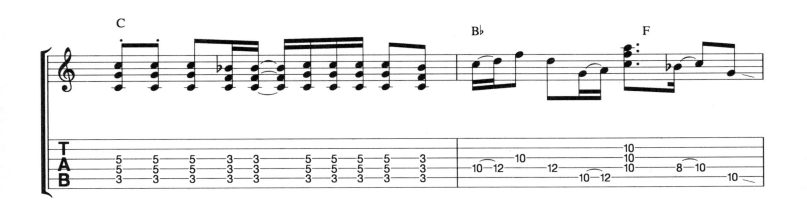

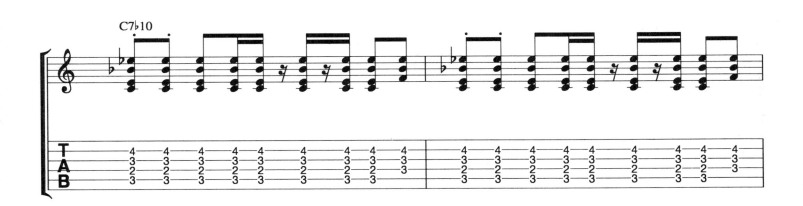

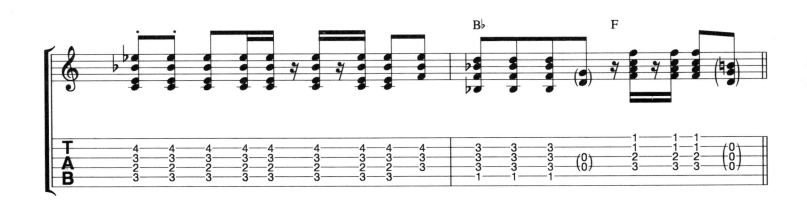

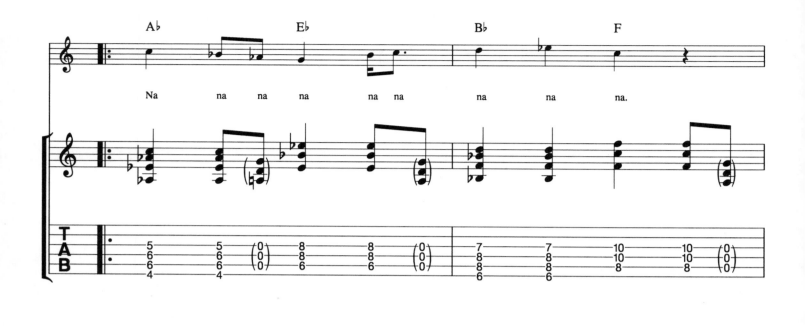

Na   na   na   na   na   na   na   na   na.

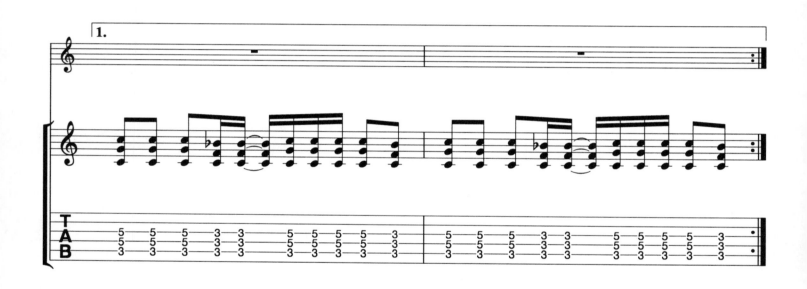

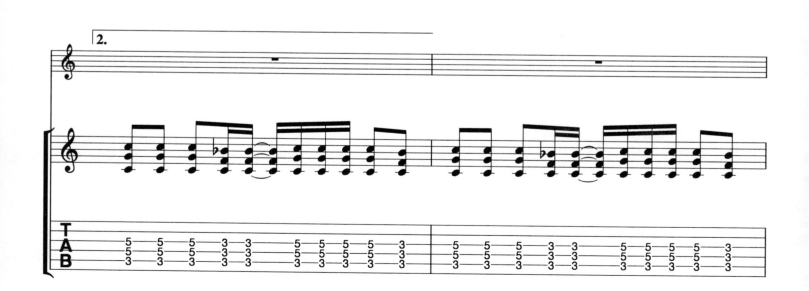

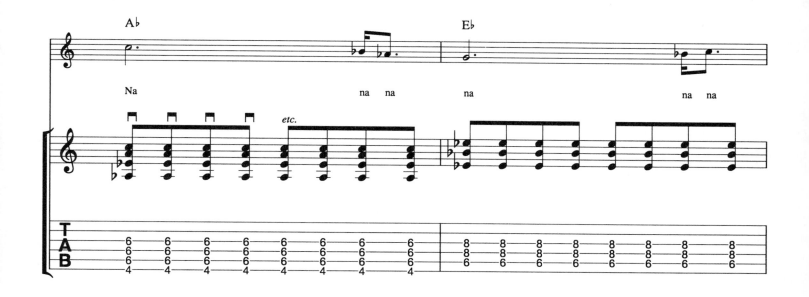

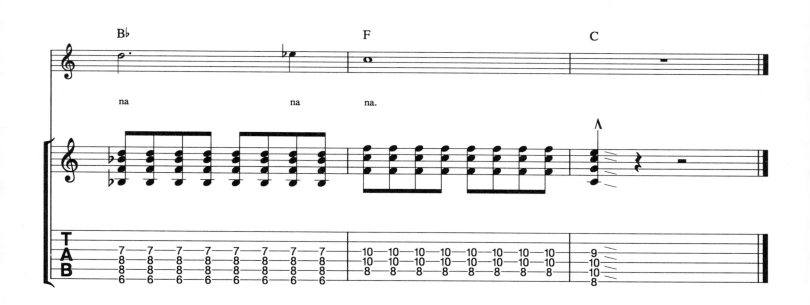

KEVIN CARTER

Music by James Dean Bradfield, Sean Moore & Nicky Wire
Lyrics by Richey James

* fret but don't necessarily play 4th string

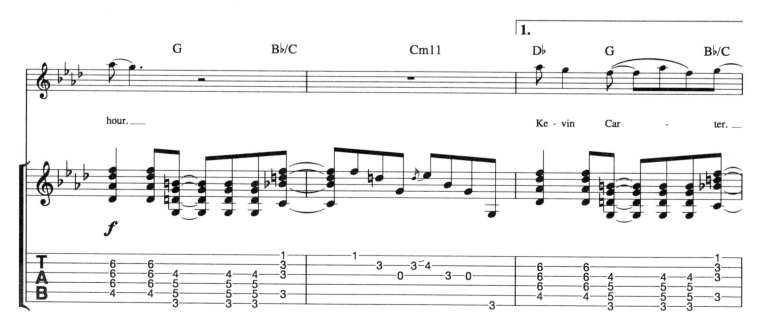

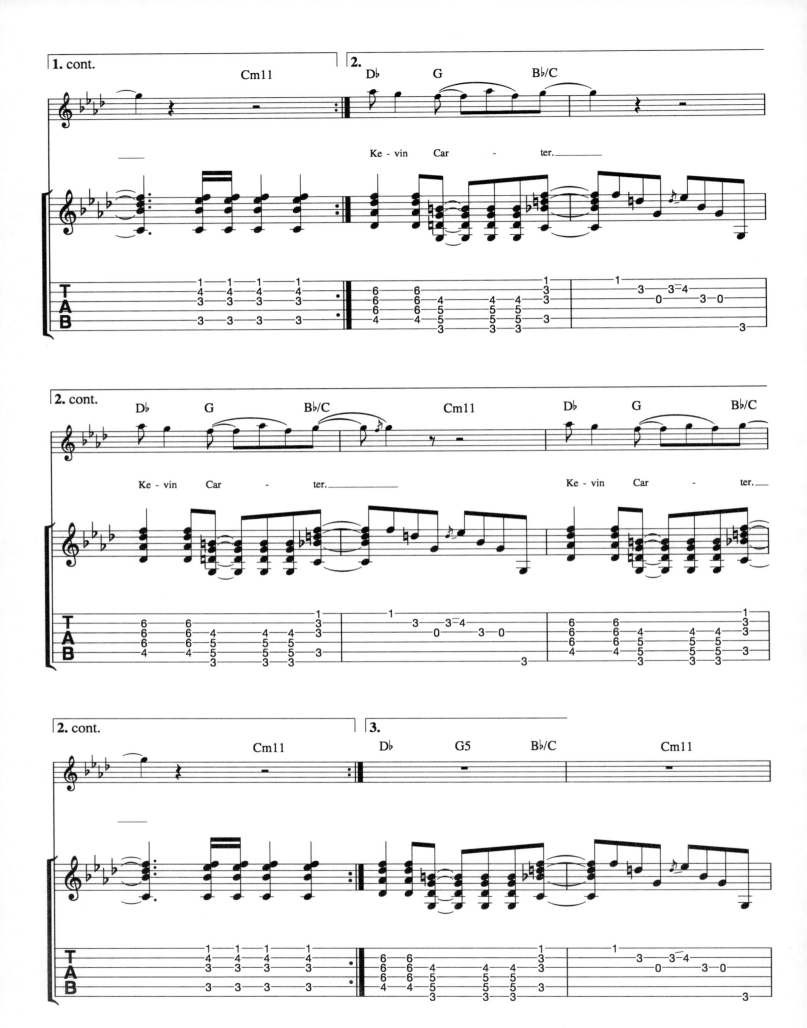

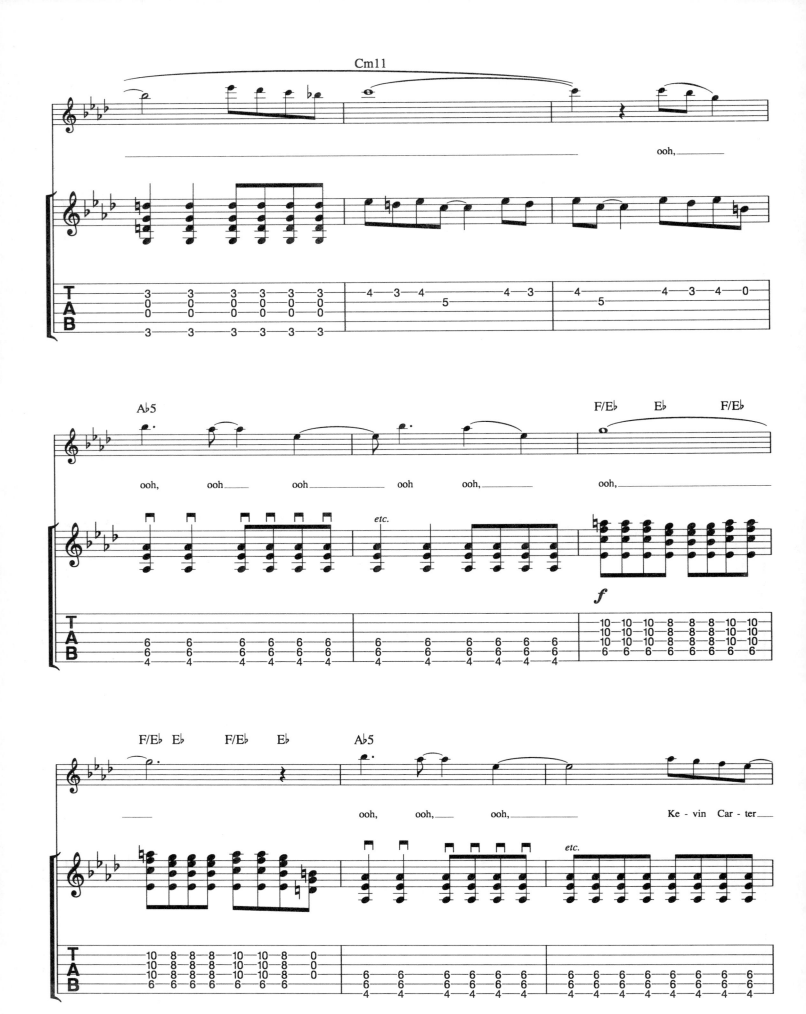

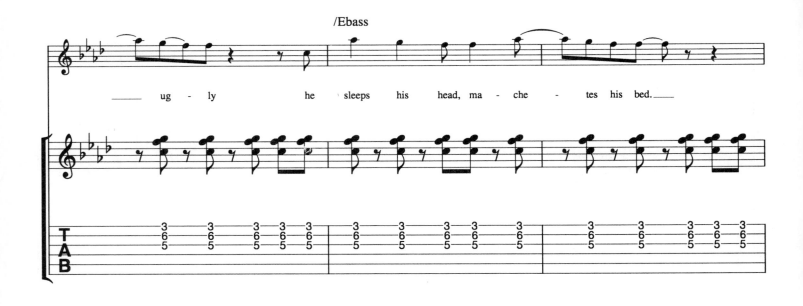

ug - ly he sleeps his head, ma - che - tes his bed.____

Ke - vin ____ Car - ter Kaf - fir lov - er for - ev - er.____

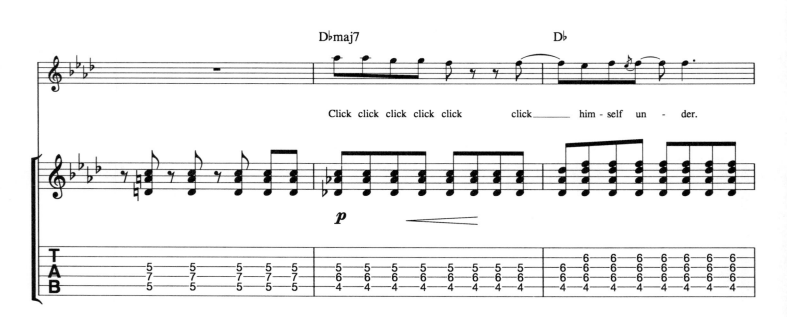

Click click click click click click____ him - self un - der.

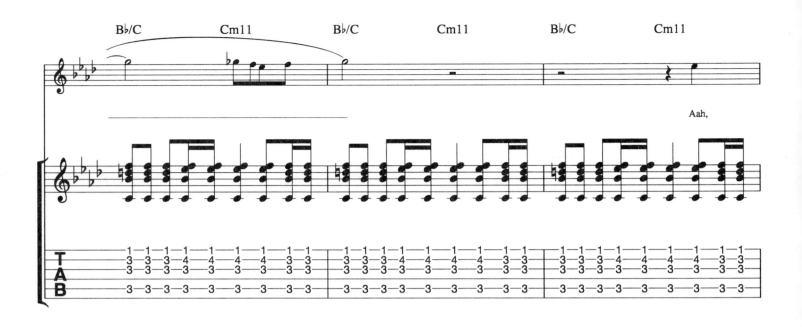

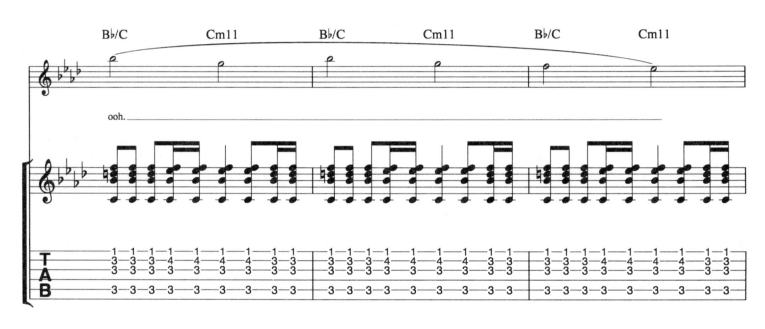

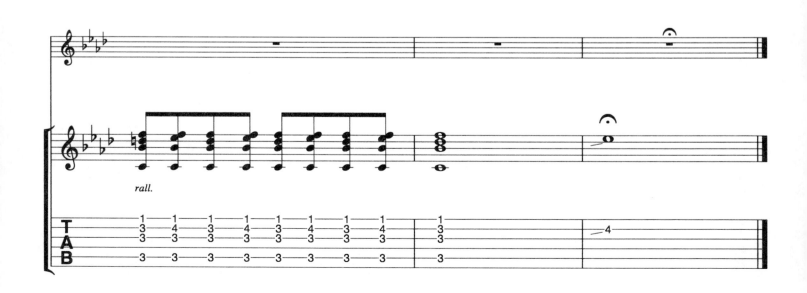

MIS-SHAPES

Music by Pulp
Lyrics by Jarvis Cocker

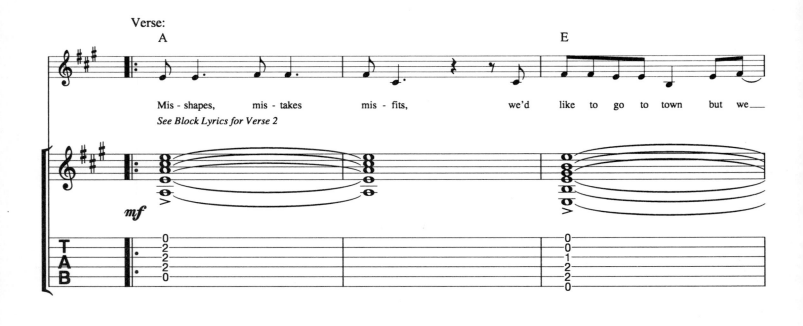

Verse:

Mis - shapes, mis - takes mis - fits, we'd like to go to town but we___
See Block Lyrics for Verse 2

___ can't risk___ it oh, 'cause they just want to keep us out,___

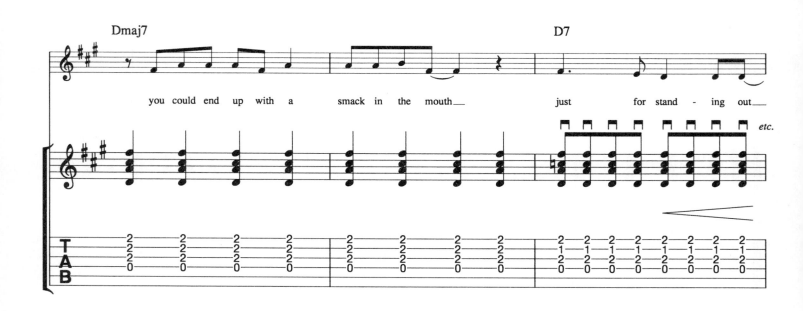

you could end up with a smack in the mouth___ just for stand - ing out___

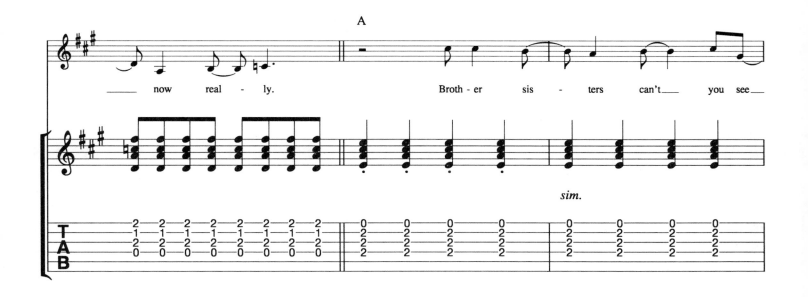

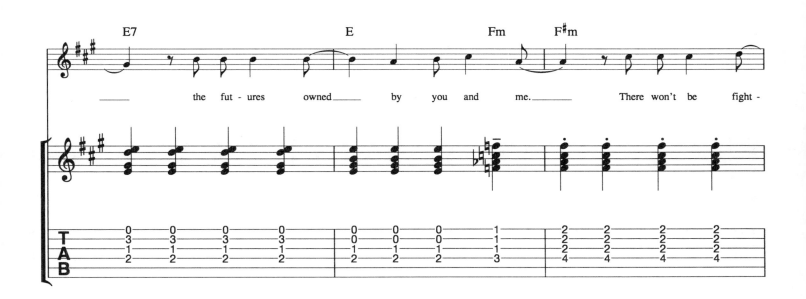

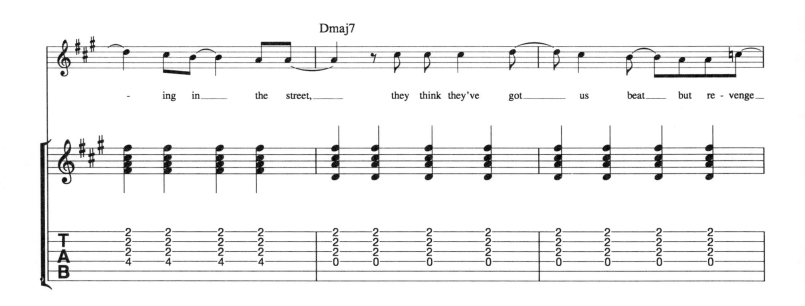

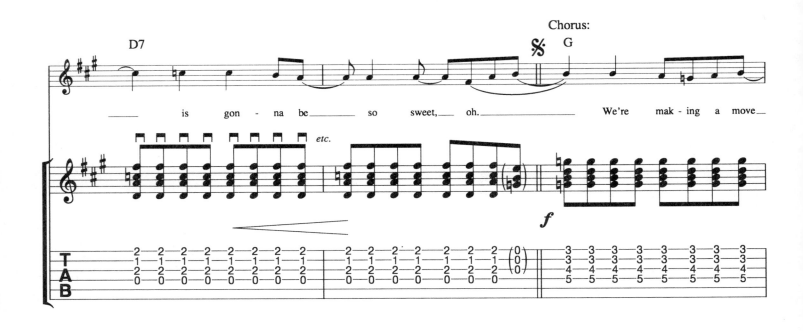

_is gon - na be____ so sweet,____ oh._____ We're mak - ing a move_

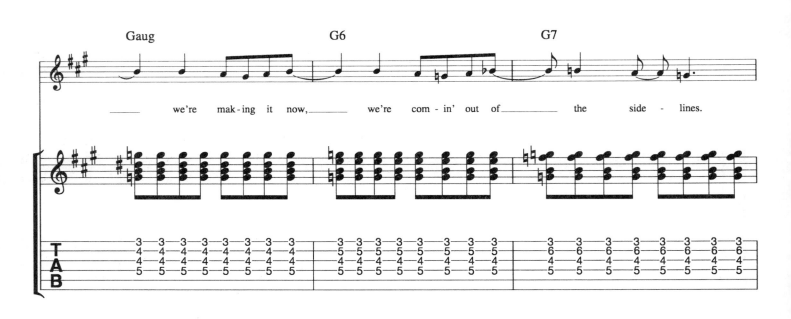

_we're mak - ing it now,_____ we're com - in' out of_____ the side - lines._

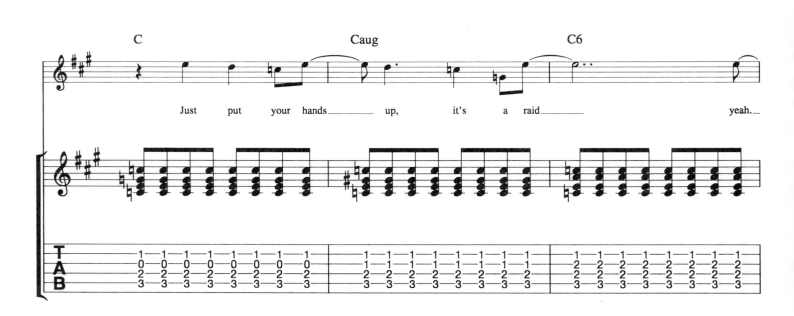

Just put your hands_____ up, it's a raid_____ yeah.____

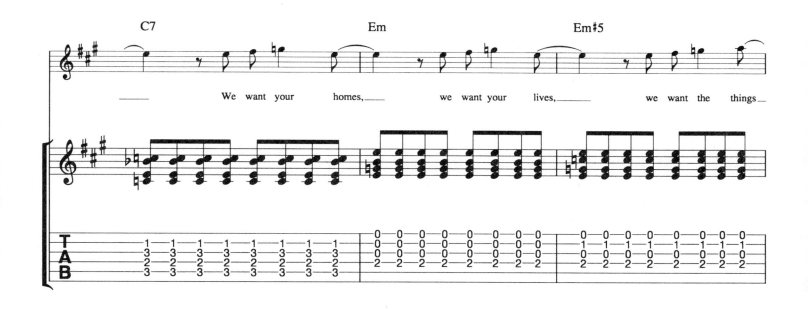

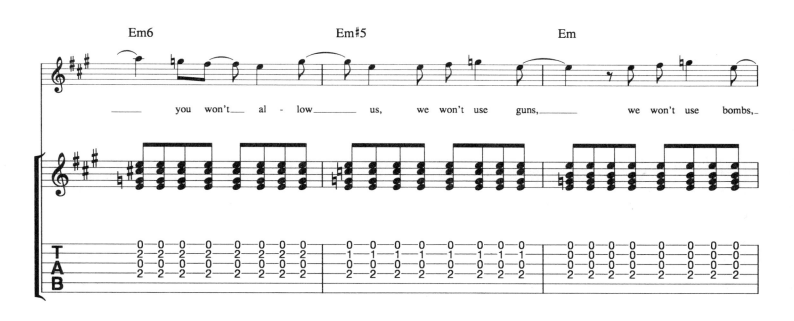

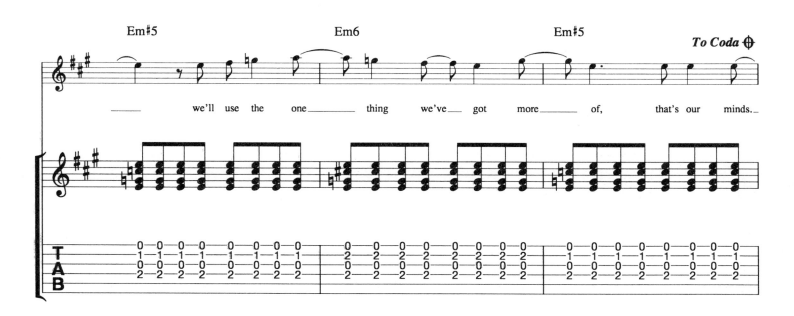

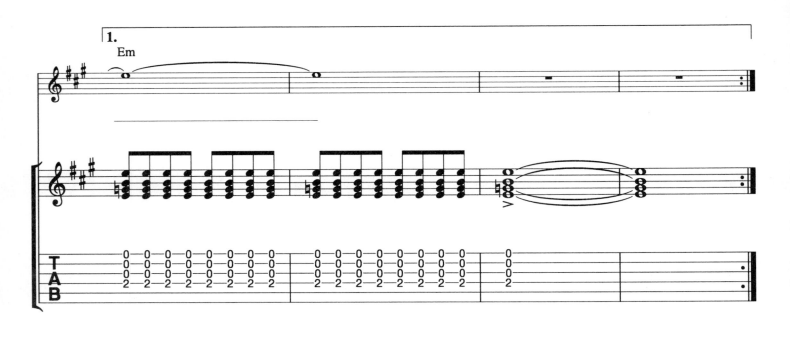

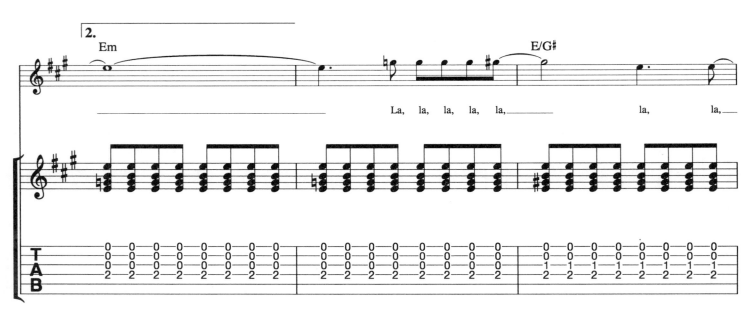

La, la, la, la, la,_____ la, la,_____

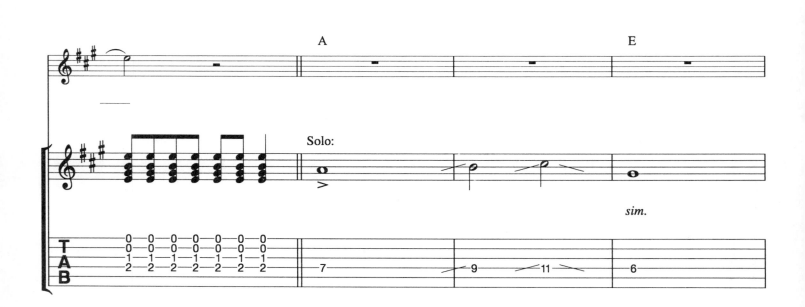

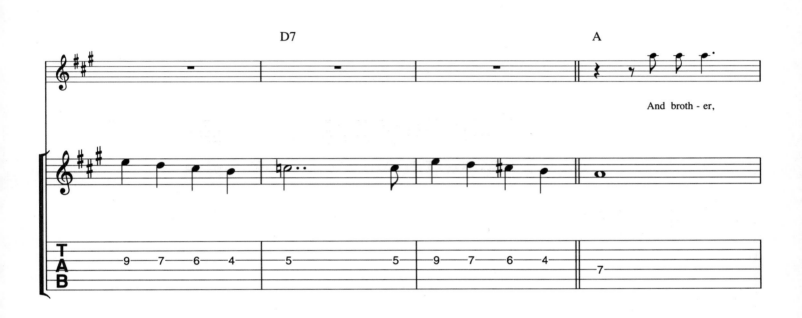

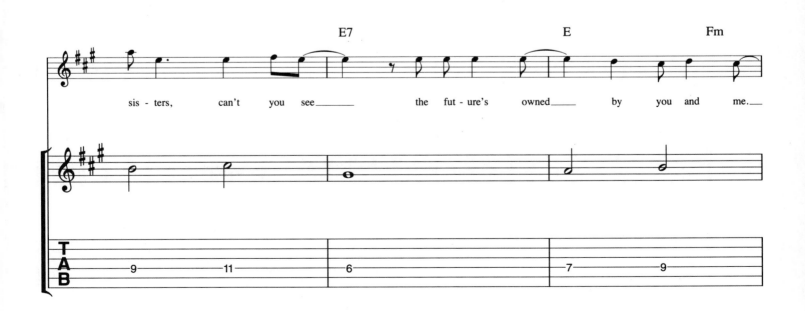

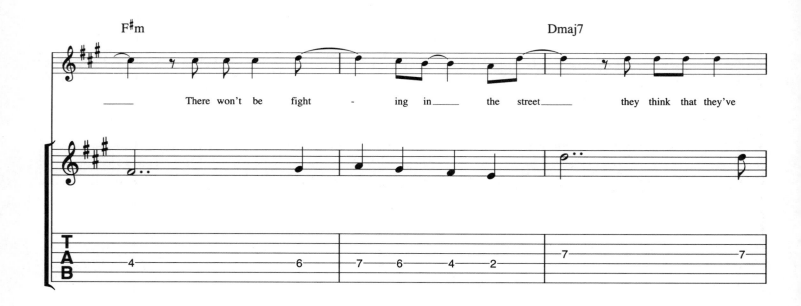

There won't be fight - ing in___ the street___ they think that they've

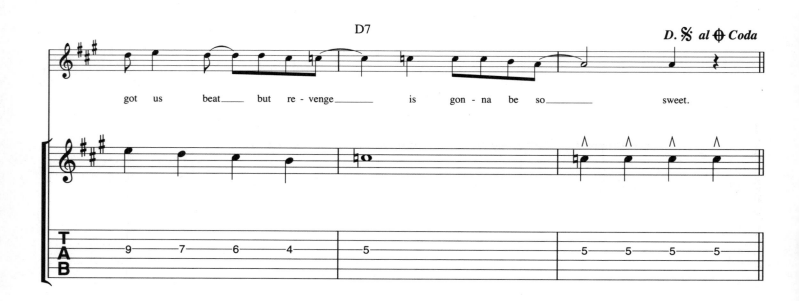

got us beat___ but re - venge___ is gon - na be so___ sweet.

D. % al Coda

Coda

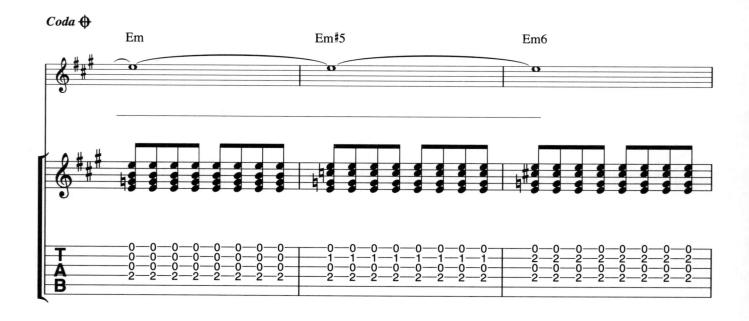

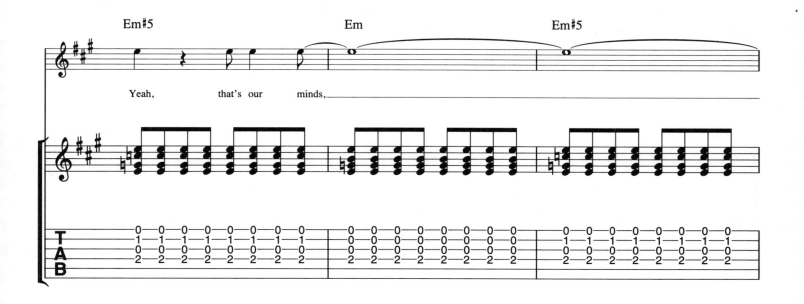

Yeah, that's our minds,_____

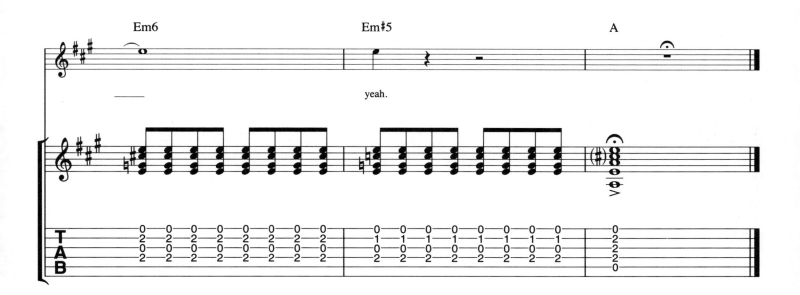

_____ yeah.

Verse 2:   Check your lucky numbers
            That much money could drag you under, oh
            What's the point of being rich
            If you can't think what to do with it
            'Cause you're so bleeding thick.
            Oh, we weren't supposed to be
            We learnt too much at school
            Now we can't help but see
            The future that you've got mapped out
            Is nothing much to shout about.

RIDICULOUS THOUGHTS

Music by Dolores O'Riordan & Noel Hogan
Words by Dolores O'Riordan

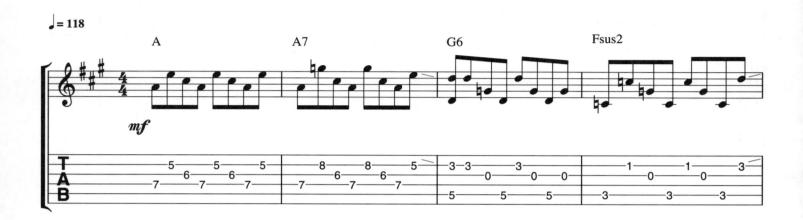

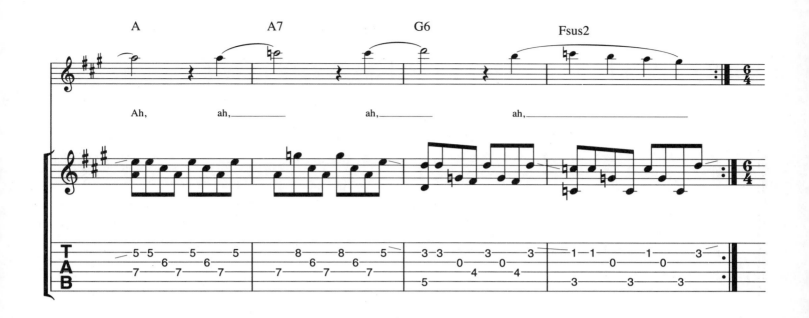

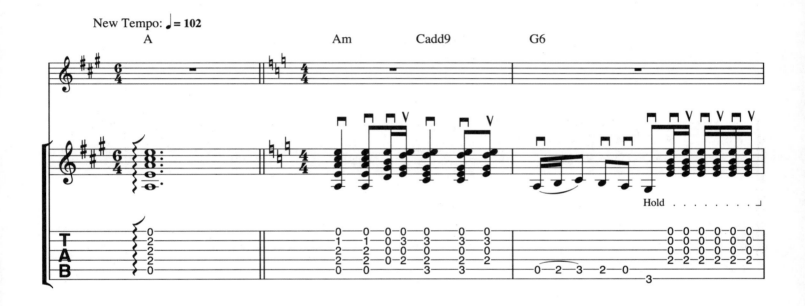

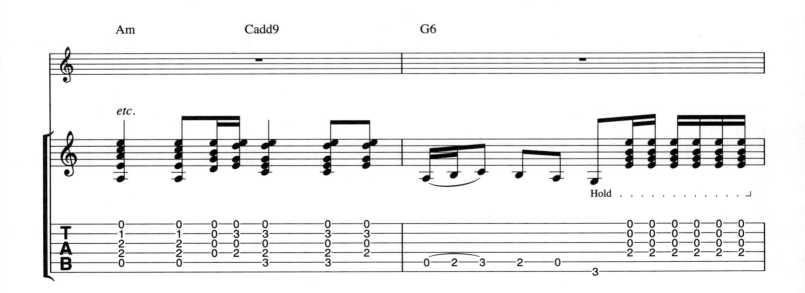

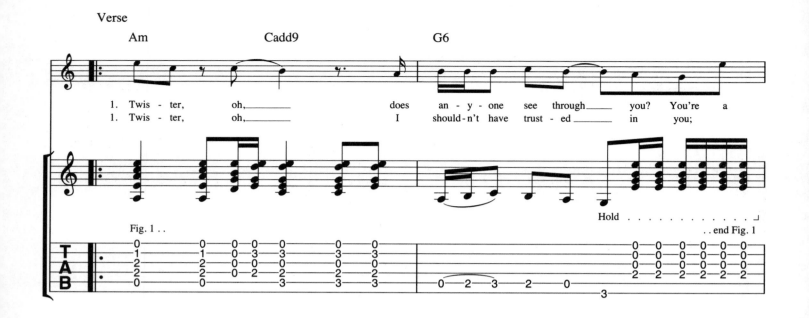

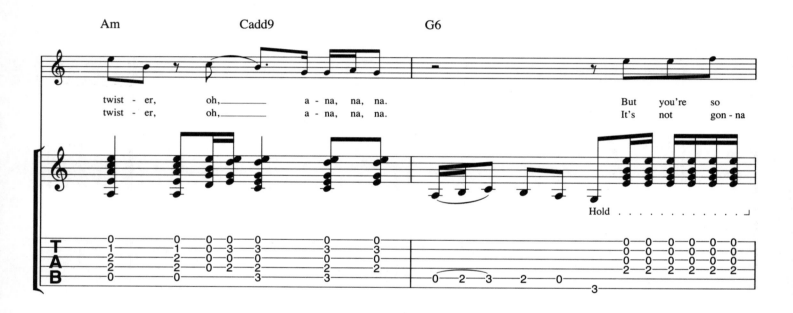

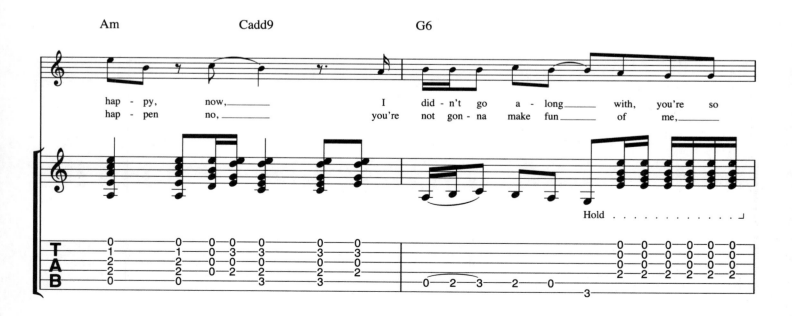

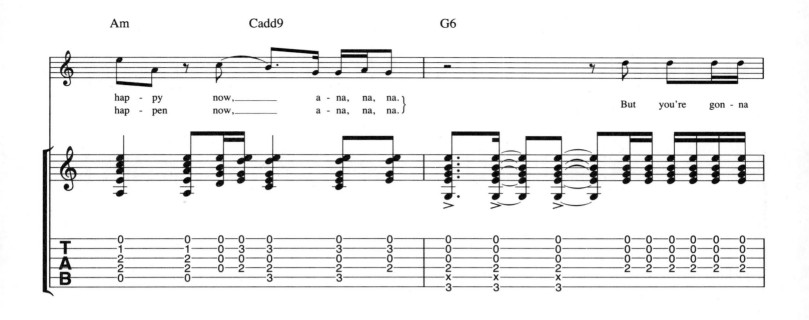

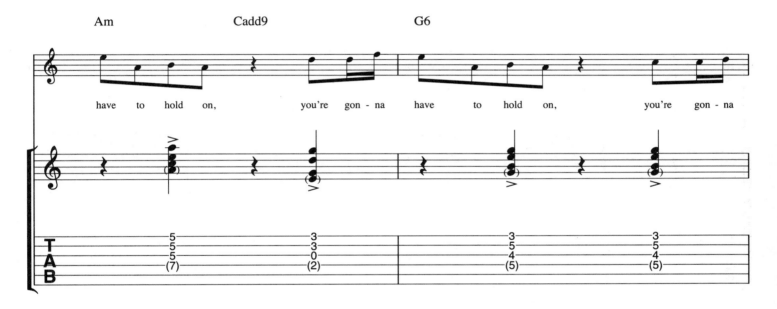

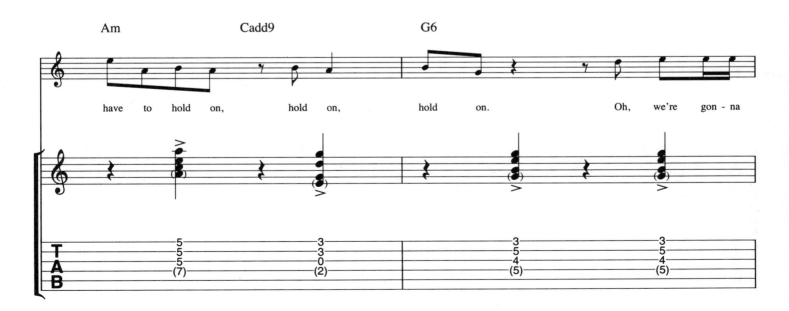

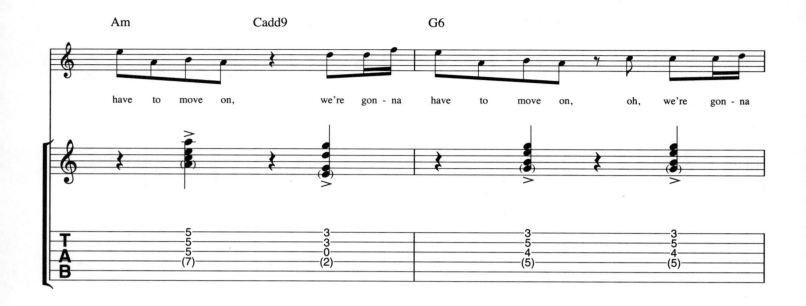

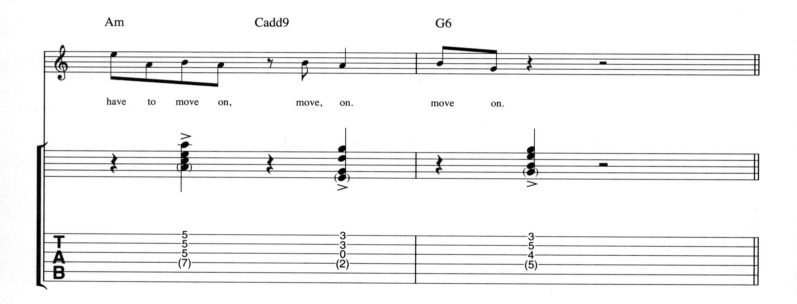

Chorus

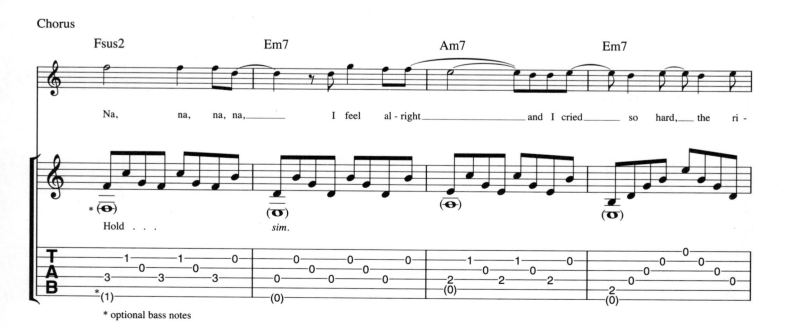

* optional bass notes

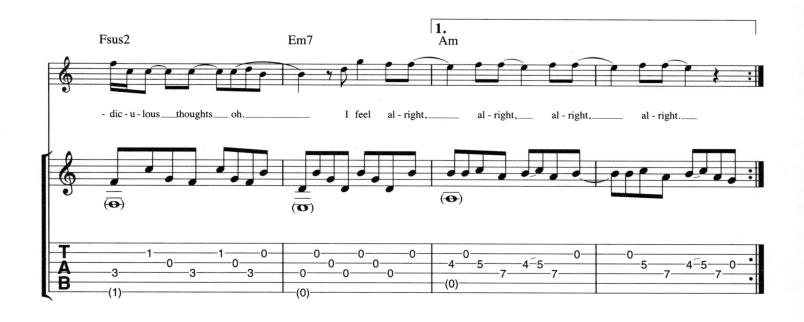

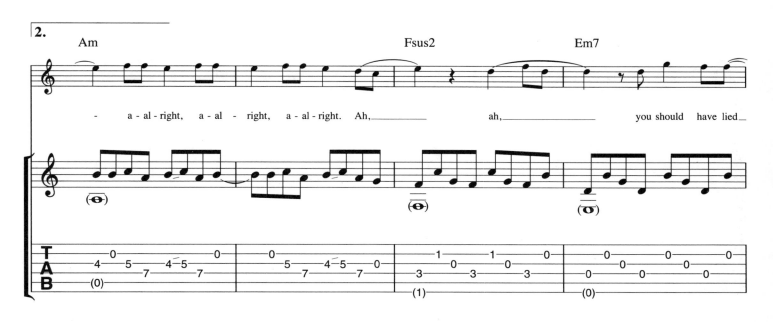

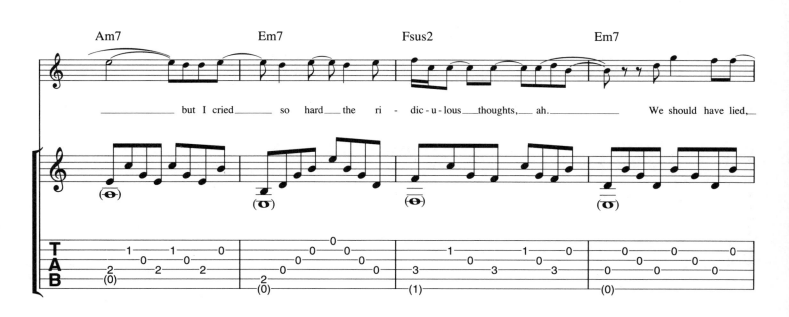

Am   Fsus2

_____ a - lied,_____ a - lied_____ a - lied._____ But you're gon - na   have to hold on,   you're gon - na

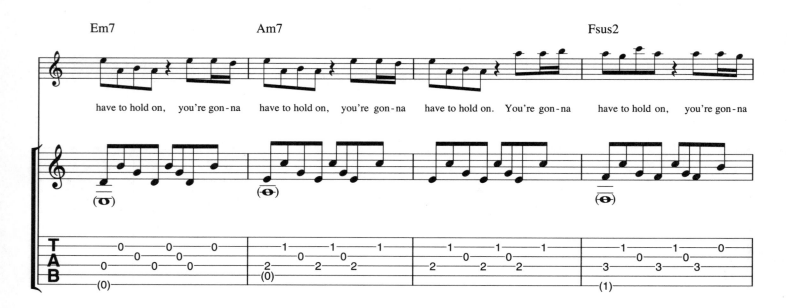

Em7   Am7   Fsus2

have to hold on,   you're gon - na   have to hold on,   you're gon - na   have to hold on.   You're gon - na   have to hold on,   you're gon - na

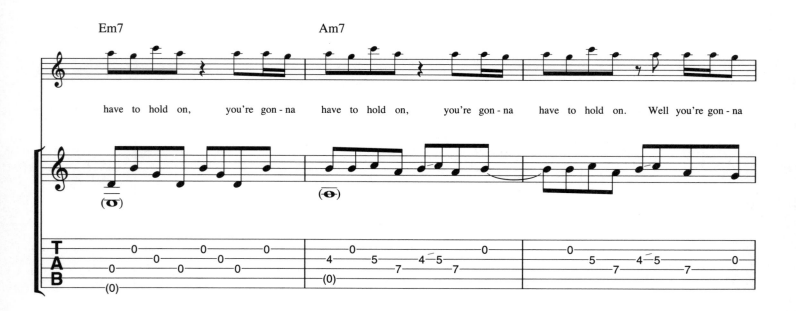

Em7   Am7

have to hold on,   you're gon - na   have to hold on,   you're gon - na   have to hold on.   Well you're gon - na

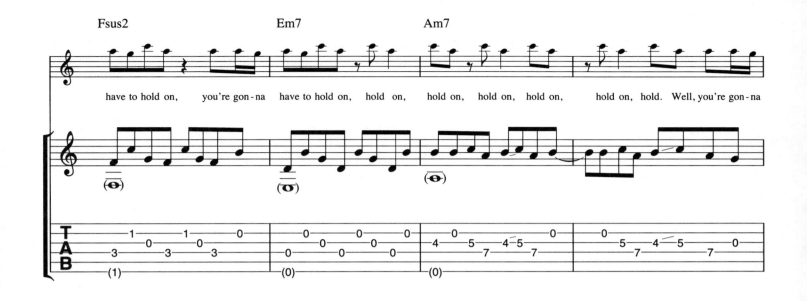

have to hold on,   you're gon-na   have to hold on,   hold   on,   hold on,   hold on,   hold on,   hold on, hold. Well, you're gon-na

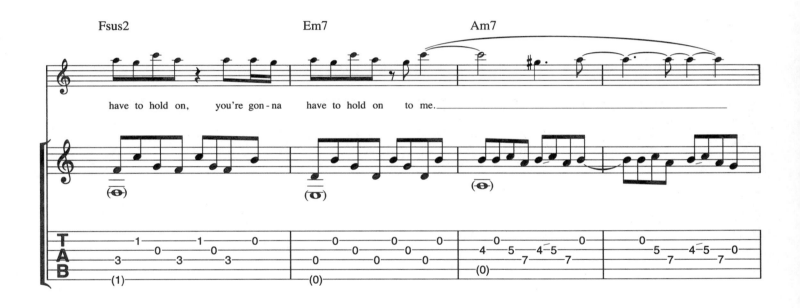

have to hold on,   you're gon-na   have to hold on   to me.

Repeat to fade

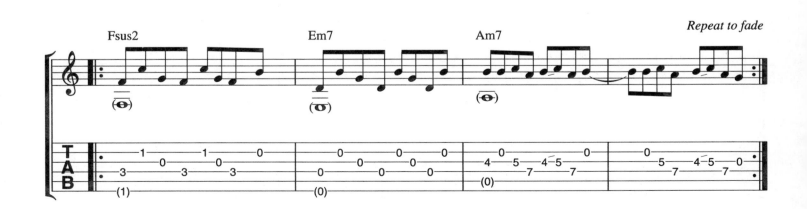

ROLL WITH IT

Words & Music by Noel Gallagher

⊓ = downstroke
∨ = upstroke

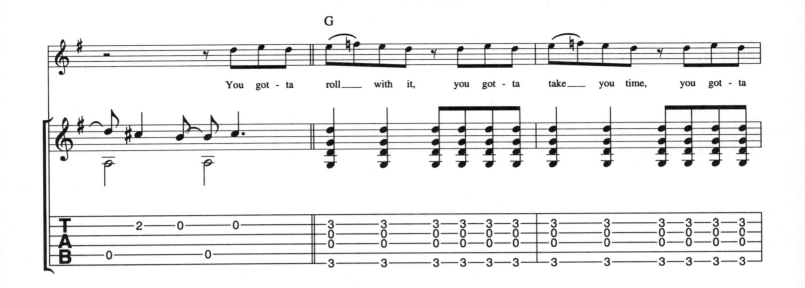

You got-ta roll___ with it, you got-ta take___ you time, you got-ta

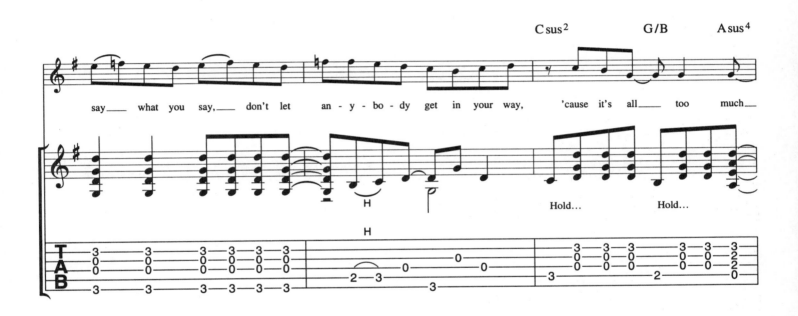

say___ what you say,___ don't let an-y-bo-dy get in your way, 'cause it's all___ too much___

Hold...   Hold...

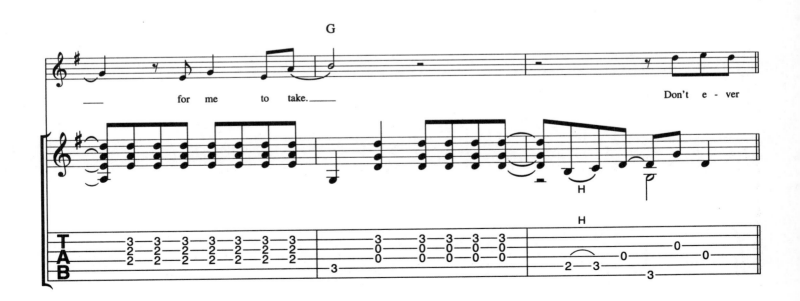

___ for me to take.___   Don't e - ver

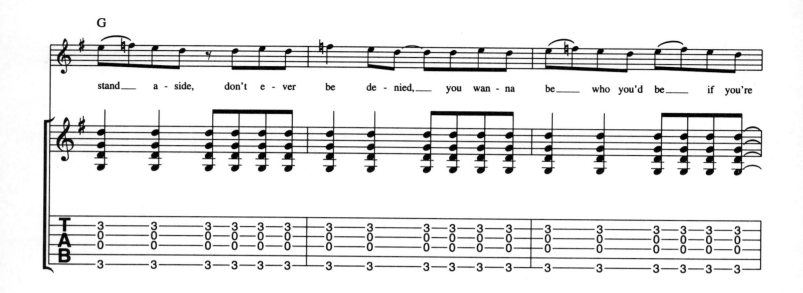

stand___ a - side, don't e - ver be de - nied,___ you wan - na be___ who you'd be___ if you're

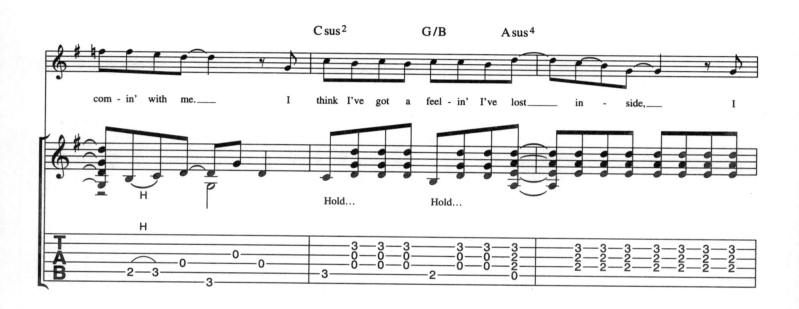

com - in' with me.___ I think I've got a feel - in' I've lost___ in - side,___ I

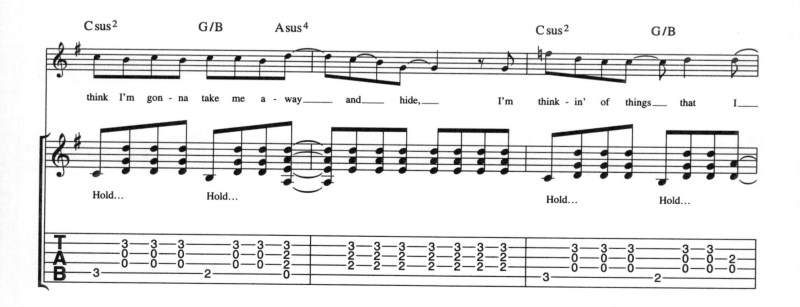

think I'm gon - na take me a - way___ and___ hide,___ I'm think - in' of things___ that I___

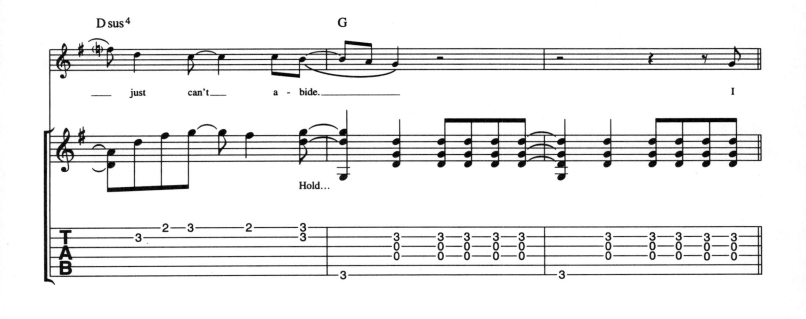

just can't a - bide. I

Hold...

know the roads down which your life will drive,

Hold...

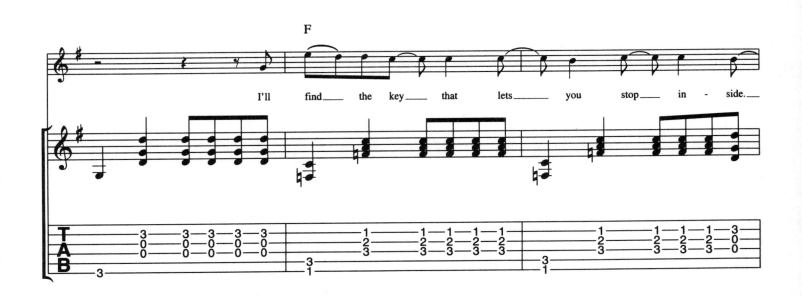

I'll find the key that lets you stop in - side.

79

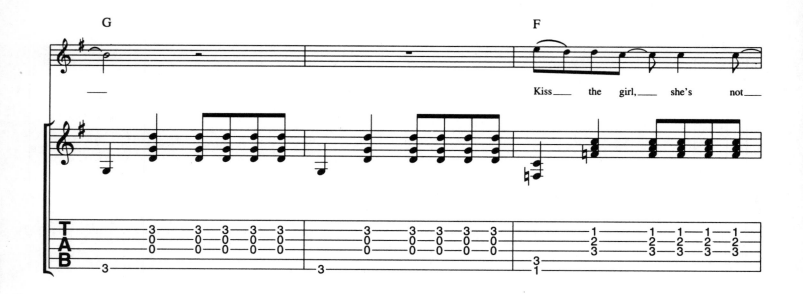

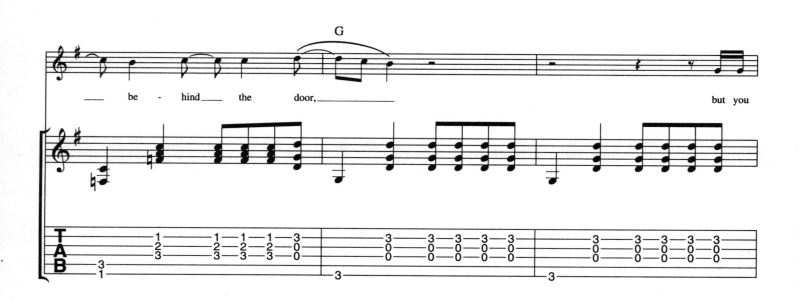

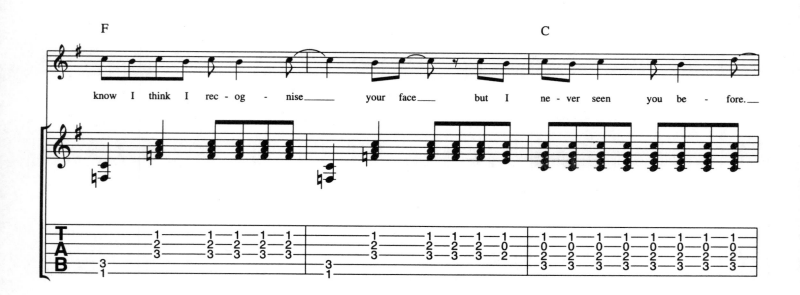

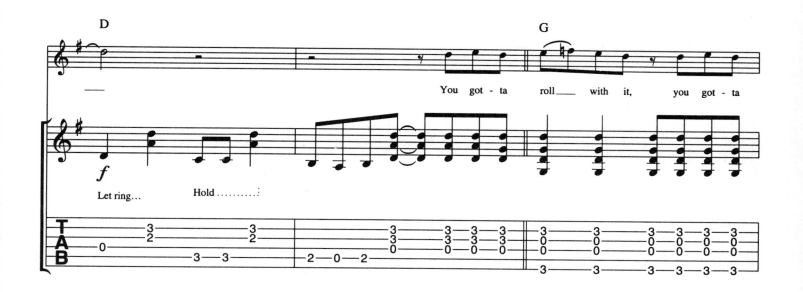

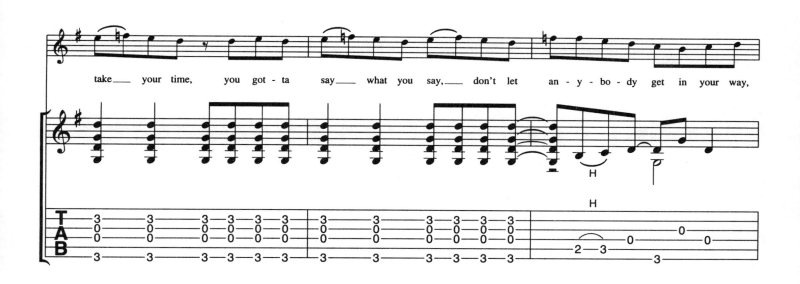

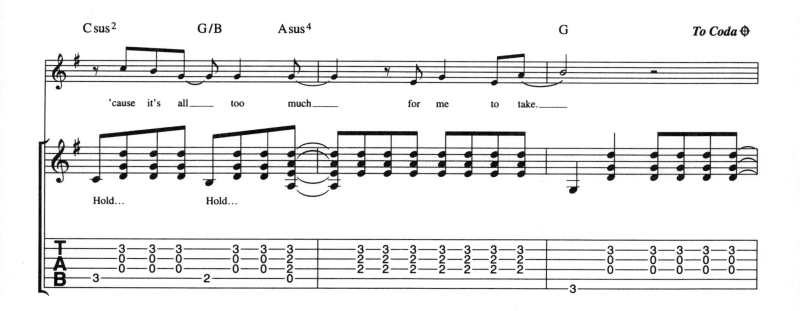

Solo:
G

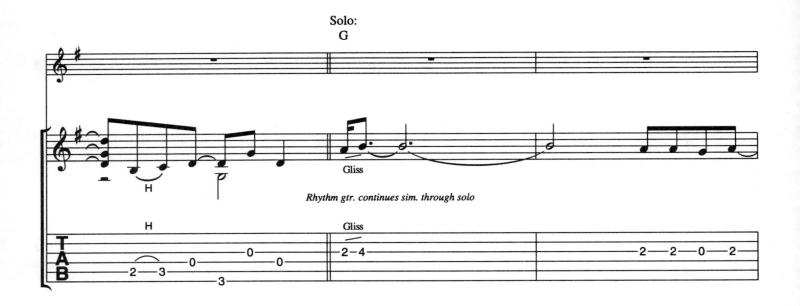

Rhythm gtr. continues sim. through solo

C add⁹   G/B   A sus⁴

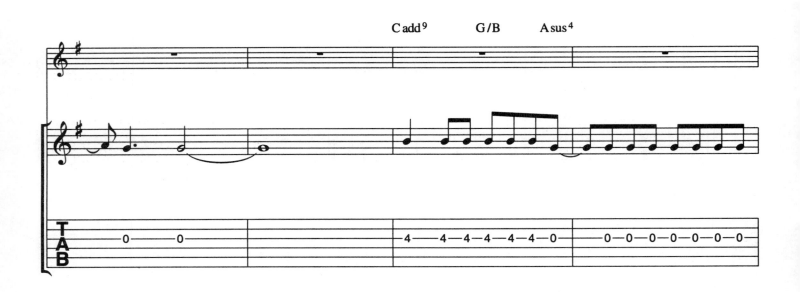

C add⁹   G/B   A sus⁴   C add⁹   G/B   D sus⁴

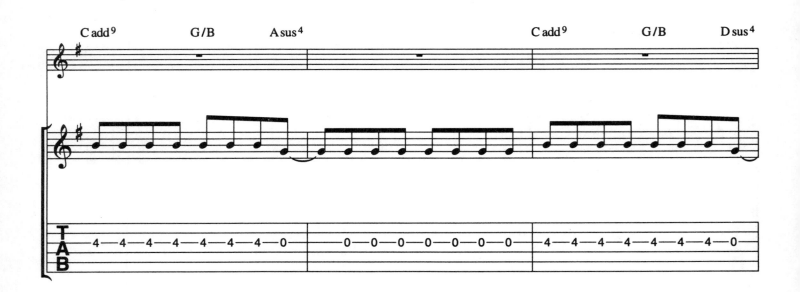

G

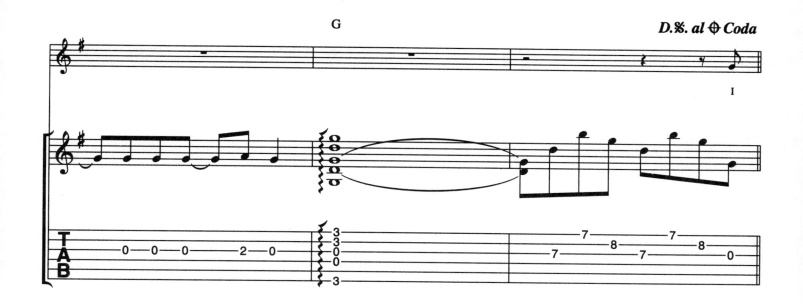

Coda ⊕

G

Don't e - ver stand____ a - side, don't e - ver

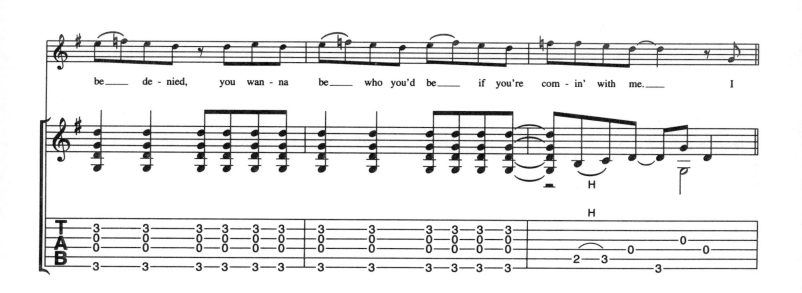

be____ de - nied, you wan - na be____ who you'd be____ if you're com - in' with me.____ I

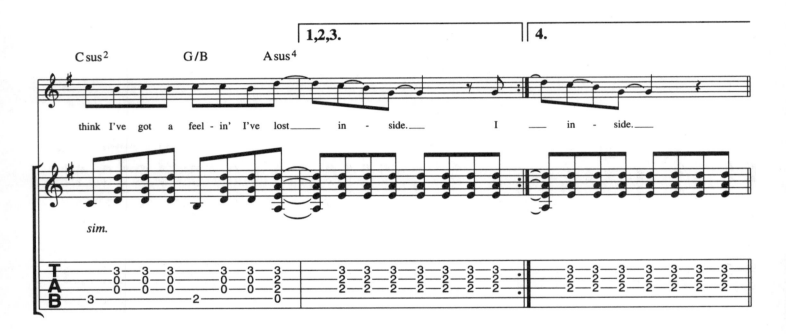

SORTED FOR E'S AND WIZZ

Music by Pulp
Words by Jarvis Cocker

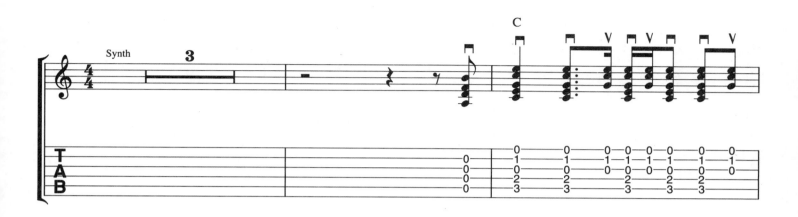

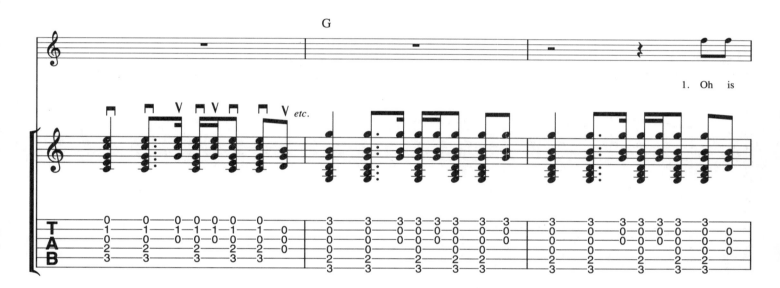

1. Oh is

Verse:

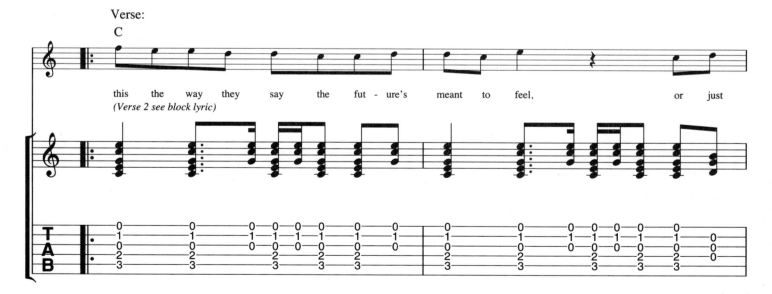

this the way they say the fut-ure's meant to feel, or just
(Verse 2 see block lyric)

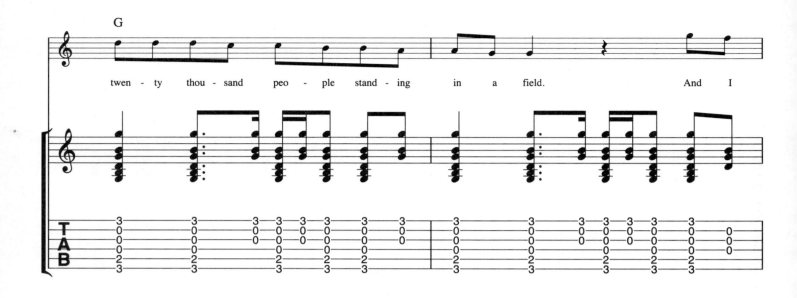

twen - ty thou - sand peo - ple stand - ing in a field. And I

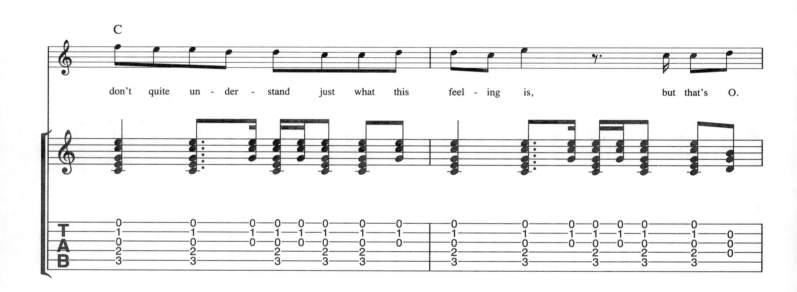

don't quite un - der - stand just what this feel - ing is, but that's O.

K. 'cause we're all sort - ed out for E's and Wizz. And

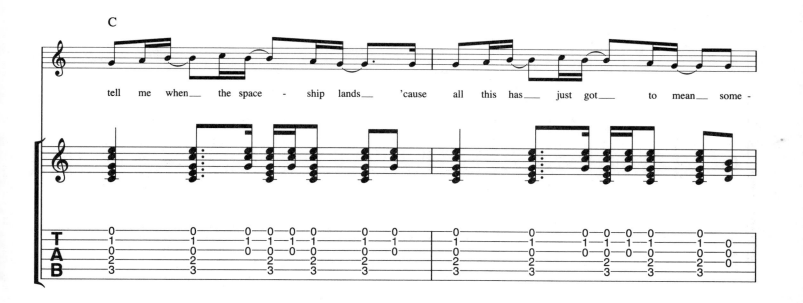

C

tell me when___ the space - ship lands___ 'cause all this has___ just got___ to mean___ some-

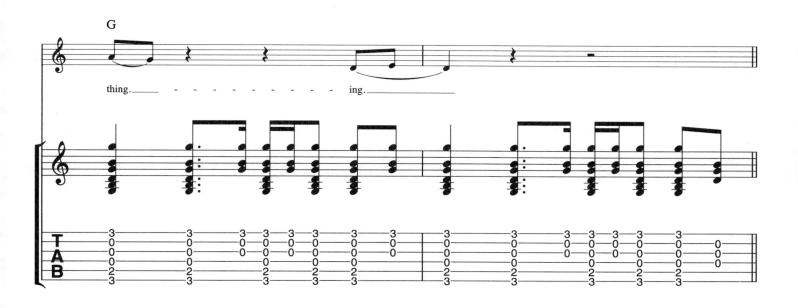

G

thing.___ - - - - - - - ing.___

Chorus:

Dm

In the mid - dle of the night, it feels al - right but then to -

F   **G**

sim.

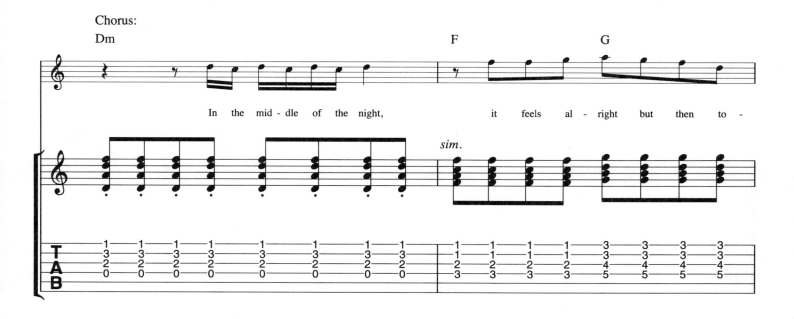

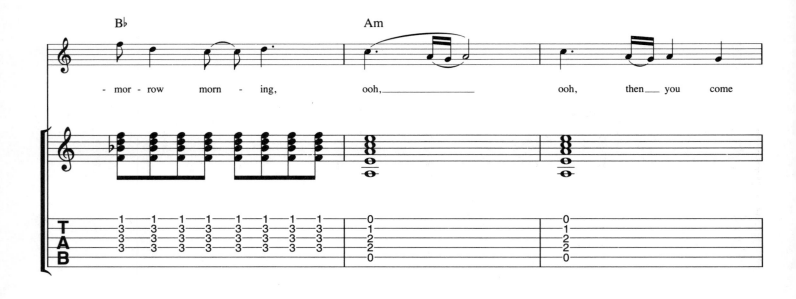

- mor - row morn - ing, ooh,_____ ooh, then___ you come

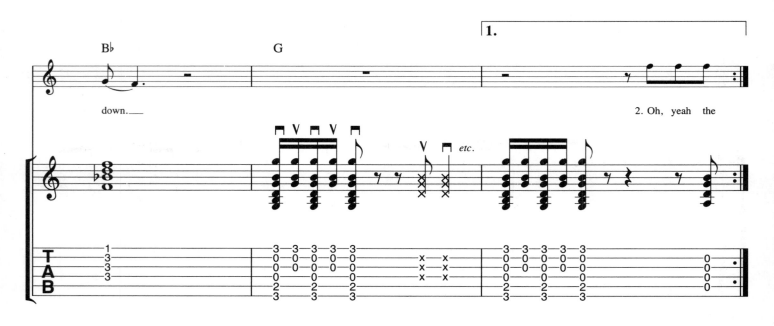

down.___

2. Oh, yeah the

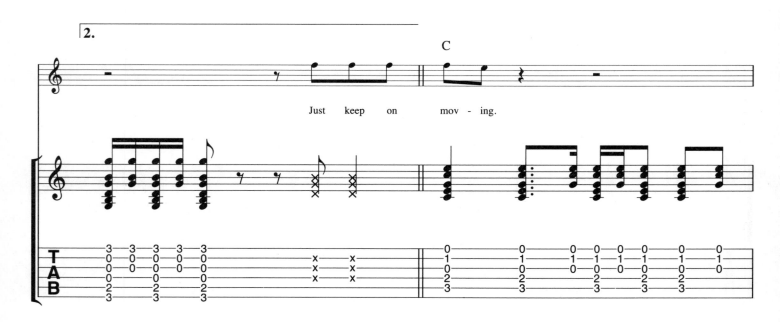

Just keep on mov - ing.

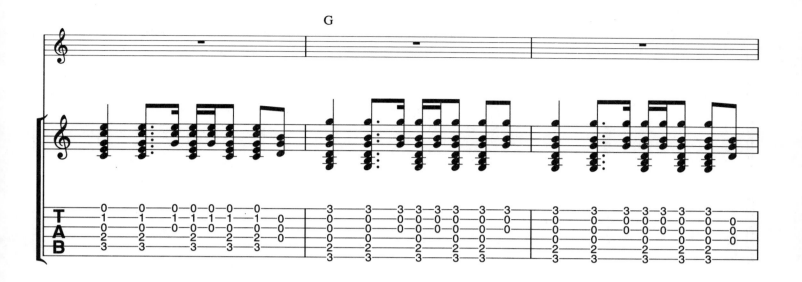

G

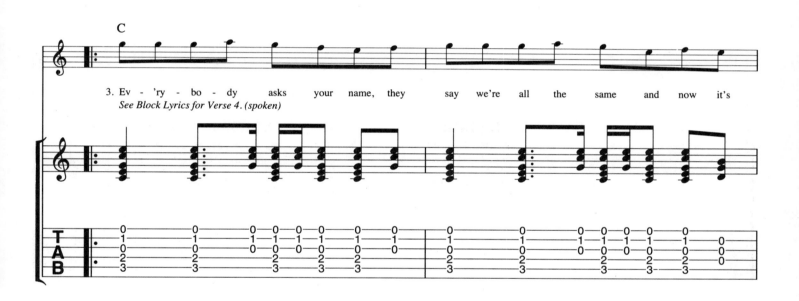

C

3. Ev - 'ry - bo - dy asks your name, they say we're all the same and now it's
See Block Lyrics for Verse 4. (spoken)

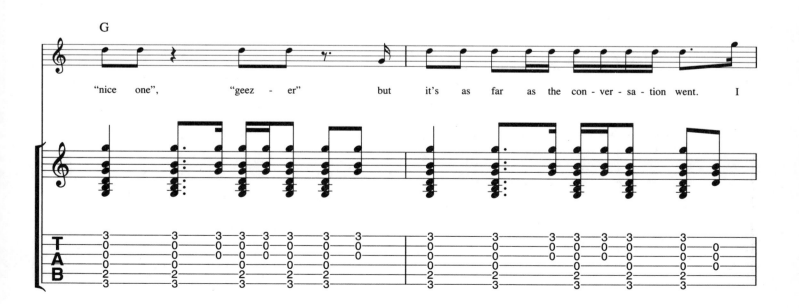

G

"nice one", "geez - er" but it's as far as the con - ver - sa - tion went. I

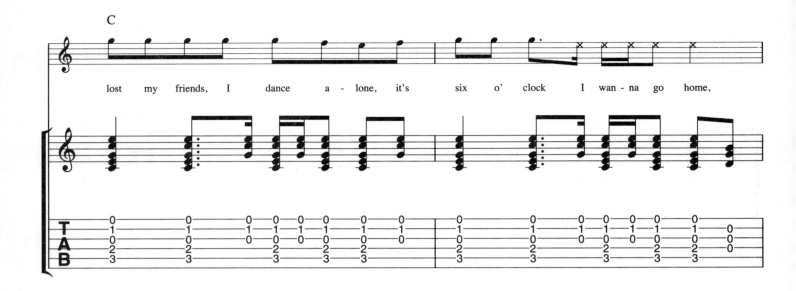

lost   my   friends, I   dance   a - lone, it's   six   o' clock   I   wan - na   go   home,

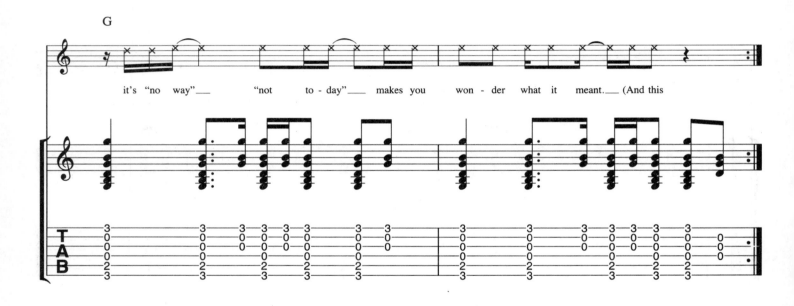

it's "no way"___   "not   to - day"___   makes you   won - der   what it   meant.___ (And this

Chorus:

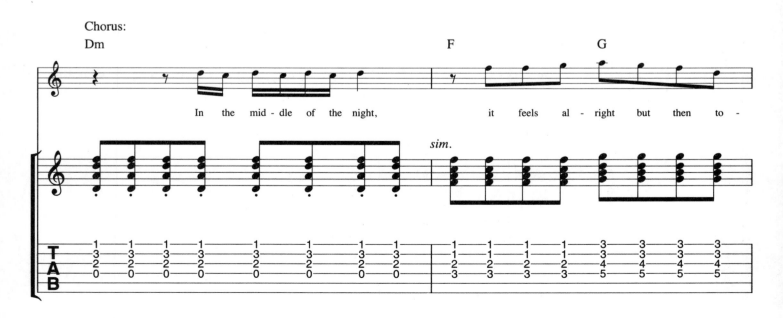

In   the   mid - dle   of   the   night,   it   feels   al - right   but   then   to -

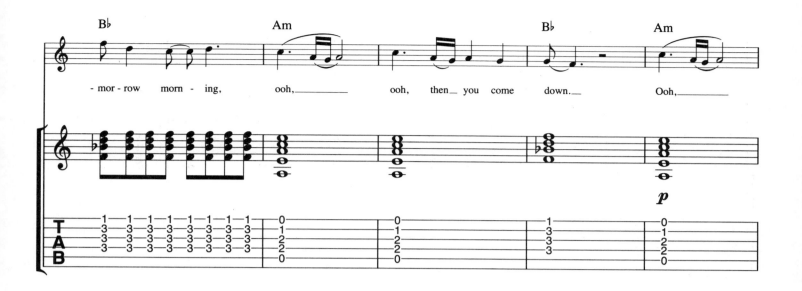

-mor - row morn - ing, ooh,_____ ooh, then_ you come down.__ Ooh,_____

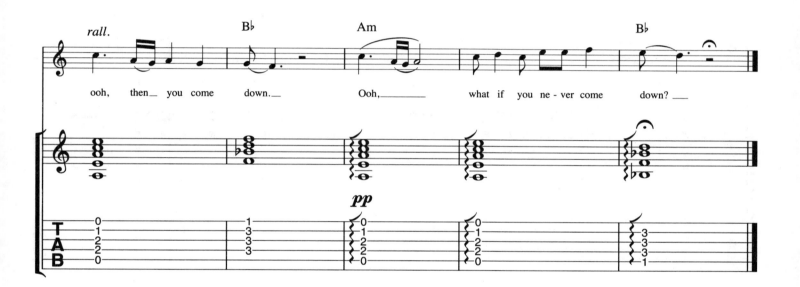

ooh, then_ you come down.__ Ooh,_____ what if you ne - ver come down? __

Verse 2:   Oh, yeah the pirate radio told us what was goin' down
            Got the tickets from some fucked up bloke in Camden Town
            Oh, and no one seems to know exactly where it is
            But that's O.K. 'cause we're all sorted out for E's and Wizz
            At four o'clock the normal world seems very, very, very far away
            Alright.

            In the middle of the night *etc...*

Verse 4:   And this hollow feeling grows
(spoken)   And grows and grows and grows
            And you want to call your mother and say
            "Mother, I can never come home again
            'cause I seem to have left an important part of my brain
            Somewhere, somewhere in a field in Hampshire"
            Alright.

            In the middle of the night *etc...*

TAXLOSS

Words & Music by Paul Draper

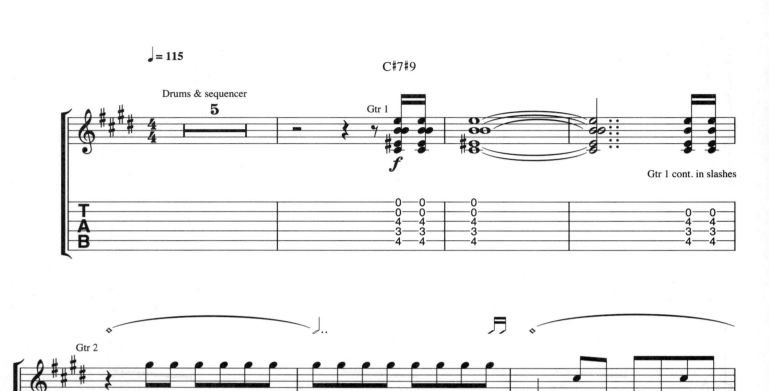

He'll be your

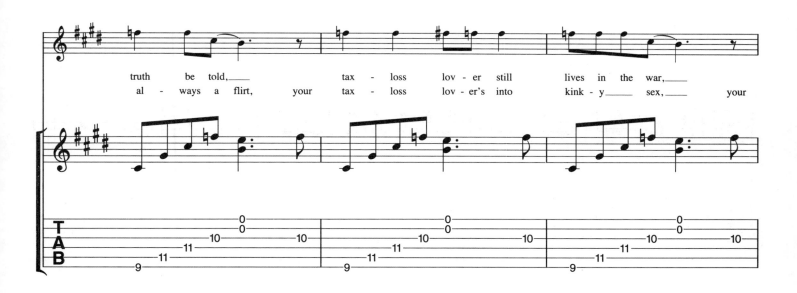

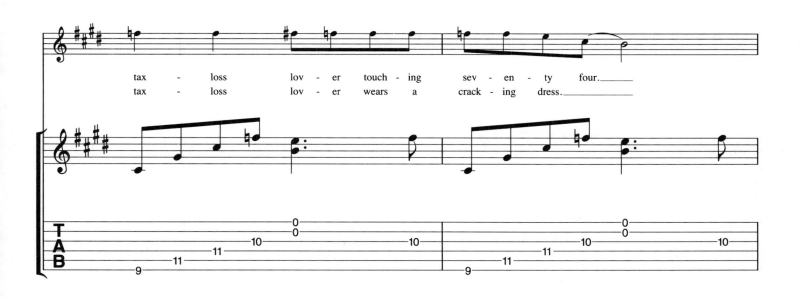

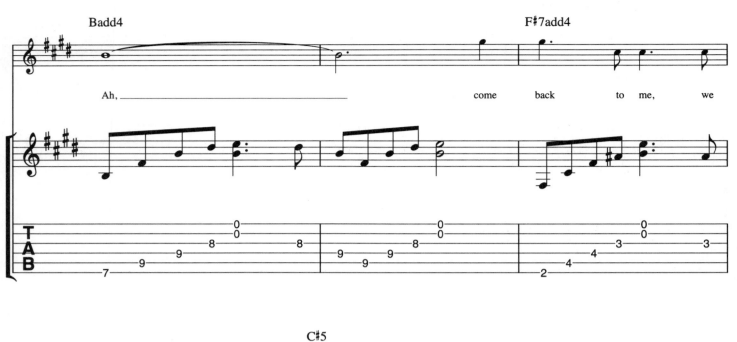

Badd4

F#7add4

Ah, _____ come back to me, we

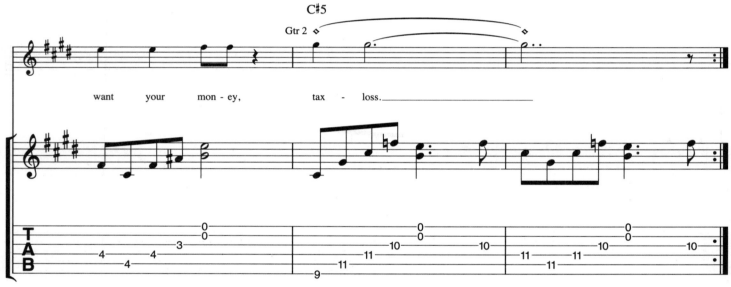

C#5

Gtr 2

want your mon - ey, tax - loss. _____

Pre-Chorus

A5

1. We think you are stu - pid, _____ we
2. sell you down the riv - er, _____

Gtrs 1 & 2 tacet on §§

then___ you'll be mine___ and we'll fly some - where sun - - ny and you'll

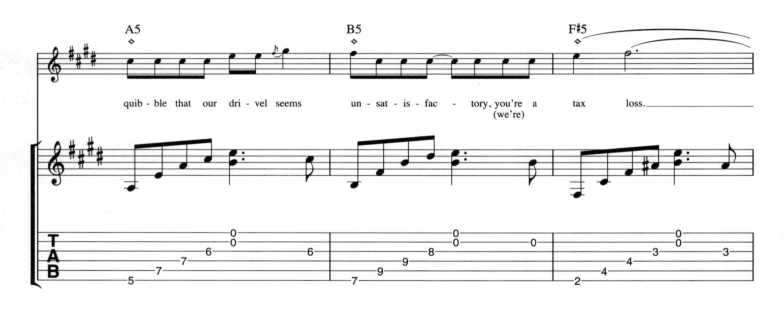

quib - ble that our dri - vel seems un - sat - is - fac - - tory, you're a tax loss.___
(we're)

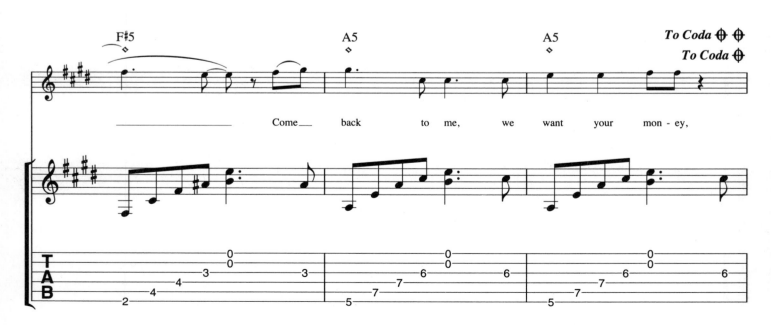

Come___ back to me, we want your mon - ey,

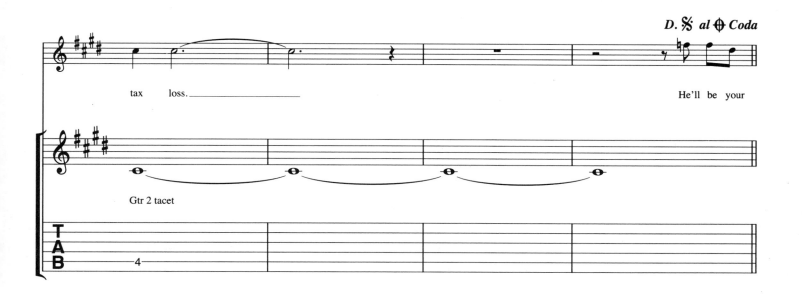

tax loss._____ He'll be your

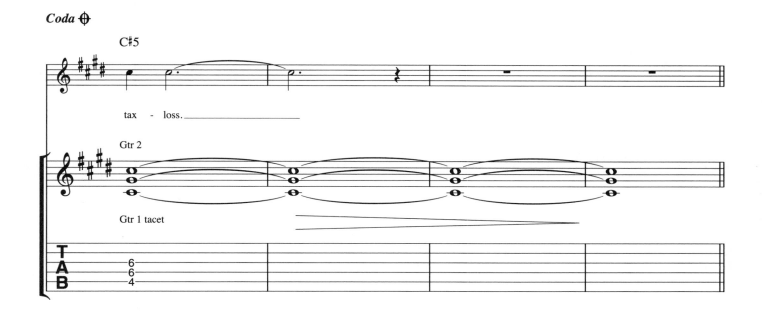

Coda ⊕

tax - loss._____

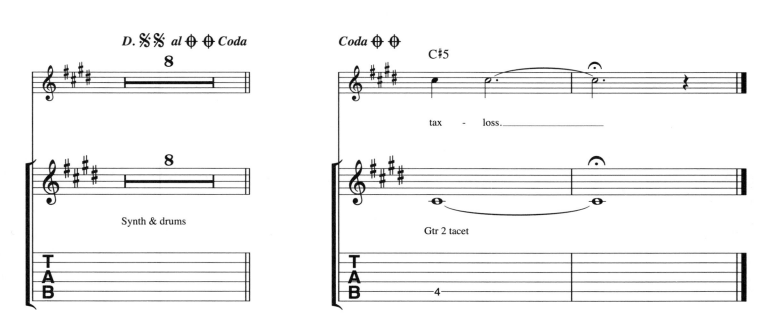

THE DAY WE CAUGHT THE TRAIN

Words & Music by Steve Cradock, Damon Minchella, Oscar Harrison & Simon Fowler

1. I nev-er saw it as the start, it's more a change of heart.
(Verse 2 see block lyrics)

Rap-ping on the win-dows, whist-ling down the chim-ney pot.

1° piano/bass arr. for Gtr.

Blow-ing off the dust in the room where I for-got, I laid my plans in

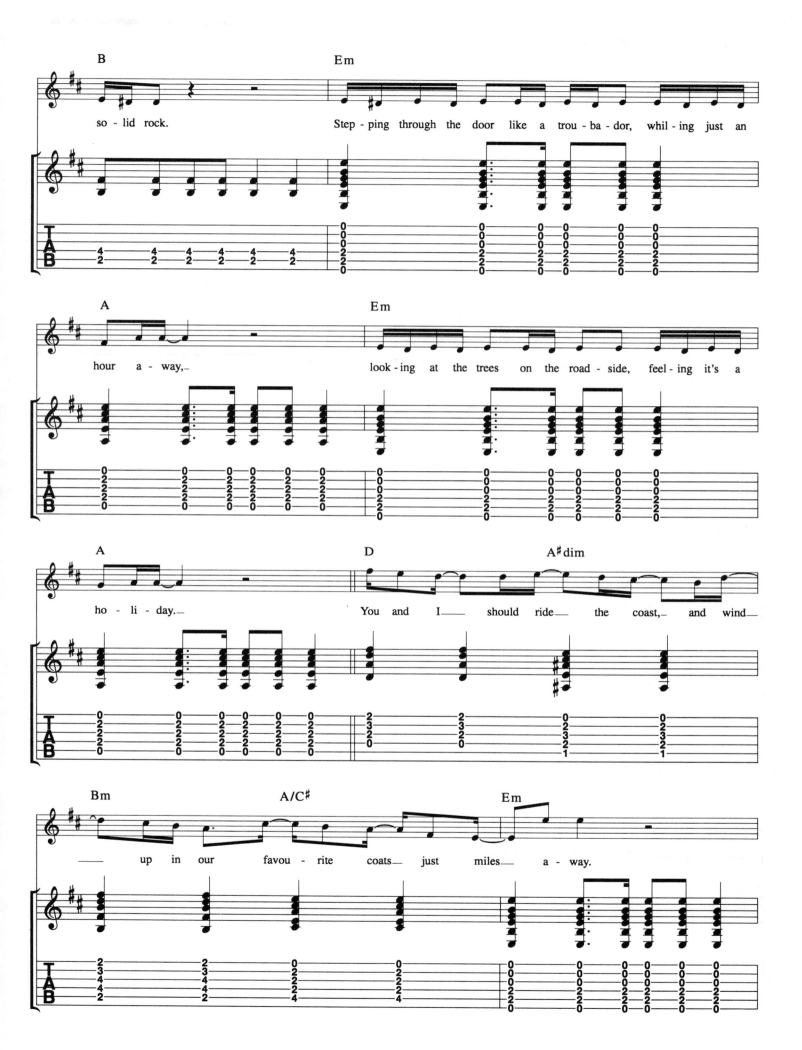

And you and I when we're com-ing down,— we're on-ly get-ting back— and you know— I feel— no sor-

Bass arr. for Gtr.

- row. We've got the whole wide world.

Oh_____ la la,_____ oh,_____ la la.

101

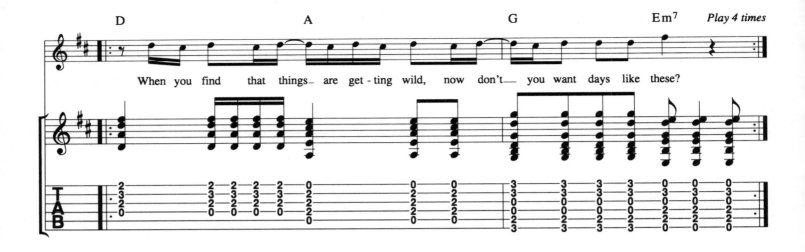

When you find that things—are get-ting wild, now don't—you want days like these?

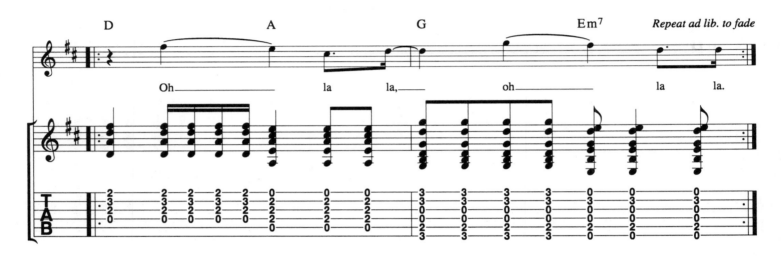

Oh——————— la la,——— oh——————— la la.

Verse 2:
He sipped a rum and coke and told a dirty joke
Walking like Groucho sucking on a number 10
Rolling on the floor with the cigarette burns walked in
I'll miss the crush and I'm home again
Stepping through the door
With the night in store whiling just an hour away
Step into the sky in the star bright feeling it's a brighter day.

WANTED DEAD OR ALIVE

Words & Music by Jon Bon Jovi & Richie Sambora

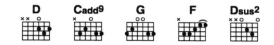

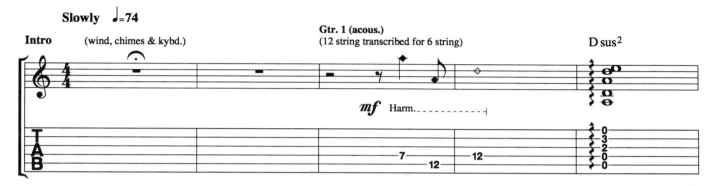

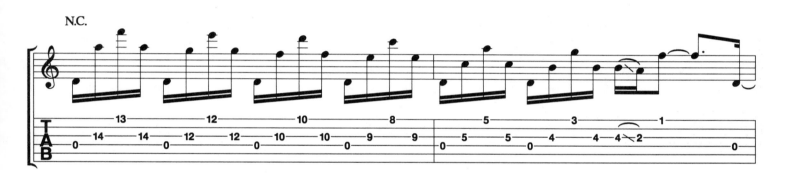

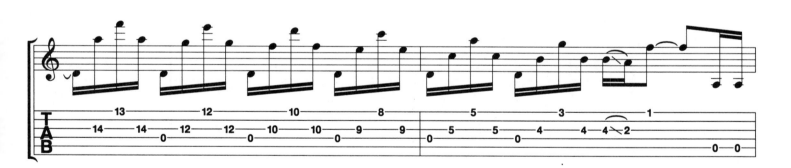

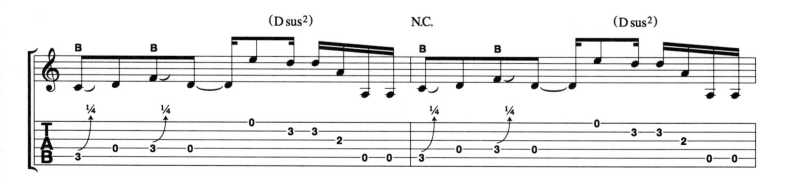

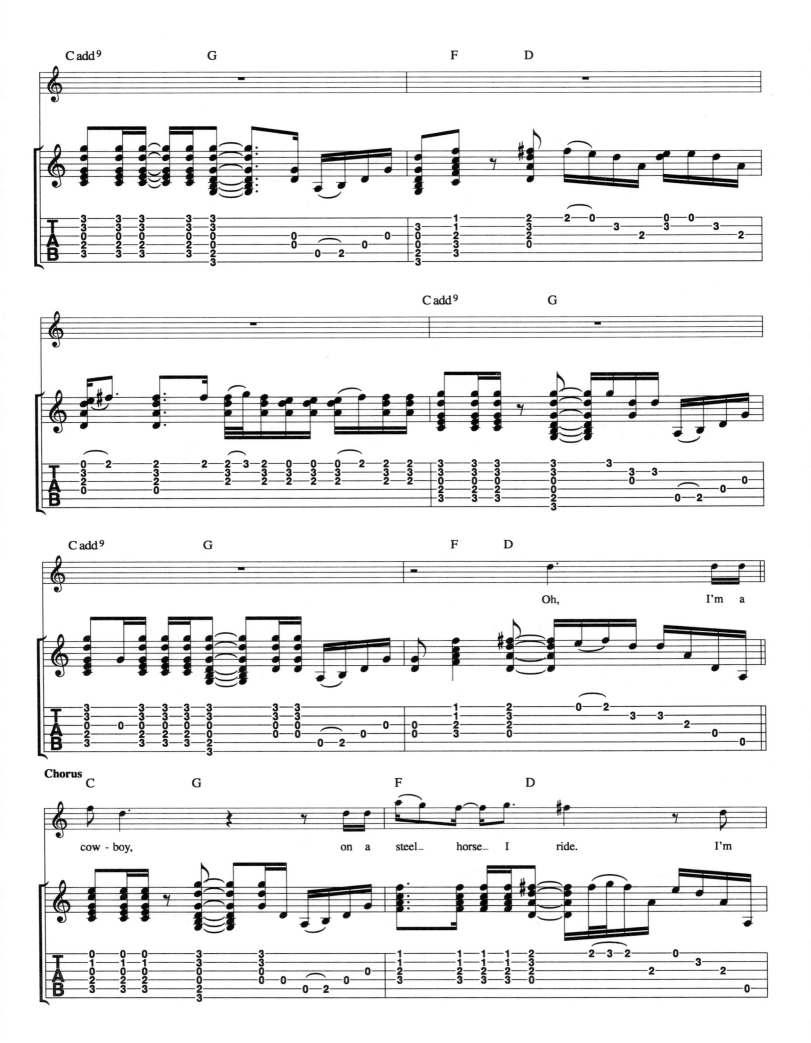

WILD WOOD

Words & Music by Paul Weller

Verse:

1. High tide,_____ mid - af - ter - noon,

See Block Lyrics for Verse 2

Fig. 1.

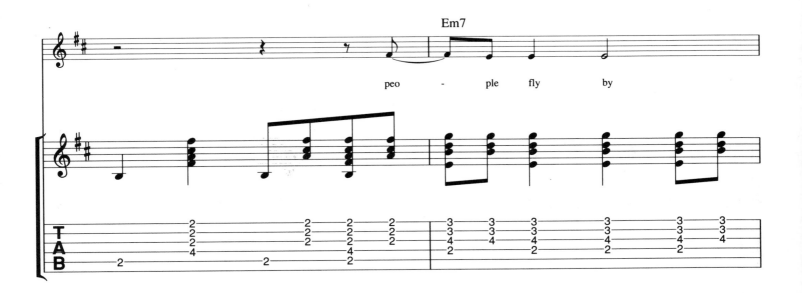

peo - ple fly by

in the traf - fic's boom._____

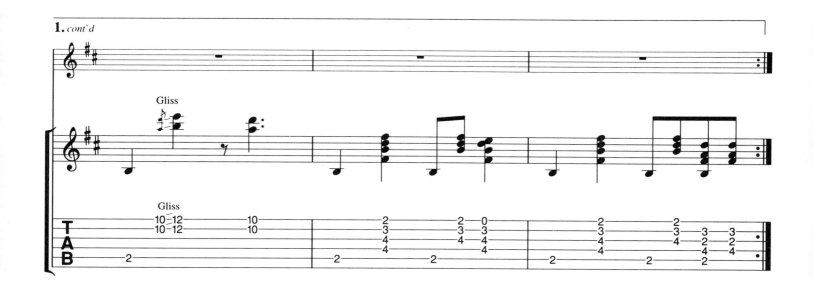

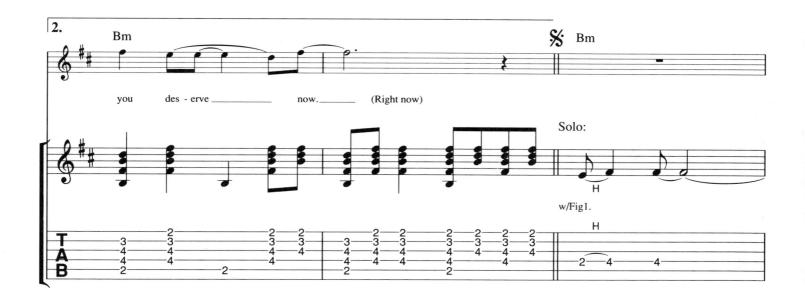

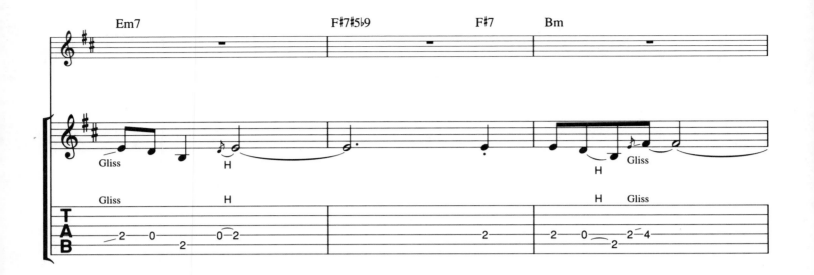

Verse:

3. Climb - ing, _____ for - ev - er_____

See Block Lyrics for Verses 4,5&6

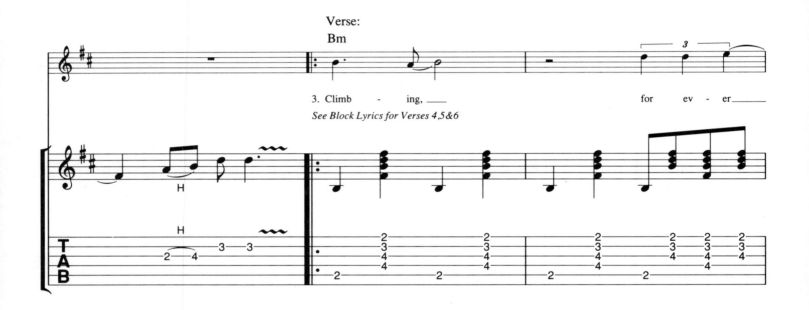

_____ try - ing, _____ find your way out

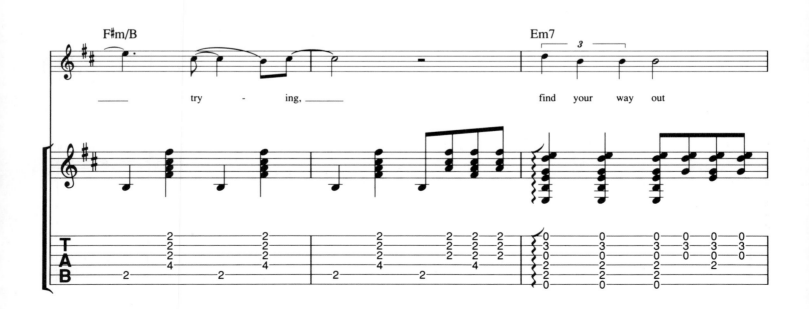

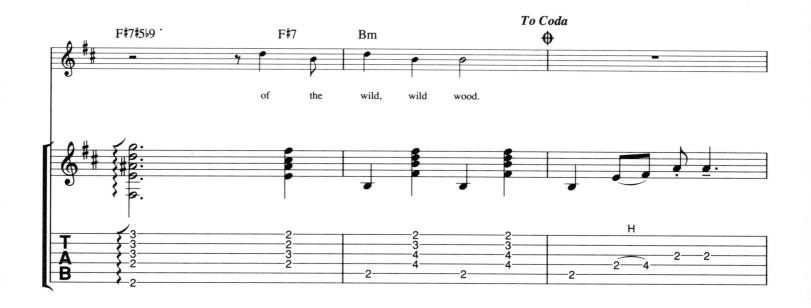

of the wild, wild wood.

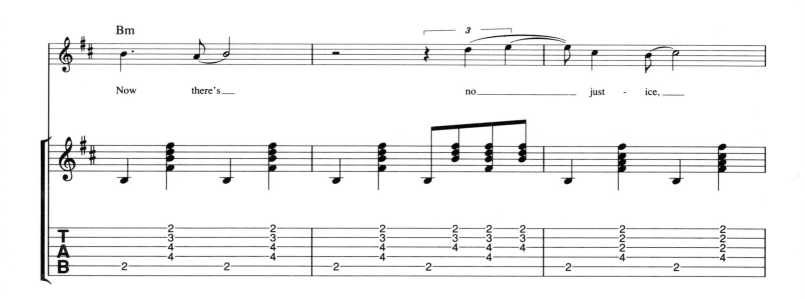

Now there's ____ no _____ just - ice, ____

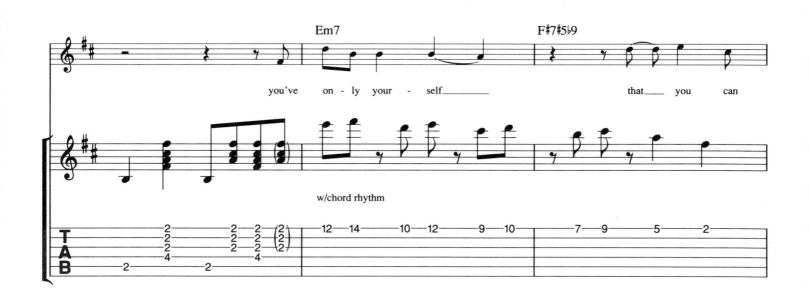

you've on - ly your - self _____ that ___ you can

w/chord rhythm

trust____ in._____ And I say____

Said you're gon - na find your way out of the

wild,____ wild____ wood._____

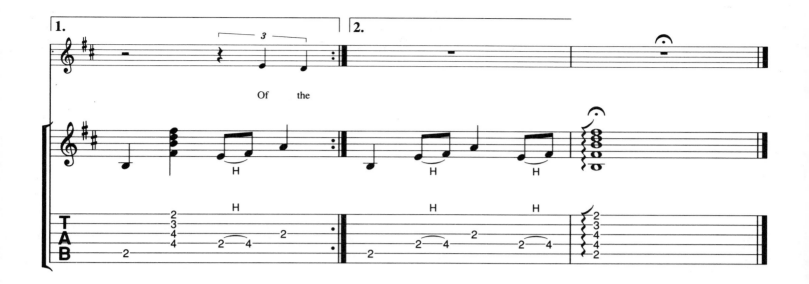

Verse 2:

Don't let them get you down
Making you feel guilty about
Golden rain will bring you riches
All the good things you deserve now.

Verse 4:

And I said high tide, mid-afternoon
People fly by in the traffic's boom
Knowing just where you're blowing
Getting to where you should be going.

Verse 5 (𝄋):

Day by day your world fades away
Waking to feel all the dreams that say
Golden rain will bring you riches
All the good things you deserve now.

Verse 6

And I say climbing, forever trying
You're gonna find your way out of the wild, wild wood.
(*To Coda*)

YOU LEARN

Music by Alanis Morissette & Glenn Ballard
Words by Alanis Morissette

Capo 1st fret

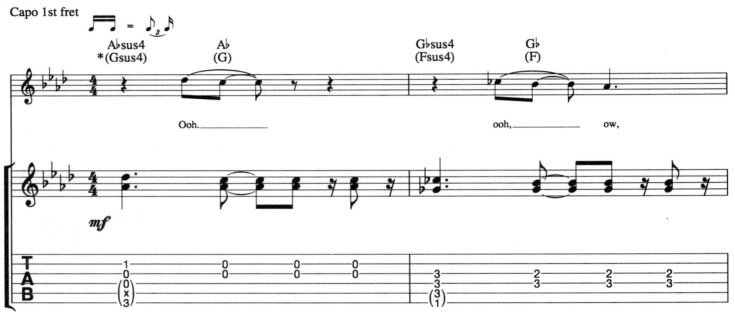

* Symbols in parentheses represent chord names with respect to capoed guitar.
Symbols above reflect actual sounding chords.

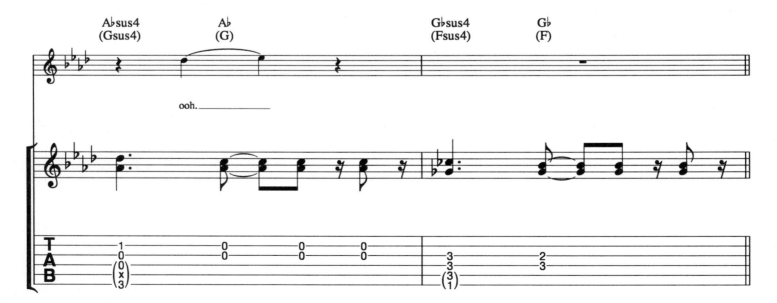

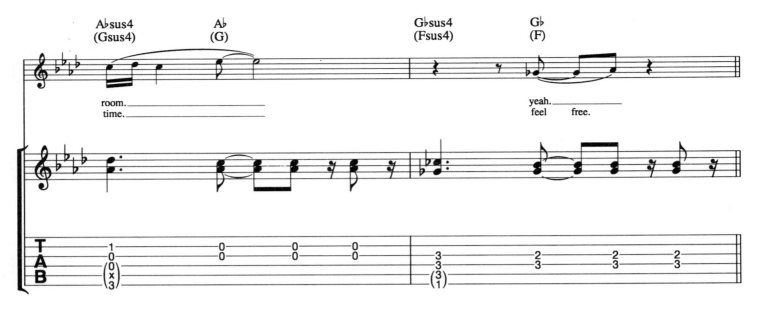

Pre-chorus

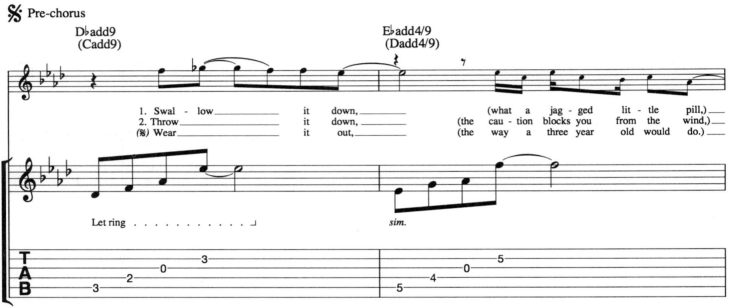

1. Swal - low _____ it down, _____ (what a jag - ged lit - tle pill,) ____
2. Throw _____ it down, _____ (the cau - tion blocks you from the wind,) ____
(%) Wear _____ it out, _____ (the way a three year old would do.) ____

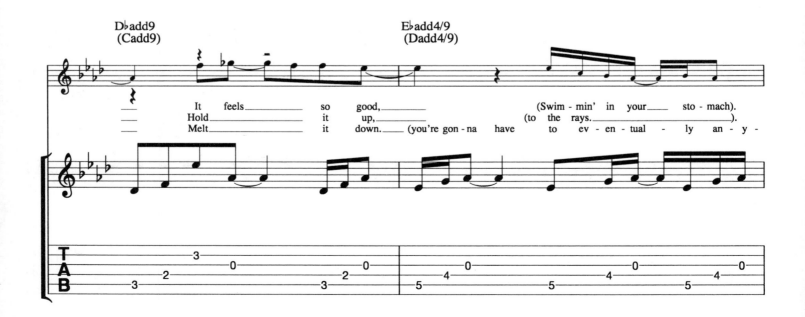

_____ It feels _____ so good, _____ (Swim - min' in your ____ sto - mach).
_____ Hold _____ it up, _____ (to the rays. _____).
_____ Melt _____ it down. _____ (you're gon - na have to ev - en - tual - ly an - y -

Hey, oh, oh.

Hold . . . . sim.

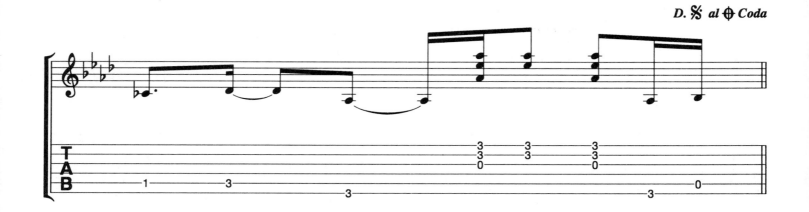

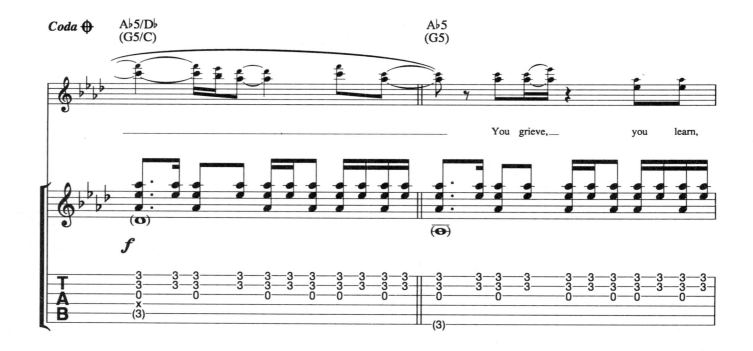

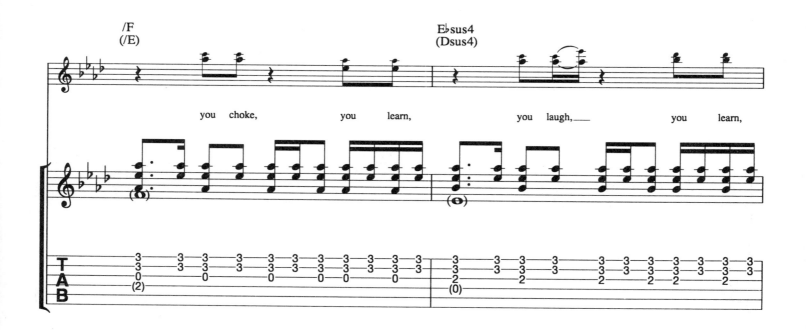

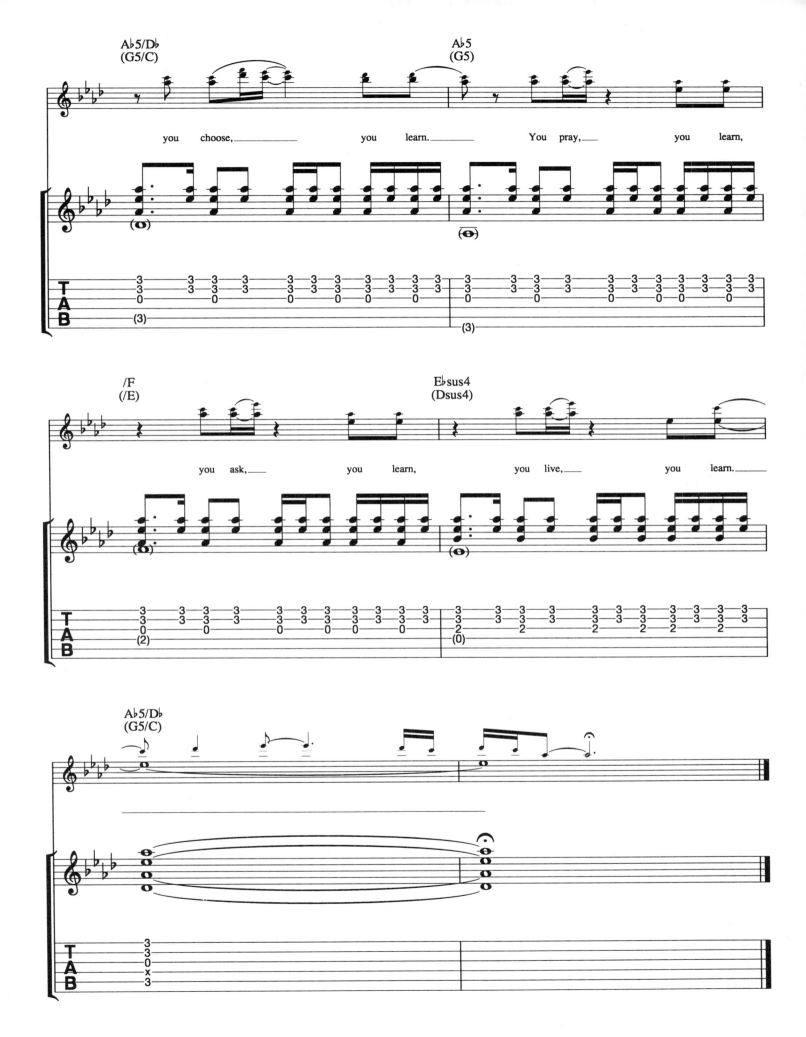

PRÉSENTATION DE LA TABLATURE DE GUITARE

Il existe trois façons différentes de noter la musique pour guitare : à l'aide d'une portée musicale, de tablatures ou de barres rythmiques

Les BARRES RYTHMIQUES sont indiquées au-dessus de la portée. Jouez les accords dans le rythme indiqué. Les notes rondes indiquent des notes réciles.

La PORTÉE MUSICALE indique les notes et rythmes et est divisée en mesures. Cette division est représentée par des lignes. Les notes sont : do, ré, mi, fa, sol, la, si.

La PORTÉE EN TABLATURE est une représentation graphique des touches de guitare. Chaque ligne horizontale correspond à une corde et chaque chiffre correspond à une case.

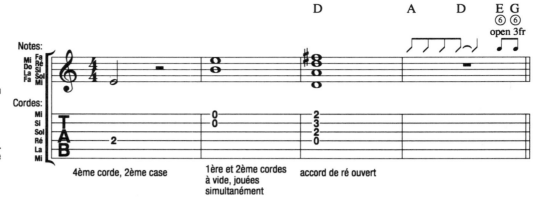

4ème corde, 2ème case — 1ère et 2ème cordes à vide, jouées simultanément — accord de ré ouvert

Notation Spéciale De Guitare : Définitions

TIRÉ DEMI-TON : Jouez la note et tirez la corde afin d'élever la note d'un demi-ton (étape à moitié).

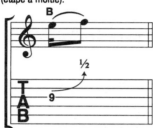

TIRÉ PLEIN : Jouez la note et tirez la corde afin d'élever la note d'un ton entier (étape entière).

TIRÉ D'AGRÉMENT : Jouez la note et tirez la corde comme indiqué. Jouez la première note aussi vite que possible.

TIRÉ QUART DE TON : Jouez la note et tirez la corde afin d'élever la note d'un quart de ton.

TIRÉ ET LÂCHÉ : Jouez la note et tirez la corde comme indiqué, puis relâchez, afin d'obtenir de nouveau la note de départ.

TIRÉ ET REJOUÉ : Jouez la note et tirez la corde comme indiqué puis rejouez la corde où le symbole apparaît.

PRÉ-TIRÉ : Tirez la corde comme indiqué puis jouez cette note.

PRÉ-TIRÉ ET LÂCHÉ : Tirez la corde comme indiqué. Jouez la note puis relâchez la corde afin d'obtenir le ton de départ.

HAMMER-ON: Jouez la première note (plus basse) avec un doigt puis jouez la note plus haute sur la même corde avec un autre doigt, sur le manche mais sans vous servir du médiator.

PULL-OFF: Positionnez deux doigts sur les notes à jouer. Jouez la première note et sans vous servir du médiator, dégagez un doigt pour obtenir la deuxième note, plus basse.

GLISSANDO : Jouez la première note puis faites glisser le doigt le long du manche pour obtenir la seconde note qui, elle, n'est pas jouée.

GLISSANDO ET REJOUÉ : Identique au glissando à ceci près que la seconde note est jouée.

HARMONIQUES NATURELLES : Jouez la note tandis qu'un doigt effleure la corde sur le manche correspondant à la case indiquée.

PICK SCRAPE (SCRATCH) : On fait glisser le médiator le long de la corde, ce qui produit un son éraillé.

ÉTOUFFÉ DE LA PAUME : La note est partiellement étouffée par la main (celle qui se sert du médiator). Elle effleure la (les) corde(s) juste au-dessus du chevalet.

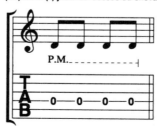

CORDES ÉTOUFFÉES : Un effet de percussion produit en posant à plat la main sur le manche sans relâcher, puis en jouant les cordes avec le médiator.

NOTE: La vitesse des tirés est indiquée par la notation musicale et le tempo.

ERLÄUTERUNG ZUR TABULATURSCHREIBWEISE

Es gibt drei Möglichkeiten, Gitarrenmusik zu notieren: im klassichen Notensystem, in Tabulaturform oder als rhythmische Akzente

RHYTHMISCHE AKZENTE werden über dem Notensystem notiert. Geschlagene Akkorde werden rhythmisch dargestellt. Ausgeschriebene Noten stellen Einzeltöne dar.

Im **NOTENSYSTEM** werden Tonhöhe und rhythmischer Verlauf festgelegt; es ist durch Taktstriche in Takte unterteilt. Die Töne werden nach den ersten acht Buchstaben des Alphabets benannt.
Beachte: "B" in der anglo-amerkanischen Schreibweise entspricht dem deutschen "H"!

DIE TABULATUR ist die optische Darstellung des Gitarrengriffbrettes. Jeder horizontalen Linie ist eine bestimmte Saite zugeordnet, jede Zahl bezeichnet einen Bund.

4. Saite, 2. Bund   1. & 2. Saite offen,   offener D Akkord
gleichzeitig anschlagen

Erklärungen zur speziellen Gitarennotation

HALBTON-ZIEHER: Spiele die Note und ziehe dann um einen Halbton höher (Halbtonschritt).

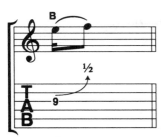

GANZTON-ZIEHER: Spiele die Note und ziehe dann einen Ganzton höher (Ganztonschritt).

ZIEHER MIT VORSCHLAG: Spiele die Note und ziehe wie notiert. Spiele die erste Note so schnell wie möglich.

VIERTELTON-ZIEHER: Spiele die Note und ziehe dann einen Viertelton höher (Vierteltonschritt).

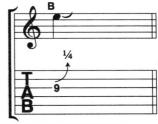

ZIEHEN UND ZURÜCKGLEITEN: Spiele die Note und ziehe wie notiert; lasse den Finger dann in die Ausgangsposition zurückgleiten. Dabei wird nur die erste Note angeschlagen.

ZIEHEN UND NOCHMALIGES ANSCHLAGEN: Spiele die Note und ziehe wie notiert, schlage die Saite neu an, wenn das Symbol "▶" erscheint und lasse den Finger dann zurückgleiten.

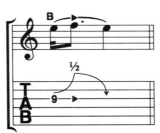

ZIEHER VOR DEM ANSCHLAGEN: Ziehe zuerst die Note wie notiert; schlage die Note dann an.

ZIEHER VOR DEM ANSCHLAGEN MIT ZURÜCKGLEITEN: Ziehe die Note wie notiert; schlage die Note dann an und lasse den Finger auf die Ausgangslage zurückgleiten.

AUFSCHLAGTECHNIK: Schlage die erste (tiefere) Note an; die höhere Note (auf der selben Saite) erklingt durch kräftiges Aufschlagen mit einem anderen Finger der Griffhand.

ABZIEHTECHNIK: Setze beide Finger auf die zu spielenden Noten und schlage die erste Note an. Ziehe dann (ohne nochmals anzuschlagen) den oberen Finger der Griffhand seitlich - abwärts ab, um die zweite (tiefere) Note zum klingen zu bringen.

GLISSANDOTECHNIK: Schlage die erste Note an und rutsche dann mit dem selben Finger der Griffhand aufwärts oder abwärts zur zweiten Note. Die zweite Note wird nicht angeschlagen.

GLISSANDOTECHNIK MIT NACHFOLGENDEM ANSCHLAG: Gleiche Technik wie das gebundene Glissando, jedoch wird die zweite Note angeschlagen.

NATÜRLICHES FLAGEOLETT: Berühre die Saite über dem angegebenen Bund leicht mit einem Finger der Griffhand. Schlage die Saite an und lasse sie frei schwingen.

PICK SCRAPE: Fahre mit dem Plektrum nach unten über die Saiten - klappt am besten bei umsponnenen Saiten.

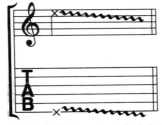

DÄMPFEN MIT DER SCHLAGHAND: Lege die Schlaghand oberhalb der Brücke leicht auf die Saite(n).

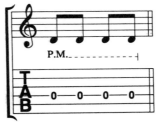

DÄMPFEN MIT DER GRIFFHAND: Du erreichst einen percussiven Sound, indem du die Griffhand leicht über die Saiten legst (ohne diese herunterzudrücken) und dann mit der Schlaghand anschlägst.

AMMERKUNG: Das Tempo der Zieher und Glissandos ist abhängig von der rhythmischen Notation und dem Grundtempo.

SPIEGAZIONI DI TABLATURA PER CHITARRA

La musica per chitarra può essere annotata in tre diversi modi: sul pentagramma, in tablatura e in taglio ritmico

IL TAGLIO RITMICO è scritto sopra il pentagramma. Percuotere le corde al ritmo indicato Le teste arrotondate delle note indicano note singole.

IL PENTAGRAMMA MUSICALE mostra toni e ritmo ed è divisa da linee in settori. I toni sono indicati con le prime sette lettere dell'alfabeto.

LA TABLATURA rappresenta graficamente la tastiera della chitarra. Ogni linea orizzontale rappresenta una corda, ed ogni corda rappresenta un tasto.

4° corda, 2° tasto   1° e 2° corda aperte, suonate insieme   accordo D aperto

Definizioni Per Annotazioni Speciali Per Chitarra

SEMI-TONO CURVATO: percuotere la nota e curvare di un semitono (1/2 passo).

TONO CURVATO: Percuotere la nota e curvare di un tono (passo intero).

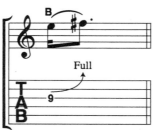

NOTA BREVE, CURVATA: percuotere la nota e curvare come indicato. Suonare la prima nota il più velocemente possibile.

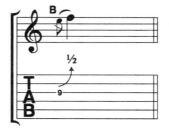

QUARTO DI TONO, CURVATO: Percuotere la nota e curvare di un quarto di passo.

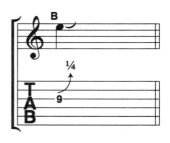

CURVA E LASCIA: Percuotere la nota e curvare come indicato, quindi rilasciare indietro alla nota originale.

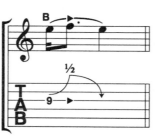

CURVA E RIPERCUOTI: Percuotere la nota e curvare come indicato poi ripercuotere la corda nel punto del simbolo.

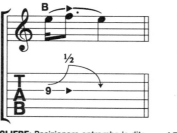

PRE-CURVA: Curvare la nota come indicato e quindi percuoterla.

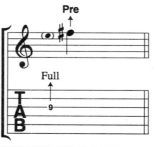

PRE-CURVA E RILASCIO: Curvare la nota come indicato. Colpire e rilasciare la nota indietro alla tonalità indicata.

MARTELLO-COLPISCI: Colpire la prima nota (in basso) con un dito; quindi suona la nota più alta (sulla stessa corda) con un altro dito, toccandola senza pizzicare.

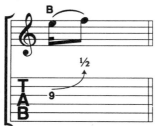

TOGLIERE: Posizionare entrambe le dita sulla nota da suonare. Colpire la prima nota e, senza pizzicare, togliere le dita per suonare la seconda nota (più in basso).

LEGATO SCIVOLATO (GLISSATO): Colpire la prima nota e quindi far scivolare lo stesso dito della mano della tastiera su o giù alla seconda nota. La seconda nota non viene colpita.

CAMBIO SCIVOLATO (GLISSARE E RICOLPIRE): Uguale al legato - scivolato eccetto che viene colpita la seconda nota.

ARMONICA NATURALE: Colpire la nota mentre la mano della tastiera tocca leggermente la corda direttamente sopra il tasto indicato.

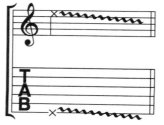

PIZZICA E GRAFFIA: Il limite del pizzicato è tirato su (o giù) lungo la corda, producendo un suono graffiante.

SORDINA CON IL PALMO: La nota è parzialmente attenuato dalla mano del pizzicato toccando la corda (le corde) appena prima del ponte.

CORDE SMORZATE: Un suono di percussione viene prodotto appoggiando la mano della tastiera attraverso la corda (le corde) senza premere, e colpendole con la mano del pizzicato.

NOTA: La velocità di ogni curvatura è indicata dalle annotazioni musicali e dal tempo.